POLITICS AND
WORLD OIL ECONOMICS

POLITICS AND
WORLD OIL ECONOMICS

An Account of the
International Oil Industry
in its Political Environment

J. E. HARTSHORN

FREDERICK A. PRAEGER, *Publisher*
NEW YORK

BOOKS THAT MATTER

Published in the United States of America in 1962
by Frederick A. Praeger, Inc., Publisher
64 University Place, New York 3, N.Y.

© J. E. Hartshorn 1962

Library of Congress Catalog Number: 62–15511

Printed in Great Britain
by Ebenezer Baylis and Son, Ltd.
Worcester and London

To
WANDA
and
DAVID

Contents

9

CONTENTS

Part Two (cont.)

Maps

Tables

11

Foreword

THIS book looks at the kaleidoscopic international circumstances of an industry in course of change: it is of necessity impressionistic and selective. For ease of reading, I have avoided footnotes and kept tables within the text to a minimum; but a short bibliography, a few maps and charts, and some pages of salient statistics about oil are appended.

For current detail I have depended heavily upon the industry's outstanding trade journals—the *Petroleum Press Service* and *Petroleum Times* in Britain; the *Oil and Gas Journal*, *World Petroleum* and the late *Petroleum Week* in the United States: *Petrole Informations* in France. I have used figures of petroleum both in the terminology of 'tons a year' that is often used on this side of the Atlantic, and that of 'barrels a day' that is used almost invariably in the United States and Middle East. In the simple rule of thumb of the trade, a barrel of oil a day roughly equals 50 tons of oil a year.

My personal acknowledgments are legion. Any understanding of the oil industry in the pages that follow has been gained from the extraordinarily patient explanation of friends in the companies, the governments, and among the consultants and commentators who serve the industry: I am indebted to them for hospitality, time, and argument. But the book is not sponsored by any company, government, or other interest: and its conclusions are entirely my own. Any understanding of business behaviour in general that I have been able to bring to this business has been gained in the service and the companionship of *The Economist* newspaper.

The mistakes may be legion too. Only those are wholly mine.

J.E.H.

Part One

against their foreign suppliers. The same principle was embodied in a new petroleum law that another large economy dependent for oil upon imports, Japan, had published some weeks before—the possibility of control 'to assure the stable and cheap supply of petroleum'.

This book was in the process of publication when these governments published their several proposals about world oil: it may perhaps be published before practical action follows upon any of them. It is unable to trace the consequences of these government moves. But what it had already been written about happened to be the circumstances out of which these government moves arose—circumstances which existed before these particular moves and will outlast their immediate significance. During the past two years, these circumstances have been coming to a head.

One of the first signs that these circumstances were sharpening was a meeting in Baghdad that may turn out to have been of seminal importance in the current history of the international oil industry. It was a meeting of governments: the governments of five countries that, at the time, were supplying some 80 per cent of all the oil that moves in world trade. After four days' discussions, it was announced that the governments of Iraq, Iran, Kuwait, Saudi Arabia and Venezuela had decided to form the Organization of the Petroleum Exporting Countries, 'for regular consultation amongst its members with a view to co-ordinating and unifying the policies of the members.'

The kind of co-ordinated policy that these governments have in mind was indicated by the first resolution they had passed at their meeting, which is worth quoting in full. They agreed:

'That members can no longer remain indifferent to the attitude heretofore adopted by the Oil Companies in effecting price modifications;

'That members shall demand that Oil Companies maintain their prices steady and free from all unnecessary fluctuation; that members shall endeavour, by all means available to them, to restore present prices to the levels prevailing before the reductions; that they shall ensure that if any new circumstances arise which in the estimation of the Oil Companies necessitate price modifications, the said companies shall enter into consultation with the member or members affected in order fully to explain the circumstances;

'That members shall study and formulate a system to ensure the

18

stabilization of prices by, among other means, the regulation of production, with due regard to the interests of the producing and the consuming nations, and to the necessity of securing a steady income to the producing countries, an efficient, economic and regular supply of this source or energy to consuming nations, and a fair return on their capital to those investing in the petroleum industry;

'That if as a result of the application of any unanimous decision of this Conference any sanctions are employed, directly or indirectly, by any interested Company against one or more of the Member Countries, no other Member shall accept any offer of a beneficial treatment, whether in the form of an increase in exports or any improvement in prices, which may be made to it by any such Company or Companies with the intention of discouraging the application of the unanimous decision reached by the Conference.'

Oil from beneath these countries of OPEC is produced and exported almost entirely by private enterprise, not by these governments. The companies that produce it, whose behaviour had been of so much interest to the framers of the OPEC resolutions, were not represented at this meeting; nobody would have expected them to be. But these resolutions, in their turn, were of deep interest to the companies. And their purport, to the big companies that produce oil in the OPEC countries, may have seemed at once ironic and menacing.

For there was little that the member governments of OPEC demanded the oil companies should do that the big companies were not, in broad terms, anxious to do; yet that little, potentially, could have disrupted the whole way that they are accustomed to do business. No government was more anxious than every company to keep prices steady and get them back to higher levels. A steady income to the producing countries, and economic and regular supplies to consuming nations, are both things that any sensible oil company is anxious to maintain in the smooth conduct of its business; and the declared purpose of its business is to obtain the fair return on capital of which the OPEC resolution spoke. Since autumn, 1960, the managements of oil companies have indeed been sighing wistfully for these things.

The demand for prior consultations with the governments of these countries before they changed their prices, however, challenged one of the central prerogatives of any businessman. These companies were not businesses given in general to exactly frenzied price competition; they are more often credited with or criticized for an extreme desire to hold

BY WAY OF INTRODUCTION

prices stable than with any wish to change them too often. But the power to set prices remains crucial to the management of their business—though it has become, by the terms of their tax arrangements in these oil-producing countries, crucial to the revenues of the OPEC countries as well. And oil revenues represent by far the largest element in the national budgets—indeed, in the national incomes—of these countries.

The Organization of the Petroleum Exporting Countries did not come out of the blue, any more than other claims of governments upon this industry had done. It came as a direct reaction, as the wording of its first resolution made plain, to one of the rather infrequent changes in price in this industry—a reduction, just about a month before, in the 'posted price' of crude oil in the Persian Gulf. That change, the first in eighteen months, was in itself unusual in timing and in sequence, though it was merely one among a train of events that had begun some years before. The attitudes that were finally expressed in the formation of OPEC had begun to form many years before, too. But it took the price cuts of August, 1960—which may turn out to have been the last that these companies were ever to make in these prices, in their then form—to crystallize them.

On 9th August, 1960, Standard Oil of New Jersey, which is the largest oil company in the world, had announced reductions ranging from 4 to 14 cents a barrel in the prices of the different crude oils that it offers at various loading points for tankers in the Gulf and the Eastern Mediterranean, bringing the level of its different 'posted prices' down by from $2\frac{3}{4}$ to 7 per cent. Four days later the Royal Dutch/Shell Group, which is the world's second largest oil company, announced similar price cuts for all the crude that it sells in the Middle East, backdating them to 9th August. Both these companies, apart from the crude that they obtain from various jointly-owned producing companies in the Middle East, buy some of their supplies from Kuwait, a shaikhdom where the oil is actually produced by a company owned jointly by British Petroleum and the Gulf Oil Corporation of Pittsburgh; Jersey Standard actually 'posts' a price in Kuwait for the oil that it receives under long-term contract with BP. When it cut its prices in August, 1960, therefore, Jersey Standard published a price for crude oil from Kuwait nominally lower than the company which supplied it was selling identical oil.

What happened next was not, as might have been expected in logic and from the world's experience of this particular industry, that the other companies selling crude oil from the same terminals in the Middle

20

BY WAY OF INTRODUCTION

East brought their prices into line. In fact, they did nothing for a day or two. There is a tradition of duplicating any changes in one's competitors' prices in this industry, for quite sensible commercial reasons. But British Petroleum, as it happened, had of late been accustomed to lead the way in price changes in the Middle East, within which it has been longer established than any other company, commands a larger share of production than any other, and has staked a larger proportion of its total investment in oil.

The first thing that BP did was quite unprecedented in the recent history of the oil industry in this part of the world: it issued a public statement deploring the price cuts initiated by Jersey Standard. A few days later, on 16th August, a week after Jersey had moved, BP did cut its prices throughout the Middle East, but in no case by more than 10 cents—a cut of only about $4\frac{1}{2}$ per cent, against the $6\frac{1}{2}$ per cent reduction that Jersey and Shell had made. For a day or two, the Middle East saw the unusual situation of three different levels of price for certain identical crudes offered at loading terminals: the new BP price, the Jersey and Shell price, and the old, higher price still quoted by one or two among the other companies trading in oil in the Middle East that had not decided which price leadership to follow.

During the whole period of this disagreement over the posted prices of Middle East crude, one of the operating companies owned jointly by most of the parties to the argument, the Iraq Petroleum Company, had been engaged in negotiations with the government of Iraq. These negotiations concerned a number of long-standing issues regarding the company's oil concession that the revolutionary government had inherited from the monarchist régime that it had overthrown in 1958, along with other demands upon the oil company that the new government had in the meantime originated itself. At the end of August, these negotiations were adjourned; after a lengthy discussion with General Abdul Karim Qasim, leader of the government, the company's negotiators returned to their headquarters in London to seek further instructions. Shortly after they did so, Shaikh Abdullah Tariki, then director of petroleum affairs (afterwards petroleum minister) of Saudi Arabia, visited Baghdad; and it was suddenly announced that the governments of a number of oil-producing countries were being invited there to discuss the latest price cuts. The countries invited included Venezuela, which is the only other large-scale exporter of oil in the Western world; crude oil prices in Venezuela had not been cut.

On 7th September, Socony-Mobil, one of the last of these companies to declare itself, decided to follow the BP example. On 8th September, just before the Baghdad meeting began, the Shell group, without explanation, put its prices up again—only a few cents a barrel, but also into line with BP. And on 14th September, the day that the Baghdad meeting was closing with the formation of OPEC, Standard Oil of New Jersey too increased its prices, bringing them, after three weeks or so, back into line with those posted on 16th August by BP. Posted prices in the Middle East were level again; but it was still a level between 2 and $5\frac{1}{4}$ per cent lower than those prices had been before the second week in August.

There was no need to assume that the partial retreat of Shell and then of Jersey Standard had had anything to do with the oil-producing governments' decision to hold a protest meeting. The explanation current in the oil business was that Jersey had originally intended a considerably larger cut in Middle East prices than on reflection it took; that Shell followed it in the milder cut that Jersey eventually decided upon in the belief that posted prices both in the Middle East and in Venezuela ought to come down from their artificially high levels; but that it became impossible for these companies to impose a cut in crude oil postings in Venezuela (which for reasons of company practice might perhaps have mattered more to Shell than to Jersey). This being so, Shell may have come back into line with the smaller price cuts set by BP partly because it had special reasons, in autumn, 1960, for not becoming unnecessarily unpopular in the Middle East. Jersey was left out on a limb: it did not care to remain.

The governments' protest meeting, however, produced OPEC. It also produced, as an immediate measure, a refusal by the four Middle East governments concerned to recognize the new levels of posted prices that had been established by this sequence of changes in price for tax purposes. They informed the companies operating in their territories that for the purpose of charging income tax as 50 per cent of the companies' gross profits they would continue to reckon profits according to the higher posted prices prevailing before August. This raised a new and important question. Had the international oil companies lost their independent commercial power to cut the price of crude oil? Two of the OPEC members, Kuwait and Saudi Arabia, did later that autumn countenance posted prices at the level that had settled down in mid-September, but not those posted by the companies that had made the cuts. They accepted this level for the initial posting of prices for crude oil by a Japanese company operating in concessions off the shores of the

BY WAY OF INTRODUCTION

Saudi-Kuwait Neutral Zone. I happened to be visiting Kuwait at the time. When I asked government officials there why they recognized a level of prices from this new company that they were not prepared to recognize when it was charged by the established companies, they had a plausible answer pat: 'The difference is that the Japanese were prepared to consult us.'

Without the price cuts that Jersey Standard initiated in August, 1960, the Organization of the Petroleum Exporting Countries would almost certainly not have come into being—at that time. To the outside observer, it seems likely that it would have come sooner or later. Five weeks after OPEC was formed, there was a public demonstration of the underlying reason why.

In late October, 1960, Shaikh Abdullah Tariki of Saudi Arabia, who was at the time a government-appointed director of the Arabian American Oil Company, presented a paper to the Second Arab Petroleum Congress in Beirut entitled 'The Pricing of Middle East Crude Oil and Refined Products'. In it he accused the eight major international companies who in various groupings own Aramco and the other main operating companies which actually produce the oil in the Middle East of swindling their 'partners', the host governments, out of $2,737,145,066, or just on a thousand million pounds.

Shaikh Abdullah's thesis was based on a complex argument about crude oil prices which it would be beside the point to summarize here; it has some consideration in a fuller discussion of pricing in this industry (which appears in Chapter X). It was not, I think he would even then have been prepared to agree, more than an attempt from outside to rationalize the pricing behaviour of the oil companies, as shown by the prices they posted for Middle East oil between August, 1953, and August, 1960; and I am not sure whether he would stand by all the details of this analysis now. But it was perhaps the first published attempt by any Arab in a position of authority to analyse pricing in the oil industry on the basis of the published information available—which nobody in the industry could pretend is adequate. And over-tortuous or not, the reasoning served to lead Shaikh Abdullah to a conclusion about which in essence if not in detail he clearly felt no doubt. This was that ever since the institution of the fifty-fifty profit-sharing system, in continuing bad faith, the eight major oil companies that control oil operations had 'posted' lower prices for Middle East crude than they were in practice able to realize, so that the half-share in profits on those posted

23

prices accruing to the host governments in the Middle East had been artificially depressed over a period of years. The Tariki paper had been prepared too early to take account of the further price cuts initiated two months before he delivered it: but as one of the chief architects of OPEC, he had left little doubt of what his views were on those particular price cuts. Few Arabs of note have been more closely exposed to the workings of the Western oil companies; and this is what this one thought of them.

Another six weeks later, at the beginning of December, 1960, came another development in the international oil industry—still as it happened in the Middle East—that broke new ground. Those so far mentioned have been instances of conflict. This was one of agreement—but on new terms. It was announced that the Ruler of Kuwait had granted a concession to the Royal Dutch/Shell group to explore for and to develop oil in the offshore area of the Gulf that belongs to Kuwait. This was the first new oil concession awarded to any of the eight major companies operating in the Middle East since 1950, and one of the very few ever awarded in recent times to any of these companies on its own, and not in partnership with any other company. It was awarded to Shell against a wide variety of extremely generous bids by competing companies; Shell's bid included some new features for any deal between any of the 'international majors' and any Middle East government.

Shell's successful bid for the Kuwait offshore concession may not formally have departed from the established 'fifty-fifty' rule under which payments to host governments, including royalties, are made up by an income tax of 50 per cent of profits reckoned at posted prices on all the oil sold. This rule had been established by the major companies at the beginning of the fifties and maintained by them ever since, though certain other oil companies had completed deals that give host countries a potentially bigger share of profits, and production has since begun under certain of the concessions granted on these lines. But Shell's bid did allow for the State of Kuwait, as and when oil is discovered off its shore, to acquire in addition to a right to 50 per cent of profits a 20 per cent shareholding in the operating company that would actually develop the oil. Kuwait would have to buy its way in, paying a corresponding share of the expenses incurred up to the point of production to exercise that option; but it would during the meantime be receiving from Shell bonuses totalling £30 million, which might reasonably be expected to cover this price of admission.

Shell entered into no commitment to consult the government of

Kuwait in advance before posting the prices for this oil, when it comes to sell any: nor did it firmly promise government participation in activities in oil operations later than the stage of production. But it did accept the state as a partner and it committed itself, if required, to take and market the state's share of production at a price only 10 cents a barrel below the posted price. When I asked one of the then managing directors of Royal Dutch/Shell whether this commitment, though in the letter relating only to a transfer price between partners, might not in effect imply consultation with the government of Kuwait about all prices posted for this Shell oil from Kuwait, he said, 'To be frank, in circumstances where we are operating with a reasonable government and without any partners among other companies, we do not believe that that particular difficulty, in practice, would ever arise.'

The Shell concession agreement with Kuwait was finally signed on 5th January, 1961. Two days later the second conference of the OPEC members, Kuwait among them, began at Caracas in Venezuela. The five members agreed to set up a formal organization and worked out its constitution; decided that its formal headquarters, with a technical, legal, and economic secretariat, should be in Geneva; and accepted a new member, the Shaikhdom of Qatar. The content of their resolutions went no farther than in September; indeed, some optimists in the industry felt that the tone was milder than before. But among its resolutions was one in which members reaffirmed their refusal to recognize the price cuts made nearly six months before. And their formal demands upon the companies in July, 1962 began with a demand that the August, 1960, cuts should be restored—though their other demands, dealing with the government revenues from sales of oil, were perhaps more important.

In the meantime, the international oil companies had twice reached apparent deadlock in the Iraq oil negotiations, and on the second breakdown, at the end of September, 1961, General Qasim had promised his people legislation to 'restore to the nation its just right in the country's oil'. The Iraq Petroleum group, owned by five of these companies, was still producing and exporting oil from the developed areas of its concessions: but in April it was forbidden to carry on exploration activities anywhere in the country, and in December, the Iraq government announced its decision to take over all of the country-wide concession area except the $\frac{1}{2}$ per cent or so where oil was currently being produced. From Libya, a new oil-exporting nation, commercial shipments had just begun: but the Western companies operating there, who had been attracted partly by the rather favourable mining law of the country, had already been told that if they wanted to get any new concessions they would have to accept a new set of much more onerous rules on their old ones as well. At the consuming end of the business, very bitter price competition in some markets had driven down the international companies' return to unusually low levels. Having had their refineries and marketing businesses in Cuba nationalized in summer 1960, and used ever since to handle Soviet oil, the same major companies had in 1962 undergone rather similar action in Ceylon and considerable use of *force majeure* in bargaining about prices by the government of India. From Brazil to Brunei, countries where oil was produced were demanding higher incomes from oil operations: from Japan to Tanganyika, countries that consume oil were seeking yet lower prices as a condition of supplying their markets. The United States government was setting in train a new study of its own three-year-old statutory import restrictions; and the European Economic Community, with Britain teetering on the edge of it, was deciding whether to adopt 'the common energy policy' we have already mentioned.

This is an outside reporter's book about the oil industry and its international circumstances, not an expert's. Its evidence is therefore at best secondhand, based on asking questions, over a period of about two years and about 30,000 miles of travel, of people inside this industry, or in a position to influence it, about what they are doing and why. Among the reasons that finally impelled me to get it down on paper were the events of 1960–62 in this industry and the background to them. Many of those I have mentioned occurred in the Middle East; but this is not a book about the Middle East, with which my acquaintance is even more glancing and occasional than with the oil industry. The background to these events lies wider; and this book is an attempt to set out analytically some of the circumstances in which the international oil industry now has to live with governments all round the world, and not merely in the under-developed countries where much of the world's oil happens to be produced.

These international circumstances, I believe, have already constricted, and for some time at least may increasingly constrict, the independence with which this industry operates, for reasons which at any rate seem legitimate to the many governments concerned, and some of which would probably seem legitimate to any unprejudiced person. Good arguments can be advanced for many of the measures that governments have taken and are taking which deliberately or incidentally limit some area of this industry's operations; at any rate, when these measures are considered singly. Together, however, they may soon reach a point where the huge job of international logistics carried out in the world oil business, as it is at present organized, could become very hard to continue efficiently. That present pattern of organization is neither perfectly efficient, nor necessarily the only one under which the international supply of a commodity becoming steadily more essential to the world could be carried on successfully. The pattern is indeed continuing, somewhat painfully, to evolve. But it is the only one we have, and its results continue to be vital to all of us. So major changes of any kind that any government is tempted to press upon the oil business have to be judged primarily in terms of how such changes—in concatenation with the other changes that other governments may be pressing at the same time—would affect the efficiency of world oil supply.

The oil business as it now exists is a curious international phenomenon, one of the few economic phenomena that have ever achieved such importance on such a stage. There is a powerful internal logic within its interlocked operations—though its structure, so far, has been organic and developing rather than simply rational, and embodies large elements of accident and luck. It cannot avoid rather more involvement in politics than most ordinary businesses: but politically as well as commercially, it would probably argue that its operating success depends upon sticking to 'strictly business' principles as much as it can. The logic of its business behaviour, however, comes of necessity into contact and at times into conflict with a phenomenon that in our century has manifested even greater power, nationalism in developed as well as in underdeveloped countries. This phenomenon is very easy to recognize and label when somebody else is displaying it—particularly for Westerners, when the somebody is in Asia or Africa. When we display it ourselves, whoever and wherever we are, we tend to identify it as 'the national interest—another thing altogether'. That is part of the universal strength of nationalism. And that is what makes the lot of any independently international organization such as the international oil industry, which exists mainly to move a resource vital to most nations across national frontiers, a vulnerable one.

The host countries where the oilfields are present themselves obviously as areas where nationalism impinges on this industry: but I believe one can both misjudge their actions and miss the main point by assuming they are in this sense exceptional. The oil industry of the

United States is tightly regulated by state agencies and of late largely insulated from the world market by government restrictions—which may have had as much to do with the world surplus that broke oil prices in 1960 as the behaviour of the state-controlled Russian industry did. The British government was the first one ever to take over a controlling share in the ownership of any major oil company: the French state owns large holdings in most French oil companies, and controls the business behaviour of all oil companies in France, whoever owns them, more tightly than almost any other country in the non-Communist world. Nationalism and governmental influence on the oil industry are not confined to any one country or group of countries.

In assessing the possible spread and effects of that influence, it is convenient to begin by considering what is being influenced. The first part of this book is designed, therefore, to give as simple a sketch as possible of the business behaviour of the international oil industry as this is at present organized. It outlines the extent to which the world depends on oil; the geography of petroleum and the long, complex chain of exploration, production, transport and marketing which that necessitates: and as clearly as an outsider can comprehend and describe them the economics of its financing, its pricing, and its company structure. Having considered the special characteristics of competitive and uncompetitive behaviour in this industry, the second part of the book goes on to describe how its operational flexibility, in almost all countries where the industry operates, is nowadays circumscribed, for good reasons or bad, in the entirely legitimate name of the national interest. Whether the industry likes it or not, it is inevitable that the governments of consumer countries in which oil has now risen to dominate the fuel market should take an interest in the economic circumstance of its provenance. And the countries from which it is produced and exported have, generally speaking, few other economic circumstances for their governments to be interested in.

This is a descriptive book with some attempt at analysis, for the person generally interested in oil rather than the expert in any particular aspect of it. I have offered some comments on the way, but not I hope irritatingly hasty solutions to other people's problems—which are not necessarily susceptible of any neat, lasting, or inevitably happy solutions. These are problems in which nobody who is at all concerned with oil—and who, nowadays, is not in some sense?—need apologize for trying to understand further. The oil industry spends more money, effort and intelligent people on explaining certain aspects of its world-wide operations to the public of every country than any other I know. Yet somehow it also often contrives to give an impression of remoteness, perhaps through its sheer size and its international depth, from any one outside its periphery. Oilmen on occasion have been apt to treat its inner workings as something of a craft mystery, beyond the ken of mere mortals outside. But more and more people—and more and more governments—are coming to feel that the oil business is too important to be left to oilmen alone. That is what this book is about.

CHAPTER II

Oil as a General Fuel

By any measure we can apply, the world is now becoming rapidly more dependent on oil and natural gas, the petroleum fuels. During the sixties, for the first time in history, man will begin to get more heat and mechanical energy from petroleum than from any other fuel. Before 1970, petroleum may be supplying more of the world's supplies of commercial energy than all other fuels put together. For something approaching a century, in these senses, coal has been the world's dominant fuel; but now the balance is tipping over.

These are broad statements; but it is only broadly that any statement about the quantities of energy consumed right across the world can pretend to be true, and historically the perspectives are even more blurred. For large parts of the world no figures exist, reliable or unreliable; and where any figures do exist, they vary enormously in scope and quality. Fortunately for this kind of figuring, most of the areas for which statistics are entirely lacking are places where people use little fuel or at least buy practically none, relying mainly on wood and farm wastes. Statisticians generally find it convenient to exclude these fuels from their figuring as 'non-commercial'. They are still burned in huge quantities: as recently as 1875, for example, three-quarters of the fuel consumed in the United States is reckoned to have been wood, and today some guesses would still put the contribution of such fuels to total energy consumption in the world as high as a sixth.

But under the heading of 'commercial energy', then, the statisticians rank only the fuels supplied for sale in response to a defined market demand—coal and other solid fuels such as lignite; petroleum, liquid and in the form of gas; hydro-electricity; and nuclear electricity, though production of this new 'primary fuel' is so far too miniscule to show at all on any graph of world supplies. During 1961, the world appears to have burned, either as raw fuel or in secondary forms, the equivalent of about 4,550 million tons of coal. Of this total, coal and lignite together accounted for some 2,350 million tons, or 52 per cent; hydro-electricity for the equivalent of 90 million tons, or about 2 per cent; production of nuclear electricity was negligible. The remaining 46 per cent came from oil products equivalent to about 1,460 million tons of coal and natural gas equivalent to just over 650 million tons. Solid fuels were still, by five per cent, in the lead; coal had not yet abdicated its kingdom. But consumption of coal, right across the world, is now growing only very slowly, while consumption of oil and natural gas, taken together, is still growing at perhaps 6–8 per cent a year. The consumption of hydro-electricity is still growing as fast as that of oil, though not nearly as fast as consumption of natural gas; but it remains a very tiny percentage of total fuel consumption in the world today. During the next few years, a shift seems inevitable. By the middle of the sixties, petroleum seems certain to catch up and pass coal's gradually slipping share of world fuel consumption; by the end of the sixties, oil and natural gas are sure to exceed 50 per cent of the commercial energy that the world uses.

Over the past thirty years, moreover, oil and natural gas have accounted for about two-thirds of all the increase in the world's consumption of fuel. They have not been the only dynamic elements in the rapid growth of the use of commercial energy during that period: the exponential curve of electricity consumption, which has continued over many years with hardly even a ripple to acknowledge the occurrence of slump or war, shows an even more dramatic rise. But electricity is a 'secondary fuel', one of the convenient ways that man has devised to make use of energy, not a source of energy in itself; it has to be made from some 'primary fuel' such as coal, oil, falling water or fissile uranium. The surge in consumption of the two petroleum primary fuels has probably also resulted partly from the fact that these are convenient to use. The specialized secondary fuels that you can refine from crude oil are convenient for many purposes and practically indispensable for some, and natural gas is a primary fuel that starts out with all the convenience that coal can only achieve rather expensively through the processes of traditional gas manufacture. But our growing dependence on petroleum has not come wholly from the fact that consumers prefer convenience. In the first decade after the Second World War, in particular, oil and natural gas supplied the lion's share of the extra energy the world required simply because they were there to be had in abundance, which coal emphatically was not. Vast new sources of petroleum were steadily developed, and the pipelines, tankers and refineries were

substitute for gasoline in this specialized role, except another petroleum product, diesel oil: kerosene had never been more than one form of lighting and heating among others. Demand for gasoline swelled enormously with the spread of motor transport, followed by other applications of the internal combustion engine, across the world; the petroleum industry could profitably allow all other products to fall in behind this one. Over certain periods in the first three decades of this century, particularly in the United States, the volumes of the black oils sold—that is, of gas, diesel and fuel—exceeded sales of kerosene or gasoline. But they never enjoyed any comparable invulnerability to competition. They were sold in competition with other general fuels on the market, as the by-products of processes operated primarily to give high yields of kerosene or of gasoline. And the amounts available were dictated by demand for these main products.

If the rapid growth of oil consumption during the first half of this century has been associated with the most widely-ramified technical innovation of that period, the internal combustion engine, it has also borrowed momentum from the fact that the industry developed first and farthest in the United States. One cannot perhaps clearly distinguish the two: the automobile and the United States, as phenomena contributing to world economic growth, overlapped during the first half of this century so far as to be in some ways inseparable. During the first half of this century, the United States was not only the largest and richest country in the world, but also the most rapidly growing of the industrial countries. During most of the hundred years that span the real history of the petroleum industry, this one country has been the largest single consumer (and producer) of commercial energy. North America still consumes close on half the world's oil, and four-fifths of all the natural gas. The oil industry of the United States was the first to be developed on any significant scale; it remains the largest in any country, and American companies own a larger share of oil production and marketing overseas than any others. The sheer size of the American economy and its possession of oil and gas reserves have been tremendous elements in the rise of world consumption of petroleum.

During the last thirty years, petroleum consumption has been growing rapidly, as standards of living have risen, in the other developed countries that are poorer than the United States, but much richer than the rest of the world. The consumption of petroleum—as indeed of most of the other commercial fuels, and of most industrial materials and manufactures—is still extraordinarily concentrated within a relatively

34

small part of the world's inhabited surface and population. About 55 per cent of all commercial fuel used in the world, in 1961, was burned in North America and Western Europe; another 20 per cent, probably, inside Russia and the European countries among its satellites. The other 70–75 per cent of the world's population used only about a quarter of the commercial energy sold in it. In the non-industrial parts of the earth, where consumption per head of fuel as of most other commodities comes down in the statistics to forbiddingly small quantities, warmth is provided by burning wood and even dung; tractive energy by the horse, the ox and the human. There is a familiar correlation between the amount of fuel used per head in each of the world's economies and the comparative standard of living there. And until very recently, at least, the statistics tended to show also that these standards are rising faster in the developed countries than in most of the underdeveloped. The rich are getting richer; and relatively, many of the poor are getting poorer.

Businessmen concerned with oil seldom like to consider it as a simple commodity, or raw material. But, in the economic sense, at present, oil and the countries that produce it are faring like other commodities and primary producers. The terms of trade have been moving against them: that is to say, the amount of manufactured goods that they can exchange with their customers for a given amount of the primary material they produce has been falling and for a time may go on down. To anyone living in a country exporting manufactured goods and importing primary materials, this remains hugely, fortuitously convenient. But it has also become one of the most disturbing tendencies in the world economy today.

Standards of living in all countries are now being raised by the fact that liquid petroleum is perhaps the first really easily transportable fuel that the world has yet developed. Oil is essentially a fuel on the move (indeed, this was vital to the formation of the oilfields from which we tap it). Flowing along a pipe or pumped, it is immeasurably easier and cheaper than coal to load into and out of every kind of container, without degradation of its quality. Being of a higher calorific value, it is anyway better able to bear the cost of transport than coal ever has been, or than electricity or gas made from coal are yet, over long distances. The economics of transporting gaseous petroleum, are favourable too, though a good deal less so than with oil. And this inherent ease of transporting oil has fitted rather neatly into the historical circumstances in which it was developed. The petroleum industry could never have grown as it has without coal, as a base for the development of iron and

35

steel and of the engineering industries that use them. But the oil, once developed, could be transported readily for use in the economies where industrialization had begun on a foundation of coal. Coal needs to be used as near the source as possible, if it is to be cheap, and a market tends to be developed wherever it happens to be. Oil does not.

It is increasingly as a general fuel rather than as a specialized one that petroleum is coming to dominate world energy consumption in the 'sixties. Gasoline, the specialized fuel to which this industry owes the biggest part of its expansion, became and has remained the industry's major product in economic terms. But sales of gasoline have never been as much as half of the total volume of oil products consumed throughout the world; and of late, consumption of certain other products refined from crude, to say nothing of natural gas, has been growing much more rapidly.

In the United States, which is still by far the world's largest market for petroleum, the total quantity of the black oils consumed—gas and diesel oils, distillate and residual fuel oils, and crude burned raw— passed that of kerosene by 1910, and was not exceeded in volume by gasoline until about 1930. Today gasoline represents about 40 per cent of oil consumption in the United States, while the black oils account for only about 35 per cent. But these are no longer the only forms of petroleum competing in the general market for fuel there; natural gas has captured a sizeable share of total fuel consumption, and its sales are still growing much more rapidly than those of the fuel oils.

In the next largest market for petroleum, Western Europe, natural gas did not appear on the market in significant quantities until recently. Throughout the fifties this market was consuming more and more oil as a general fuel—its consumption was growing much more rapidly than the American. The petroleum that was used as a general fuel on the European market consisted almost entirely of the black oils refined from crude. So far as oil alone is concerned, therefore, European demand for the heavier oil products, in the fifties, rose faster than for gasolines. In broad terms, across the world, one can say that consumption of natural gas and of the black oils, together or separately, have been growing faster throughout the world than sales of any specialized fuel.

Its steadily widening involvement in the general fuel market during the fifties, began to present the oil industry with some new problems, economic and political. During the late fifties, these problems were sharpened. At the same time certain economic problems with which the industry had become grimly familiar in the past returned to plague it.

Of these, the central problem was the return of a world surplus of oil—or rather of capacity to move the surplus of oil available to market. As late as 1955, in economic terms, and as late as 1957, in political terms that were still blurred by the consequences of shared folly at Suez, forecasters inside and outside this industry were dominated by the mental climate of anxiety over fuel shortage that had prevailed since the end of the Second World War. It is easy, as we look back on it, to recognize that climate of opinion as shot through with large patches of illusion. In the general fuel market of most European countries, at any rate, our judgment was blurred at that time by the apparent continued impossibility of getting enough of the general fuel upon which we were accustomed to depend, coal, in spite of the investment that had been poured into attempts to raise the output. So far as the oil industry itself was concerned, potent business decisions had been made and vast sums had been staked upon the assumption that the oil business in the United States would prefer to buy its oil in the cheapest market and hence to rely to an increasing degree upon importing foreign oil more cheaply than it could produce oil at home; made, incidentally, by some of the most astute businessmen concerned with oil both inside and outside the United States.

Fortunes—including those of whole nations—depended upon those decisions; and they began to appear wrong, in some cases, within months of being made. The United States decided not to rely on increased imports of oil, and has not so far been obviously the worse for it. Coal output outside the United States and the Communist sphere remained almost as hard to increase; but the ranks of the customers who had been forced to switch to oil were soon swelled by others who positively liked the idea, and within a couple of years coal changed from being hard to get to being hard to sell. The host governments of oil producing countries who had been made partners in the bonanza of cheap oil flowing from under their deserts, and given half of the richest 'economic rent' of all time, were suddenly asked to share lower unit profits in leaner years. World demand for fuel was still increasing, and petroleum was still the abundant residual supplier of all the extra fuel the world wanted. But there was more of it ready for delivery at once than the world was prepared to buy for the moment; and more was becoming available every day.

37

OIL AS A GENERAL FUEL

Today's short term surplus of oil, offering the world a potential abundance of cheap energy, has to be considered against a certainty of continued growth in energy demand. Some investment decisions being taken now, in a climate of fuel surplus, may turn out to be as wrong as those were in the last years of an illusory fuel shortage. Forecasting of energy demand, over the last decade or so, has undergone considerable refinement in technique. But the nature of the data upon which forecasts have to be based may still be so unreliable as to offset this. Also, it is often impossible to appreciate in advance the eventual 'net' significance of major technological shifts in consumption or supply.

At the beginning of this century, forecasters had to try to assess the consequences of electricity, a fuel that was clearly fantastically easy and efficient to use, though in terms of thermal efficiency inherently wasteful to produce. On balance, what effect would it have on the growth of fuel consumption? In fact, it accelerated the consumption of energy—and the general rate of growth—in the industrialized economies where it was first applied. But at the same time, from the nineteen-twenties onward, its efficiency in use, and its substitution for other fuels, brought about a significant growth in general productivity, and a reduction in the amount of extra energy and other resources, needed for any given amount of general economic growth. It does not seem likely, writing in 1962, that the eventual if delayed arrival of competitive and cheapening nuclear energy will have as profound a net effect upon productivity and growth in mature or developing economies as electricity has already had on the mature ones. But it would be stupid to pretend to any certainty.

Today, forecasts of world energy demand over the next years postulate rates of growth varying from $2\frac{1}{2}$ to 4 per cent compound per annum. In 25 years' time, that range implies that total effective demand for commercial energy may be from 85 to 167 per cent more than it is today. Hydro-electricity is unlikely to contribute much of that massive increase. Coal production will certainly grow more slowly than total energy demand for a generation or so, though it is possible that by the end of the century the ruling price of energy, through rising costs in other fuels, may rise enough to justify some more rapid growth in coal exploitation, and perhaps some recovery in its share of world energy supply. Within ten years, nuclear energy may be setting an upper limit to the price at which it will be possible to sell fossil fuels, and contributing much of the increase in electricity generated in areas where these fuels are expensive. But its contribution to the growing total of world energy will probably still, by the end of the century, be a limited one. The bulk of the increase in energy requirements, for a generation at least, can only come from one basic source—petroleum, liquid and gaseous. And the circumstances of its provenance will be a vital national interest in every country in the world.

CHAPTER III

Geography: Sources and Markets

'Oil is where you find it' is perhaps the most frequently quoted truism in this industry: but rather often during oil's commercial history, that has not been where you want it. Sheer geography would have been an inhibiting factor in the oil industry, sharply limiting the areas over which its markets could economically spread and imposing checks on its rate of development, if oil had not, providentially, turned out to be inherently easy to transport. As it is, the pattern of its geography has gradually made this industry, during this century at any rate, more genuinely international than perhaps any other has ever been. There are still, certainly, two great areas of relative self-sufficiency for oil, in North America and the Soviet Union. But no other fuel—including so far, natural gas—has ever been consumed in such vast quantities so far away from where it is produced.

The physical geography of petroleum, as its name indicates, derives from geology, which might be called the petrified history of the earth. The fuel's own historical origins remain a matter of some argument among geologists (and are the first of the many fascinating technical aspects of oil into which this book is not competent to follow the expert). Most of them appear now to agree that it was formed, over many millions of years, from organic materials of one kind or another accumulated at the bottom of oceans or inland seas, or washed inland during periods of inundation, and gradually covered by mud or lime deposited on top; there is less agreement about just how. Through the action of temperature or pressure, of particular processes of decomposition, or perhaps simply of time, these organic sources became converted into the characteristic mixture of hydrocarbon compounds that constitute petroleum—varying from nearly solid asphalt, through the liquid form, to gaseous forms such as methane. Being formed as a fluid, petroleum could move through any underground strata that were porous and permeable. Being lighter than the salt water also found in the pore spaces of the strata surrounding it, it tended to make its way gradually upwards. So where it is now discovered may not necessarily be where it began to be formed. That propensity to migrate has considerably complicated the geologists' ideas of just how petroleum could have originated; however, it is also mainly what has made petroleum available to man. For the characteristic underground pool of oil-permeated rock that forms an oilfield seems generally to have come into being when oil, moving upward or laterally through porous layers of rock, had its general progress towards the surface stopped by some impervious layer or 'caprock'. These deposits are found in particular where folding and wrinkling of the earth's crust has formed 'anticlines', dome-shaped formations under which the upward-migrating oil was sealed and gradually collected. There are many other formations and faults of rock strata in which oilfields have been located, but almost all seem to satisfy certain prerequisites: porous strata such as sand or limestone in which the oil can collect, and impervious rock or clay above and around parts of such strata that can hold the petroleum sealed in. And those geological prerequisites, as it happens, seem more often than not to exist under parts of the earth's surface where so far industrial civilization has not been developed sufficiently to use the products of petroleum in really large quantities.

Any fuel or mineral extracted from the earth, to the extent that it can be used raw or processed simply, obviously creates as much of a local market as it can. But from almost the beginning of the large-scale commercial exploitation of petroleum—which to all practical purposes one can date from the opening up in Pennsylvania of the Appalachian fields, from 1859 onwards—most of the oil began to be moved quite a long way to market. Some of the biggest sales of kerosene for lighting and heating, as the American market developed, were in rural areas and behind the frontier as it moved westward. In the more developed markets of the Eastern cities, coal, and later gas and electricity, could offer kerosene much more competition. During the first thirty years of oil's history in the United States, moreover, it was nearly always exporting a third of its total output of refined products, and sometimes selling as much as two-thirds to foreign markets. On the earth's surface as well as under it, oil has proved a migratory fuel.

For lighting and to a lesser extent for general heating, kerosene was only one fuel among others, and one best able to compete in rural or underdeveloped areas; hence 'oil for the lamps of China'. Gasoline, on the other hand, was a fuel almost without a rival, and essentially a fuel of advancing industrialization and rising standards of living. And the first great surge of automotive consumption happened in the United States where the crude oil was produced. But even there the markets that developed earliest and fastest were rather remote from where the oil came out of the ground.

By the time that the gasoline era of this industry was beginning, the great centres of oil production had shifted from Pennsylvania, New York, West Virginia and Ohio to Texas, California and Oklahoma. In these areas, remote from coal, the black oils could develop local markets as a general fuel for railroads, heating and industrial steam-raising. But automobiles were bought all over the continent, and particularly in the larger centres of population in the East, and the oil had to be taken there. In the same way, in Europe, Russian and Rumanian oil was originally developed for small-scale local use, but demand for it rose faster in the cities and later in the richer and more developed economies of Western Europe. North America has remained even until today the greatest single source of oil produced and market for it. But the very size and rate of expansion of its market caused early anxiety about exhaustion of reserves—anxieties that have been regularly disproved, but have recurred, during the whole history of the petroleum industry. It sent the nation's oilmen overseas to look for fresh supplies; and all the biggest reserves of oil discovered since about 1935 have been outside the United States.

At the turn of the century the only oil industries developed on any significant scale were in the United States and Russia; there was some production in Burma as indeed there had been for centuries, and the exploration for oil was beginning in Persia. In the first twenty-five years of this century oil consumption grew at a rapidly rising rate in the United States, much faster than extra reserves were discovered there; but there were important discoveries in Mexico, Venezuela, and Persia. Fears of exhaustion of American reserves spurred the search at home; in the late twenties and early thirties huge new fields were opened up in East Texas, California and Oklahoma. But these fears also encouraged American oilmen and American diplomats to seek a firm footing in the developing Middle East (as against the British, who were already largely established there economically and politically, developing oil in Persia and later in Iraq). Moreover, there came a sharp decline in demand as slump spread throughout the world; the new American fields were produced at high rates that simply pushed prices and returns on investments down to ruinous levels until the governments of the main oil-producing states began to regulate the level of output. Between 1935/45 the growth of oil production and reserves in the United States, which had already been very heavily drilled, tended to slacken: five years of that decade were years of war and materials shortage, admittedly. But for the world as a whole, reserves 'proved' by exploration rose much more than production of oil did. In the Middle East, in particular, the thirties were a period of major oil discoveries, in Bahrein, Kuwait and Saudi Arabia, as well as in Iran and Iraq. Since the war, significant new oilfields have been discovered in Venezuela and the Middle East; moreover, the estimates of oil reserves in already developed fields have gone up steadily. Canada came in at the end of the forties as a new producer, and by the end of the fifties a sustained effort of exploration was developing large-scale production in certain parts of Africa, primarily the Sahara, Libya, and Nigeria.

The significance of the truism quoted at the opening of this chapter is that in spite of all the preliminary surveys and scientific assessment one can make of likely areas, oil can defy the geological signs and still not be where the indications suggest. Broadly, one can rule out large areas of the world's surface where oil almost certainly isn't. Without drilling, however, one cannot say definitely where it is, even in promising areas; and without further drilling once an oilfield is discovered one cannot estimate how much oil it may be possible to get out of it. As a result the number of new fields discovered must be to some extent a function of the amount of effort and money that companies have been prepared to put into all the costly techniques of explorations, especially into drilling.

The amount of oil that one actually discovers for a given amount of drilling varies enormously, not only between areas already heavily explored and exploited such as the United States and newer areas such as the Middle East, but also between different areas developed more recently. In all, fewer than 400 wells have been drilled in Kuwait since exploration began there, 'proving' reserves estimated (conservatively) at 62,000 million barrels of oil. In the Sahara, from 1952 to 1958, about the same number of wells were drilled, but only some 5,000,000,000 barrels of oil have been located. It is said that it took only 17 'wildcat' wells to find the first 13 major oil reservoirs in Saudi Arabia, Kuwait, Qatar, and the Basrah area; yet 130 wells were drilled in Canada before the discovery of its first significant field, Leduc. In any given programme of exploration, the dominating factor is the uncertainty and randomness of reward for this effort.

43

GEOGRAPHY

The reserve-production ratio, which is an important yardstick for oil-fields, countries, and for companies in this industry, takes into account also the current output of any given area; and unless more oil is located as fast as output rises, this ratio will necessarily tend to decline as the years go by. And there are other factors, not wholly economic, that are still, even with far more oil on tap today than the world needs, encouraging a very high rate of exploration. One can count on some continuing improvement in the techniques of searching for oil: but the area of the main sedimentary regions of the earth's surface still unsurveyed, from dry land at least, is steadily decreasing. The industry has only just begun on oil exploration in the 'continental shelves' of the oceans: there are intriguing possibilities too, in the 'seaway' beyond territorial limits. Drilling in already intensively explored areas has steadily to go deeper: in the United States, fewer 'barrels of oil proved per thousand feet' drilled are being added from exploratory wells as the years go by.

For the world as a whole, the total of 'proved oil reserves', over the industry's whole history, has at most times kept pace with the growth of consumption, and following the huge discoveries in the Middle East during the thirties the reserve production ratio rose sharply for a time. In 1939, total proved reserves were put at 32,000 million barrels, representing 16 years' production at the previous year's rate; by 1950, they had nearly trebled, representing twenty-four years' output at a much higher rate; and at the beginning of the sixties 'published proved reserves' were more than three times as high again, at 312,000 million barrels, about 37 years' production at 1961 rates. But the geographical distribution of the world's proved reserves had also altered radically during this period of increase. In 1959, half of the total was located in the United States—as against about 60 per cent both of world output and of world consumption. By the end of 1961, the United States, still producing 34 per cent and consuming 42 per cent of the world's oil products, possessed only about 12 per cent of proved reserves. No less than 60 per cent of reserves were in the Middle East Nations, though countries in this area were producing only about a quarter of current world output—and they were themselves consuming no more than two per cent of the world's oil. Another rapidly rising share of world proved reserves has been in the Communist bloc, where proved reserves of oil now exceed those of the United States.

What one means by 'proved' reserves, in the most rigorous definition so far worked out, is a measure of the quantities of oil that have been located by drilling and are estimated to be recoverable by the production systems in operation at the time, plus undrilled resources so close to the drilled areas that there is every probability that they will produce when drilled. Even that definition, framed by the American Petroleum Institute, involves a large amount of estimation and leaves a good deal of room for optimism or pessimism. It is important to remember, moreover, that the number of years' production in the reserves that any country or oil company has proved and published is related within limits to the amount of effort it has chosen, or found profitable, to put into drilling. This is an expensive exercise in which to tie up one's working capital, but provisions in the tax systems of certain countries make a high rate of exploration and development of new wells advantageous financially as well as in maintaining a company's technical position. The United States is one of the most expensive places in the world to find an additional barrel of oil for one's reserves; at the beginning of the sixties its reserves represented about 12 years' production. To keep that ratio around 12–13 years, certainly, was involving the American oil industry in a prodigious and steadily growing drilling effort—some 50,000 wells a year, exploration and development. Perhaps 10,000 of these were exploratory 'wildcat' wells, of which no more than one in nine finds oil and no more than one in forty-five finds a million barrel field, which is what one needs to make it worth commercial production. The rest of the wells drilled are development wells, of which three in four reach oil; these 'prove up' existing oilfields but don't really locate fresh oil.

In other parts of the world it is very doubtful whether 'proved reserves' prove as much as in the United States. Not all companies or even producing countries want to advertise just how much oil they know they have. One or two countries, perhaps, are close-mouthed because they wish they had more; but some of those in the Middle East find it more convenient to be conservative about their inventory of buried wealth. Total 'proved reserves' for that area, in 1961, were published as 188,000 million barrels: yet Mr. Wallace Pratt, one of the industry's leading geologists, reckoned in 1955–56 that the Middle East had 240,000 million barrels of 'conservative and proved reserves'. Companies operating in Kuwait and Saudi Arabia, for example, publish proved reserves totalling about 60 and 50 billion barrels respectively: many oilmen in the Middle East are prepared to guess that the companies on the spot have something very close to proof, at any rate, of the existence of reserves two to four times that size. Moreover, there is considerable latitude open to a company in deciding how much it shall 'prove' and publish of the oil that it thinks it has found. When the present consortium began operations in Iran in 1954, it published figures of proved reserves a good deal higher than had ever been reported by Anglo-Iranian: yet there had been no drilling in the meantime. Companies striking it rich in new areas, such as Standard Oil of New Jersey, towards the end of the fifties, in Libya, are cautious about indicating reserve figures: and their rivals in the oil business are even more cautious about taking any figures at face value. Figures of proved reserves, collected according to as rigorous and stable a definition as one can hope to get observed, are meaningful in indicating the state of development of the general 'resource base' of the industry; but one should not ignore the fact that the primary data represent no more than companies want to tell their competitors.

Estimates of 'ultimate reserves', on the other hand, have generally been made for the industry as a whole. And these figures, from the outside, sometimes seem to represent so little that has any tangible meaning that the industry does not care in the least what it tells its competitors (though it would as soon dismay them as not). Definitions of the term vary, but it is usually taken to imply an estimate of the total petroleum recoverable, both from current proved reserves and from reserves that will be discovered in future, in terms of current production techniques (usually assuming an unchanged level of recovery techniques). This last convention has been challenged, quite logically within the terms of such speculation, by two American economists in a recent and controversial study, which suggests the alternative concept of the 'resource base'. This is an estimate of the total quantity of oil *in situ*, to which one may if necessary then apply recovery percentages based on the techniques that one hopes may have been invented by the time that the oil in question comes to be taken out. The trouble is that what you arrive at is not susceptible of any form of periodical checking with what is actually discovered in the meantime; and that opens the question whether such estimates have any practical meaning at all.

One of the few purposes served by estimates of ultimate reserves is to reassure people who fear the world may soon run out of oil, as people may who simply apply current rates of growth in consumption till, say, the end of the century and compare how much oil we may by then cumulatively have taken out of the earth against the figures of 'proved reserves'. Another purpose, it is difficult not to suspect, may be simply to bedevil forecasters in other fuel industries. Some planners in other industries, such as coal, base their own ideas of the amount of capacity they ought to keep in being on the argument that the oil industry's own forecasts of growth in consumption imply quite sharply rising costs for petroleum by about the end of the century. Whether or not such estimation is ever wise, it is almost predictably upset, within a year or so, by some far more optimistic estimate of the 'ultimate reserves' of oil likely to be available by another (or even the same) famous oil geologist: the latest figures suggest that some 2,000,000 million barrels may be recoverable by primary techniques, and another 1,500,000 million barrels by 'secondary recovery' techniques. Steadily growing exploration of oil structures in the Middle East, for example, and a more systematic survey of many areas of the earth, are largely responsible for the recurrent revision upward of such estimates. But the constant upward revision also seems to represent in part simply the geologists' state of mind— which is characteristically sanguine, and on experience so far has good reason to be.

It is probably safer to settle for another of the oil industry's generalizations—'There is still a good deal more oil left in the earth than has ever been taken out.' Even in terms of 'published proved reserves', that is still true, as a statistical statement; and estimates of the world's proved reserves, as we have seen, have of late been growing rapidly. Whether it is true of the United States alone may be becoming more arguable; at least in terms of oil economically recoverable at costs comparable to those at which it could be imported from elsewhere. In any case, given current orders of cost and a finite reservoir of this exhausting resource, many oilmen there believe that the peak rate of American output may be passed during the next 10–15 years. And North America is the only major area of the world that has ever supported a really high rate of petroleum consumption out of its own resources. (Russia in the late fifties used no more oil per head than Hawaii.) The only other centres of really high consumption, primarily Western Europe and certain parts of the British Commonwealth, have never had very significant proved oil reserves of their own at all: about half of one per cent of the world's oil reserves. In 1961, Western Europe produced in fact about one and a half per cent of the world output; but this amounted to no more than one-thirteenth of the amount of oil that it consumed.

This pattern of oil geography, therefore, makes a very large part of the world's consumption of oil dependent on long-distance seaborne trade between the main exporting countries that produce most of it but use hardly any, and a group of consuming countries which use large and growing amounts but produce practically none. Until the mid-twenties most of the oil moving around the world came from Mexico and the United States. For the next generation Venezuela was the dominant supplier. Since about 1950, the Middle East has been in the lead. The United States began to import oil between the wars, but did not become a steady net importer until about 1948. Up to 1961, though its imports covered only about a fifth of its consumption, they were still the largest of any country in the world. As a region, however, Western Europe has long been the destination for the biggest imports; in 1961, it brought in about 4½ million barrels a day, twice as much as North America. Gradual shifts between the sources from which oil is carried to the main importing countries, allied with the switch of certain countries from exporting to importing, have transformed the pattern of the world's oil trade, at the same time that its total volume has been growing rapidly like everything else in oil. But they have only sharpened the distinction between have and have-not, consume-not and consume, which is responsible for that trade.

Are any developments in sight in the world's oil industry that may greatly alter this interlocking pattern—and basic interdependence—of consumer and producer nations? In what it is fashionable to call 'the foreseeable future'—say over the next 25 years—one can obviously expect the countries from which oil is exported, some of them already rich though not industrialized countries, to develop standards of living that consume much more energy; and what they consume is unlikely to be anything but petroleum. The United States, as an act of policy, has reduced the rate of growth of its net imports; and if it remains prepared to accept the somewhat higher—though not necessarily rising—cost of energy produced at home, it may not make such demands on the main exporting countries as it expected some years ago. New major oil-producing areas, such as North Africa, are already rising in importance, particularly where they are located nearer the big importing areas than the present Middle East and Caribbean suppliers. The present industrialized importing areas—in particular, Western Europe—are beginning to be explored for oil more intensively than ever before; and they cannot necessarily be written off in terms of petroleum production of one kind or another—particularly of natural gas.

Nevertheless, if one assumes peace and even moderate rates of economic growth, it is difficult to expect anything but a continued rise in imports of energy into Western Europe. Less developed economies are likely to be growing faster and so will their consumption of oil. But the absolute lead in living standard of the highly industrialized societies, and their lead in population over all but a few of the others such as India and China, are likely to mean that their total consumption remains a very large proportion of the world total. There seems little chance, moreover, of any massive shift in the geographical balance of world industrialization during say the next twenty-five years.

The world's industrial centres were originally developed according to the location of coal and iron ore, and though much of the original iron ore in such centres has gone and the coal is getting expensive, the concentrations of technology and high consumption developed around those locations last a long time. The economies newly becoming industrialized are far less dependent on coal than those developed earlier, and certain materials of construction which are now rising in importance, such as aluminium and the plastics, can reduce a developing economy's dependence even on steel. Natural gas, again, might possibly turn out to be more of a 'resource-locating' fuel than oil has ever been. It certainly seems likely that certain bulk chemical commodities will be made from natural gas at source, and moved by tanker around the world in large volumes, from now on. But one specialized job that petroleum has not until recently been able to do, the smelting of iron, has served coal well. Moreover the institutional 'weight' in the world market of the economies built on coal retain a considerable magnetism for capital—and for educated manpower.

If the import requirements of the developed Western economies are then certain to remain a huge and possibly growing proportion of the world oil trade over the next generation or so, where they may be met from is perhaps something that it is less wise to prophesy, even in purely economic terms. Did many experts guess in 1929 how the centre of gravity of world petroleum would shift, over the next thirty years, to the Middle East? Yet when one considers the reserves of oil now certainly available in that region, and the likelihood of further discoveries there, given any really intensive drilling—even apart from the relatively low cost of oil there, of which we have said nothing so far—it is hard to believe that any other area can replace it over the next generation. Diversity in sources of supply is something that customers might seek for economic reasons alone, even if there were no political reasons pressing them into doing so. It is also something that companies that develop and purvey oil throughout the world may logically also go on seeking, even in times of surplus. But we ought probably to assume that the industrialized areas of the world are likely, on balance, to become even less self-sufficient in fuel; and that a very high proportion of the

49   D

fuel they import will still have to come from the major exporting regions of today, give or take one or two significant areas.

This separation of oil resources from oil markets, over the industry's history, has brought immense benefits to many otherwise under-developed parts of the world, as well as to the developed powers that supplied the knowhow and capital, and the companies that have done the job. Oil is a kind of fuel for which there is still no practical way of providing autarchic substitutes. It has been the source of possibly the greatest single wave of overseas investment in history, and of a fantastic acceleration of economic advancement in some areas. It has been developed, so far, by companies domiciled originally in developed countries—and in particular by a handful of very big ones, inter-national in scope, mobile in operations and dealing on terms approach-ing equality with the governments not only of exporting, but of con-suming countries. These oil companies fulfil, primarily, an economic role—though it quite often does not seem to the governments concerned to remain simply economic, and perhaps could never have been expected to remain so. For both the economics of oil development and the institutions that have evolved to carry it out are rather unusual.

CHAPTER IV

Operating Economics: I. Crude Oil

Nobody outside the oil industry can hope to gain more than the sketchiest idea of its technology; indeed, few people inside would claim they know it all. Along with the chemical industry, it was among the first of the 'science-based' industries; today, from one end of its long chain of operations to the other, it is still involved in steady improvement of the complex techniques that it employs. It is a safe generalization to say that this industry has a characteristic pattern of high fixed costs and low running costs, so that almost always the next barrel of oil that passes along the line costs less than the last one did. But to put meaning on the bones of that generalization, we need to consider the cost pattern of each of the main stages in the industry's operations.

The production of oil can logically be linked with exploration for it (in the past; unfortunately, there is no automatic link between present exploration and future production). For convenience rather than in logic, this chapter also includes a sketch of the specialized forms of long distance transport used to move oil. Tankers and pipelines, obviously, are used to move products as well as crude oil. But as crude accounts for a growing proportion—now some 65–70 per cent—of the oil moved in international trade, and a considerable proportion of the products move within self-sufficient countries such as the United States and Russia, it is convenient to consider oil transport primarily in terms of crude movement from producing areas onward towards the market. In a following chapter, the operating economics of processing crude oil into products that consumers can use and getting those products to the customers are considered. A third one glances at the economics of natural gas, which is a part of the petroleum industry and to a large extent overlaps oil operations, but over a large part of the world is now emerging as a partly competitive fuel in distinct circumstances of its own.

OPERATING ECONOMICS

Production and Exploration

At the end of 1960, about 698,000 oil wells were in operation through the world; with almost 21 million barrels a day, or 1,100 million tons a year, of total output, that gave an average yield of less than 30 barrels a day, or 1,450 tons a year, for each well. But that average is utterly misleading. About 620,000 of those wells were in the United States, producing in all about 7·8 million barrels a day, which is a sizeable proportion of the world's output, but an average of no more than 13 barrels a day, or 650 tons a year, from each well. In the Middle East, on the other hand, fewer than 1,300 wells were in operation throughout the oil-producing territories, for an output of 5·2 million barrels a day, producing an average of 4,300 barrels a day (215,000 tons a year) each. In Iran and Iraq, each with only about a hundred wells in operation, the average was nearly 10,000 barrels a day from each well. Between these extremes of dribble and flood came the 10,500 wells in Venezuela, each producing about 280 barrels a day; those in Indonesia, with an average of about 200 barrels a day; and the 32,000 or so wells of the U.S.S.R., producing about 95 barrels a day each. And within each of these countries, there are further variations between the old and the new, the richer and the less productive oilfields.

This fantastically wide variation between rates of output from the wells that this industry considers it worth while keeping in operation results from various factors. These include the different volumes and conditions in which the oil lies in the earth in different places, the depths from which it is being taken out, the working age of any given well, and the number of them that have been drilled to tap the same oil reservoir. When the pressure in the oil reservoir that one is tapping is high, it will gush to the surface at a very high rate; and so will crudes in which there is a very high proportion of dissolved gas, even if they are found at great depths. Over the working 'life cycle' of an oil well, again, one would normally expect an initial period on 'natural drive' with the oil flowing to the surface of its own accord. Then comes one form or another of 'artificial lift' which lengthens the wells' working life. Both these phases are classed as 'primary recovery'. Finally the well declines to operation as 'a stripper', exhausting its last few barrels a day, unless the operator has in the meantime decided to invest in more elaborate forms of 'secondary recovery'. The techniques used are generally those of 'fluid injection' with gas or water. When applied early in a well's producing life, this is known as 'pressure maintenance'. But when

I. CRUDE OIL

it is applied only when the well's natural pressure is becoming exhausted, as 're-pressuring' and 'water flooding' along with more complex techniques, it ranks as 'secondary recovery'.

The period that any well runs on 'natural drive'—obviously its time of lowest costs—will vary according to underground conditions and possibly also according to the number of wells that have been drilled into its reservoir of oil. Over-drilling, which has occurred in some parts of the United States and elsewhere at certain periods, can waste the underground pressure in a reservoir and indeed reduce the proportion of the oil in it that one can hope to get out without resort to costly methods of secondary recovery. Most of the wells in the Middle East are still on natural drive, and conditions in the reservoirs there are such as to keep them flowing without assistance from the surface for many years; but pressure maintenance is already being applied. In the United States, on the other hand, nearly 90 per cent of all producing wells, in 1960, were 'on the pump'; that is to say, that the oil was being raised with the help of various kinds of pump or by other techniques such as 'gas lift', which involves injecting gas under pressure into the column of oil contained in the well, to reduce the weight of it and enable underground pressure to keep it flowing to the surface.

Many of the 700,000-odd oil wells in production across the world in 1960 were producing far less oil than they could have been, though comparatively few, except in Venezuela, were actually 'shut in' for lack of demand. In the free world in 1961, it was reckoned that there existed extra capacity for perhaps 7–8 million barrels of oil a day, or 40 per cent more oil a year than was in fact being used. Whether that capacity could have been brought into production and moved to market very quickly was another matter; but it was available, and about 3,000,000 barrels a day of it was in the United States and Canada. In part, this reflected a situation of surplus in the world oil market; but it also reflected the past history of oil exploitation in the United States, and the continuing incentives that drive oil companies to go on looking for more oil even when they cannot easily sell all that is already available.

Between the end of the Second World War and the beginning of the sixties, the total of proved oil reserves in the world rose by about 230 billion barrels, or 30 billion tons. During the same period, from the end of 1945 to the end of 1959, the oil industries of the world produced about 72 billion barrels or nearly 10,000 million tons of oil for consumers. The amount of new oil proven in reserves, therefore, was of the order of 300 billion barrels. This was the result of a prodigious effort of exploration and development of known oilfields. Together, exploration and production in the free world alone have been reckoned during the period to have absorbed some $50–60 billion (about $20,000 million) during these fourteen years.

This postwar surge of exploration for oil was partly to match a rapid expansion in demand and to provide for the maintenance of a greatly expanded capacity in being. Oil, like other extractive industries, has constantly to provide against the depletion of the resources it is working. In terms of the actual physical depletion of reservoirs, this factor is really significant perhaps only in the areas where production has been established on a large scale for a long time. In the United States, for example, every producer seeks to find another barrel for each barrel of oil he takes out (and he may have to spend practically all the profit he gets out of the one in finding the other). Oil leases there are granted for extremely small areas, and there may be many operators drilling in a given field. In the past, therefore, there was an incentive to drill as many wells as one could to tap the maximum amount of oil from a reservoir before your competitors also tapped so much as to reduce production. Conservation laws there now control this to some extent; even so, the depletion allowance granted in U.S. tax law on income from production, and the ability to write off the costs of preliminary exploration as an expense, plus the preferential production rights allowed to new wells, encourage an uneconomic rate of drilling.

Outside America this seldom occurs, because the concession areas in which a given company acquires the right to drill are so much larger that competitors are unlikely to have rights near the new oil deposits one may locate. But against that, nowadays, a concessionaire is generally obliged to carry through a minimum programme of drilling and to bring any fields located into production within a given period, or relinquish his rights to explore. And to abandon or drastically to reduce exploration in an area where one may have invested many millions is a heavy decision to make because of the current state of the market for finished petroleum products. It is seldom, after all, that any significant supplies of oil come on to the market from a new oilfield in less than about three years from the time the find is made, and in that time the state of demand can have altered quite radically. Outside the Soviet sphere, again, we are not concerned in this industry with managements who imagine they can do what is best for whole industries. The people who have to decide are concerned with the present and future of individual companies. Moreover, they may always be pushed into

I. CRUDE OIL

exploring any given area by the feeling that if they do not somebody else will take the gamble—and perhaps the winnings, which may eventually be huge.

In the process of finding oil and developing production, very large amounts of money have first to be gambled on what may be no more than an experienced geologist's hunch. Even if this gamble pays off, a great deal more money will have to be invested, not only in determining the extent of the field and installing the production facilities. Often, particularly in the underdeveloped areas where most drilling goes on, much capital has to be invested in providing transport facilities to move the oil and living accommodation, with some standards of amenity, for the people who will be responsible for getting it out of the ground. A large proportion of the money spent on exploration, particularly the early stages of it, tends to be wasted; and practically all the money ploughed into production has to be invested before the venture pays a penny of return on capital.

The chances of finding oil when one drills a 'wildcat' well in exploration are often quoted at one in nine; in practice, this figure comes from the United States, where the statistics are more reliable than anywhere else but the circumstances encourage drilling in less promising conditions than would be commercially wise almost anywhere else. In the same way, one might relate estimates of the industry's total investment in exploration and production to the volume of new reserves added to proven reserves in a year, and come up with an average cost per barrel of oil added to reserves. Once again, such averages are misleading. There are areas of the world where the chances of finding oil are extremely good, and the chances that if you do it will be cheap to produce and bring to ocean-going transport are very high. One has only to cite the Kuwait off-shore area for which Shell secured a concession to explore at the end of 1960. The Japanese Arabian Oil Company, which began drilling off the shore of the Kuwait Neutral Zone, somewhat to the south of this a year or two earlier, discovered oil with the first well that it sank. Yet during the same twelve months a number of major companies had decided to pull out of Papua, where some years and millions had been spent in pursuing what seemed a good chance of finding oil; and Shell and B.P. were finally able to achieve an output of 10,000 barrels a day from two fields in Nigeria, in finding which they had spent about £30 million over a period of nearly twenty-one years.

An oil company does not begin to put down the heavy stakes in the gamble of exploration until it begins drilling; any refinement in preliminary techniques that will reduce the risk of 'dry holes', therefore, is eagerly sought. The ordinary sequence of searching for oil begins with a preliminary reconnaissance by the geologists, which may take anything up to a year for a large area on which little data exists. If this is favourable, it will be followed by surface geological mapping and air photography. Geophysical survey of likely areas, by techniques that measure fractional differences in the earth's gravitational or magnetic fields, or by seismic methods akin to echo-sounding, follows. But all these stages can at best assess the probability that oil may be found in certain places. Nowadays, petroleum can only be found with the drill—and indeed it may be necessary to drill 'stratigraphic' test wells to investigate the nature of the rock strata before taking the decision whether or not to go ahead in drilling actual test wells for oil. The preliminaries will probably cost hundreds of thousands of pounds, when you count in the cost of accommodating and administering the expeditions involved, and may run into millions. A drilling programme is fairly certain to cost millions.

It was estimated in the middle fifties that 60 per cent of the oil contained in proved reserves in the major oil-producing areas of the free world lay between 1,000 feet and 5,000 feet below the surface, and another 30 per cent between 5,000 and 8,000 feet down. It is still possible to happen on new and highly productive fields within these depths; but exploration teams are tending to have to drill more and more of their wells between say 3,000 and 10,000 feet, and many go much deeper. The deepest hole ever drilled into the earth's crust (until American and Russian geophysicists began seeing who could dig down farthest purely in the interests of national science) was by an oil company in West Texas. It went to some 25,000 feet, before the company decided to stop. Almost inevitably, it was a dry hole (though production has now been achieved from wells below 21,000 feet). The rigs involved in drilling are large and fairly elaborate pieces of equipment. Though they are constantly being rendered more mobile, in remote areas they need backing up with supply services and all the people concerned need accommodation and provisions, so that the exercise is inherently costly, at times running into hundreds of pounds per foot drilled. To say that rotary drilling consists of rotating a toothed bit in the earth on the end of a string of pipes, while pumping through it a specially-compounded mud that carries to the surface the debris—and the evidence—is broadly true but hopelessly inadequate to describe what goes on. Over the years drillers have perfected ways of dealing with the

I. CRUDE OIL

myriad difficulties that can arise in carrying on a boring operation in which the bit may be two or three miles out of sight below your feet, but test drilling will probably never become a routine operation. Nor can it ever be anything but a financial risk.

Even to locate oil is not nearly enough. You have to estimate the 'pay thickness' and then the extent of the oil reservoir. Then you have to decide whether the investment so far and the probable life of the reservoir at a rate of extraction that will justify putting in transport facilities—almost certainly a tanker terminal, and frequently a long pipeline to feed it—make the further investment of bringing the find into production worth while. Once the decision is made, an oil company has to invest more years and millions before the first oil from this new underground source flows into world trade. Getting the oil to the surface, in the initial stages, may be no problem, since it often lifts itself up to be stoppered and led off from the characteristic 'Christmas tree' of valves and gauges. But the correct spacing of wells to take off the required volumes of oil, the assessment and utilization of pressure conditions in the underground reservoir, and the installation of surface equipment to separate gas in solution and to treat any of its other special properties, are technically demanding and costly. Pipes to take the oil away, tank farms to hold some limited amount in store (though one seldom wants to store much crude anywhere but in the best place, under the earth), and ocean terminals to load it into tankers (assuming that the oil is discovered remote from refineries and markets) require further investment. Complete townships, such as Ahmadi in Kuwait and Dhahran in Saudi Arabia, may have to be developed to house the technical staff and management involved, in what may well be in its own right a very big business indeed.

In economic terms, this business of oil exploration, development, and production is highly capital-intensive; and the time-table of the investment involved has a peculiar effect upon the production costs of oil. For almost all the investment involved has to be committed before the entrepreneur gets his first barrel of oil to market or nets any return at all. In many cases the running costs of producing oil are very low indeed; they are almost always low in relation to the burden of capital charges that the product has to bear. As a result, oil production is in a situation of 'decreasing marginal costs' over a much longer part of its 'plant's' working life than most other industries are. In particular it is in a cost situation sharply contrasted with that of the other extractive industries, which includes one of its main competitors, coal. Oilmen generally bridle if you say to them that oil mines itself; and when you consider the vast effort and expense, in many cases fruitless, that has to be put in before a barrel of oil is produced from a new well, they have every reason. But after those resources are committed, successfully, for a while the oil comes up on its own.

At some point in the working life of a given well—say twenty-five to forty years—it can be argued that the normal pattern of diminishing returns that must eventually apply to any industry extracting a wasting asset does begin to assert itself. So long as the well is flowing freely— mining itself?—its marginal costs diminish; when it is shifted over to its next stage of artificial lift, such as straight pumping or the injection of gas to help it to the surface, its costs rise sharply by one further 'step'. But this upward step again is mainly a fixed addition to the capital investment embodied in the well; the running costs are increased, but do not become very high and remain the same for a considerable time. So for another longish period in the well's working life its incremental costs are again probably diminishing. Eventually, perhaps, it reaches a point where the flow, even assisted, becomes such a trickle that without exceptional and yet more costly techniques of secondary recovery, the owner may turn off the tap. The well, or on a rather wider scale the field, is gone; so is the investment. The owner has undoubtedly been looking for reserves to replace those he is taking out; indeed, the point at which he finally decides to take the expiring well out of production may well be influenced by the relative cheapness of new production he has found elsewhere. But across a whole industry where steady exploration eventually finds enough new oil fairly cheaply, the situation of diminishing returns that eventually shows in the working life of a single well may not necessarily begin to declare itself for many many years, until far more of the world's oil-producing areas begin to move into the situation of the United States. There, reckoning all the industry's costs according to their peculiar pattern, some experts would say oil is already in a situation of diminishing returns; the next barrel may not cost more to produce, but it tends to cost more to replace than the last.

This pattern of cost makes competition with oil intensely difficult for coal, an industry extracting solids from the earth by cutting them out of the seams underground and lifting them. Mechanically or with hand labour—and there is no doubt that most of the coal industries of the world have stayed more dependent on hand labour, and over a longer period, than they should have done—this job is one in which running costs are high and usually increasing, if only because each next ton one wins is farther away from the surface or the shaft bottom. Where it comes into direct competition with coal, oil's peculiar pattern of production cost—a pattern that tends to be repeated in later stages of its progress to market—gives it tremendous inherent advantages. But this same pattern of cost can have considerable embarrassments for the oil industry itself in internal competition. Large amounts of new capital may be attracted into oil, particularly in the most productive areas, by the very high returns that entrepreneurs can on occasion earn there. But the return that can be earned on oil production depends on getting the oil to market—and without command of the facilities to do so, the new producer may be forced to unload his oil at prices that offer very low returns indeed.

TRANSPORT

Once at the top of the well, oil is ready to flow where the producer wishes. Its very nature as a liquid is the essence of the ease and cheapness with which it can be transported, in comparison with other fuels and indeed with most other commodities that move in world trade—just as it is essential to the consumption of oil and is the property around which the technology of its processing has been developed. This liquid has to be contained to be handled at all, and generally in a specialized container: once the volume is large enough, it is convenient to combine the container and the means of transport. In the pipeline the product moves, not the container. The ocean tanker, on the other hand, gains economies of scale from the principle that the containing 'skin' of any receptacle rises as the square of its dimensions, whereas the volume enclosed rises as the cube of them.

On any one day at the beginning of the sixties, there might have been about 15 million tons of crude oil and products moving in perhaps 25 million deadweight tons of tankers around the world, and a like tonnage of tankers in ballast on their way back to be filled up again. There are not many return hauls in the crude oil trade, and vessels are generally employed over any given period on crude or on products, but not both. In the movement of petroleum products, some of which may be in surplus in one refinery area and some in others, the shipping departments of the oil companies can make rather more use of 'triangular' routeing of their ships, but this too is limited. World-wide movement of oil, at the beginning of the sixties, was using about 90 per cent of a world tanker fleet that totalled, at the end of 1961, some 67 million deadweight tons, representing about one-third of all merchant shipping in the world. This total was about three times as big as in 1939, and 25 times as much as in 1914: over the last generation, in particular, tanker tonnage has been by far the most rapidly growing element in world shipping. And it has been increasing much faster in carrying capacity than in tonnage, because average speeds have steadily risen too, and the new, faster tankers are the larger ones. Before the war, companies were building tankers mostly of say 12,000 tons deadweight and operating speeds of say 11–12 knots. The T–2 standard tanker, turned out in vast numbers by American shipyards during the war, is of 16,800 tons with an operating speed of 14–16 knots. Since the war standard sizes have risen rapidly, from 28,000 tons and 32,500 tons d.w. until today, when most new tankers are of 40,000–50,000 tons d.w. and a growing number are of 50,000–80,000, with some giants of 100,000–130,000 tons d.w. in service. Operating speeds have risen to 17–18 knots.

One can hardly give any comparable figure of the total capacity of pipelines throughout the world: sufficient statistics do not exist. The total length of pipelines in being in 1960 has been put at 700,000 miles (apart from the Communist countries, where large developments are in train): of this total some 540,000 miles carried natural gas, and 250,000 miles carried oil. The majority of this was crude oil; so far the main use of pipelines in this industry has been to carry this from inland oilfields to refineries or tanker terminals. The use of pipelines for the movement of refined products, hitherto economic only in the United States, is now spreading to Europe, where another fresh development is the building of crude pipelines from ports to refineries far inland. There is talk of building undersea pipelines for both oil and gas from North African oil terminals across the Mediterranean to the coast of South-West Europe; but so far there is only one major crude pipeline in the world that operates in direct competition with ocean tankers. This is TAPline, the 754-mile line completed in 1950 from Sidon in the Lebanon to Qaisumah in Saudi Arabia, where it joins a 314-mile pipeline to the Abqaiq oilfields in Arabia. TAPline can deliver 470,000 barrels of crude a day (23 million tons a year) to the Eastern Mediterranean; when working to full capacity, it will at any time contain about 5 million barrels of oil. In operation, it has somewhat reduced the growth of seaborne movement of oil, by reducing the number of tankers that have to go from the West right round to the Persian Gulf. A similar

I. CRUDE OIL

effect has been experienced from the use of the trunk pipelines from Northern Iraq to the Eastern Mediterranean, though these lines, from far inland, can hardly be called directly competitive with tankers. Certain large trunk lines were built from Texas to the north-east coast of the United States during the war for the movement of crude, but the distances involved then offered insufficient advantage over coastwise tanker shipment, and these lines are now used to move natural gas. As the big trunk lines from the Russian oilfields to Central Europe come into operation, they will be playing a real part in the world oil trade and moving oil that might have come from the Black Sea by tanker. But so far TAPline has been the only major line to play a big part in the free world's international trade in crude oil, and practically all the oil that it delivers to Sidon is loaded into tankers for further movement. In the movement of crude oil, so far, pipelines and tankers have been much more complementary than competitive.

In Western Europe, however, now pipelines are beginning to play a larger part, by moving crude oil from the southern coast of Europe to refineries built inland. Once oil from the Persian Gulf that moves to the Eastern Mediterranean by TAPline instead of tanker can go from Marseilles to Stuttgart or Strasbourg by pipeline instead, possibly, of sailing round the North Sea to be transhipped into smaller tankers to sail up the Rhine, a long distance is lopped off each end of the tanker haul to North-West Europe. That is one new development that is tending to moderate the growth of the total ton-miles travelled by tankers in the seaborne movement of oil. Another is the rapid development of production much nearer Europe, in Algeria and in Libya. A third—which is only partly economic, and belongs properly to our later discussion of nationalism—is that the movement of oil from the Middle East to the United States has not grown to the degree that that was foreseen in the fifties.

The greater part of the oil movement around the world flows towards the shores of the North Atlantic; but in comparison with pre-war years, a far larger amount now comes from the Eastern hemisphere, and the bulk of this from the Middle East. At the end of the fifties, indeed, the movement of crude oil from the Western hemisphere to consuming countries in Europe and points East was down to a trickle. Considerable quantities of products were still being exported from Venezuela to Europe (not least because the most rapid rise in European demand was for fuel oil, and Venezuelan crudes offer relatively high yields of fuel oil).

61

During the early postwar years, with this big shift in the network of oil movement, the average distance that a ton of oil moved to market steadily rose: it was about 3,600 miles, 12 days' steaming for a 14-knot tanker, by 1955, some 13 per cent farther than the average for 1938. During the fifties, looking forward ten years or more as it is necessary to do in planning all the facilities that a capital-intensive industry such as oil needs in a period of fast and steady growth, forecasters in the major companies reckoned that the average distance would continue to lengthen. The interruption of oil supplies during the Suez crisis emphasized that in future large quantities of oil might have to be shipped from the Persian Gulf round the Cape, instead of through an international waterway under nationalist and potentially hostile control. This strengthened the forecasters' conclusions; they may indeed have put an extra margin for security into their calculations about the tanker tonnage required. By the beginnings of the sixties, some of the factors we have mentioned above—supplies nearer Europe, pipelines within Europe, and restrictions on American imports—were beginning to weaken the basis of that reasoning. But the tankers—some 35 million tons ordered between 1954 and 1957—were coming down the slipways by then; the money was spent.

It was a vast amount of money; the 30 million tons on shipyard order-books around the world at the peak in 1956–58 represented, at then prices, perhaps £2,750,000,000. Means of transporting oil represent a sizeable investment—one among the many in this industry. There is one saving, however, of which the company investing in tankers can take advantage: remarkable economies of scale. It takes less labour, steel, and shipyard design to build a tanker to carry 60,000 tons of crude oil than it does to build two to carry 30,000 tons each; and less than twice as much shaft horse power to drive it through the water at a given speed, and hence less bunker fuel. The crew needed on the larger tanker is little larger than on one of the smaller ones, and up to a point insurance costs per ton of cargo fall as size increases. 'Up to a point' applies to all these economies; there may come a point where the construction costs and certain running costs 'fault' upward sharply, before economies of scale again begin to apply at the higher level.

Another factor that limited the extent to which tanker owners were prepared to seek economies by building bigger, even during the building boom just after the Suez incident, was the question where the vessels could sail and could profitably be employed. If the Suez Canal had remained closed, and the same amount of oil had had to be moved to the West from the Persian Gulf, the industry would have needed more capacity to move it round the Cape. This might have been had most cheaply by building very big tankers; or more pipeline capacity from the Gulf to the Eastern Mediterranean; or some combination of both. The most economical tanker capacity to build for the longer run, indeed, might have been vessels of say 80,000–100,000 tons d.w. But these would not have had the alternative of going through the canal if it were open, because they would draw too much water to transit the waterway even after all existing plans to deepen it were carried out, and even if they were only part-loaded and riding high in the water. The canal did not stay closed. Shifts in the rate of growth of American demand for Middle East oil, and in the sources of supply for Europe, gave a chance of moderating the flow of crude oil to the West if the companies had to do so. And the companies pressed forward with plans to increase the capacity of the existing pipelines to the Mediterranean, though the cutting of the line from Kirkuk to Tripoli, during the Suez affair, did not exactly predispose them to lay down more capital immovably on the ground in the shape of new lines; and by the time the new pumping capacity on existing lines from Iraq was completed the companies were in bitter dispute with its government. They did, certainly, begin to construct a number of large terminals in Europe as well as the United States, to and from which super-tankers could operate. Moreover, supplies from the Middle East to Japan, and also to the United States, favoured use of the 100,000-tonner. The limited depth of anchorage within reach of the main consuming centres of the world, and the need to keep as costly a single item of capital as a tanker of this size fully and regularly employed, mean that an investment in super-tankers has to be supported by heavy investment in terminals to take them.

The big ocean-going tanker is still probably the cheapest way of moving oil—provided that it is not so big that apart from other increases in cost it has to forfeit the flexibility of operations that tankers ordinarily enjoy. It is a highly mobile unit of 'fixed capital'; by contrast, the pipeline is fixed in the physical as well as in the accounting sense. The pipeline is a highly efficient form of continuous one-way transport of fluids; but it is itself immovable. Its costs are almost entirely fixed costs, and the unit cost of moving oil therefore falls fairly steadily up to the limits of its capacity. This capacity depends largely on the diameter of the pipe and the pressure gradient from one end to the other: you can move the same amount of oil in a given time by a large-diameter pipe

63

with a small pressure drop, or a smaller diameter with a larger pressure drop, and the choice may depend on the cost of pumping stations, to move the oil along the pipe. One can move 800,000 barrels of oil a day, or 40 million tons a year along a 36-inch pipeline, the largest diameter so far in general use.

Unit costs of fluid movement along a pipeline, unlike those in most other forms of transport, depend hardly at all on distance. The main cost is the pipe, and another mile of route takes another mile of pipe and a corresponding fraction more power. Administrative costs tend to fall as the length of a line extends: but these are relatively insignificant anyway. But the unit costs that a pipeline actually achieves, as against those it can potentially offer, depends upon the extent to which it is used. Its costs rise significantly when it is used below full capacity, and in the short term it has a rigidly defined total capacity without the possibilities of overload in times of emergency possible for most other forms of transport—and for most of the other expensive capital plant that the oil industry uses.

It is usual to begin operating a pipeline with the minimum pumping power—a single pumping station theoretically, would do for a line some hundreds of miles long, provided it traversed flat country—and later build up its capacity towards the theoretical limit by installing more stations. The optimum for large-diameter lines has been put at one pumping station per 60 to 150 miles; obviously costs of pumping are higher where a station has to be installed in remote country without any basic services at all, but the stations can use the fuel that is being moved in the line, and are increasingly being remotely controlled. Since TAPline was installed in 1950, its capacity has been increased almost 60 per cent by increasing the permissible pressure and putting in extra pumping units; the extra investment required amounted to no more than 12 per cent of the $200 million that it originally cost to lay the line. But in 1960 TAPline was moving oil at only about half its full rated capacity—some 240,000 barrels a day during the year, compared with 368,000 barrels a day in 1958. Its costs were unable to compete with those of large efficient tankers in a very depressed freight market.

Many comparisons have been published from time to time of the cost of moving oil in various forms of transport; it is not easy to keep these realistic when costs of one form of transport vary primarily with the utilization of capacity and those of most others mainly with distance. Moreover, the cost of tanker operations is one thing: freight rates at any

I. CRUDE OIL

particular time may be another. Over equal distances, no crude pipeline has ever yet been able to compete even with the average tankers of today, let alone the super-tanker on an efficiently organized run. Product pipelines are probably cheaper than road or railway movement over equal distances for quantities of half a million tons a year or more; and cheaper than major river transport for quantities of a million tons or more. And it has to be remembered that the pipeline can usually go for a shorter way from A to B than any other form of transport and can operate regardless of weather conditions. Costs for tankers and most other forms of transport fall with distance, because one only has to load and unload once however long the journey: those of the pipeline do not. For the movement of crude, pipelines are an essential complement to tankers, but seldom compete except where much shorter distances can be achieved. For products, though problems arise for viscous fluids such as heavy fuel oil, which may need preheating and heavy insulation of a pipe (or the mixing of fuel oil, like some solid fuels, with water), they are coming in logically as inland centres of consumption develop. For natural gas, as will be seen later, they form so far the only practicable means of transport, though others may soon be able to compete in technical terms at least. The operating economics of petroleum transport, as we have seen, vary considerably in detail. But both of the main specialized forms require very large capital investment, and need operating to high capacity in order to achieve their inherent economies in cost.

E

CHAPTER V

Operating Economics: II. Refined Products

O il, which is now becoming the world's most widely used fuel, is hardly ever burned raw. All crude oil is a mixture of a long series of hydro-carbon compounds, but the nature of the mixture varies considerably between crudes from different oilfields and types of sedimentary strata. Here we are concerned with the chemistry of petroleum only in terms of the range of products that can be processed from these crudes; broadly, they can be ranked in three main families, paraffinic, asphaltic, and mixed base crudes. Paraffin based crudes, when refined, will give a high yield of gasoline and a fairly high yield of kerosene, a residue from which lubricating oils can be made, and solid paraffin waxes as a by-product. Asphaltic based crudes give a low yield of the lighter products, and a large yield of the black oils, with a semi-solid residue that is marketed as bitumen. Mixed base crudes come in between the other two. The first crude oils commercially refined, from the Pennsylvania fields in the eighteen-sixties, were paraffinic crudes rich in light products (which suited the early demand for lamp oil, though the gasoline yield was a nuisance). Venezuelan, Mexican and Californian crudes are asphaltic with a particularly high yield of fuel oil. Most of the crudes produced in the Middle East and in the main basins of the United States are of mixed base, with yields of products between the two extremes.

The main range of liquid petroleum products, again, can be ranked in terms of end-use. There are a range of light products, primarily the gasolines, but including diesel oil, from which energy is best obtained by explosive combustion; these are mainly used in road and air transport. Then come a range of diverse general fuels, from paraffin to heavy fuel oil, from which one obtains energy mainly by simple burning— though paraffin is used in aircraft jet engines and attempts have long been made to run gas turbines on heavy fuel oil. Certain gases, in particular butane and propane, are separated as by-products of refining

66

II. REFINED PRODUCTS

processes: these have long had a role as fuels for special purposes, and are now, like natural gas, entering the general fuel market, though in far smaller quantities. And outside the fuel field, there comes the vast family of lubricants, general and specialized; waxes and bitumens for a variety of uses; and the range of hydro-carbon compounds used as raw materials in chemical industry, which represent a small proportion of the volume of oil products used throughout the world but have been growing in importance and value to the industry faster of late than any other single group of oil products.

The translation of liquid petroleum from its original complicated mixture into a range of still complex but better-sorted-out products ready for use is effected by a specialized technology of petroleum engineering. This begins by distillation, boiling off the different fractions of the crude oil; so that in refining terms, one talks of the variable yield of products one can get from any given crude in terms of the proportion of its volume that boils off within different bands of the temperature range. Distillation is the main process of separation available to the refiner; but some compounds can also be separated out by solvent extraction, in which a particular solvent may be added to a mixture of hydro-carbon compounds to dissolve and thus separate out those compounds that are soluble in it and leave those that are not. But these 'straight run' processes, which separate the products naturally available in the crude, do not give the refiner the various products in the proportions that he may have a market for them.

A wide range of conversion processes have therefore been developed in order to convert those of which he gets more than he can sell into those of which he cannot get enough to satisfy the market. This family of processes, which began with thermal cracking, the treatment of surplus separated products under high temperature and pressure, has been steadily elaborated through various forms of catalytic conversion and polymerization. Almost always so far, the elaboration of the refinery technique has been in the direction of obtaining more light products, in particular high-grade gasolines, from a barrel of crude oil. Since the late fifties, with demand for fuel oil rising faster than for motor spirit there has been a theoretical case for processes to produce more fuel oil out of the barrel, which would be technically possible providing a market could also be found for large amounts of products such as liquid petroleum gases. But in practice this shift in demand has been met by building more of the new refineries as the simpler types, such as 'topping units' which merely 'skim off' the light products and leave the straight-run residue of black oils. The third main family of processes in refining is concerned with the purification of the products produced, one particular impurity with which refiners are concerned being sulphur. But many other impurities have to be cleaned out of oil products before they are sold to the customer; the general degree of purity across the whole range of products is far higher than could have been achieved thirty years ago.

That over-simplified classification of the main types of process that go on in oil refining can give no idea of the wide variety of techniques employed and the complicated way in which these are linked together. But the fact of their linkage is not without importance in petroleum economics. The continued development of oil refining has brought into being over the last forty years or so a new 'steady-state' technology of chemical processes. In a modern refinery there is a sequence of processes going on unceasingly while the mobile feedstock flows from one on to the next, continuously undergoing chemical and physical change. In continuous flow processes such as these the operating conditions in any one vessel or item of plant remain the same all the time; the liquids and gases undergo the change as they move spatially through the successive items of plant. This assemblage of processing units in each of which conditions are unchanging, but between which balance has continuously to be maintained, do not so much lend themselves to automatic control as require it. In the balancing of certain modern refinery units, it is no longer a question of how many men a given bank of instruments and automatic controllers has replaced. Men could not do the job at all as it is now set up, because it would be impossible for a group of them to co-ordinate their own manipulation of pressure, temperature, flow and the other variables quickly and precisely enough.

Any form of technology where labour simply cannot do much of the operating is by definition capital-intensive; once again, this basic characteristic of the oil industry asserts itself. An oil refinery is one of the most capital-intensive among a group of industries in which capitalization is generally high, the industries that process basic industrial fuels and materials from their raw state. At the beginning of the sixties, there were refineries in the world with a total capacity of close on 25 million barrels a day, or 1,200 million tons a year, representing a capital investment of perhaps $20,000 million. Like tankers and pipelines, refineries can take advantage of economies of scale in their construction and operating costs. There is a minimum scale of throughput below which it is hardly economic to build one—say 15,000 barrels a

II. REFINED PRODUCTS

day—though the further economies to be gained become smaller as one moves up the scale.

Limits to refinery size may be set by the managerial capacity required to head such a plant and make all the decisions that have to be made (though the computer is coming in here to lighten the executive load of actual operations). Limits are in practice rather more likely to be set by external factors—the size and stability of the market that can economically be served from the refinery, which at giant size will have heavy additional costs to bear from operating at times below capacity. According to the present thinking of refinery designers, there may never be any more giant refineries built such as Abadan. The present tendency seems to be to argue that with a throughput of say 60,000 barrels a day or 3 million tons a year, one has attained all the economies of scale that one can achieve without bringing in extra complications.

As an exceptionally highly-capitalized item of process plant, with high overheads and comparatively low running costs, the refinery has the same characteristic pattern we have seen in exploration and transport of oil—diminishing costs and increasing returns for each incremental barrel up to the limits of its capacity. But the nature of its processing—the separation and conversion of the crude oil into a wide range of different products—introduces another special complexity into its operating economics. Almost all its costs are joint costs, in economic jargon—i.e., one cannot have any of the final products without the whole cost, and incidentally without each other. (As noted above, the refiner has a battery of techniques that enable him to get a larger proportion of any one product; but he can never wholly eliminate the rest of the range.)

This situation of joint costs is a familiar concept in economics (the classic example is another fuel industry, the joint manufacture of gas and coke). With only two products coming from a process, one can postulate a formula for allocating these costs, not in terms of any technical valuation (e.g. the calorific value of the two fuels in heat units), but on the demand for them. One charges all the costs on to the one which is in most demand and which therefore sets the scale of operations; sells the other for whatever it will fetch in the market; and credits its proceeds against the cost of the whole operation to determine the price at which one can sell one's primary product. That is broadly the rule of thumb used in the pricing of gas, coke and the other by-products of the traditional manufacture of coal gas. Either gas (in a gasworks) or coke (in coking plant) can be the major product of the process. But one can never properly speak of the 'cost' of gas or coke (apart from the cost

69

of ancillary operations peculiar to either one). And in the same way, in oil refining, it is hardly meaningful to speak of 'the cost of gasoline' or 'the cost of fuel oil'.

Refining a barrel of oil has a perfectly measurable cost, and the refiner has to get this cost back plus a return on his investment; but none of the products he sells from that barrel has any fully identifiable cost at all. This is not a point that the oil industry has ever managed to get over to the public, or to its competitors, very effectively. Coalminers, for example, feel that some swindle is going on when fuel oil, competing with their product, is sold for less than the price that the crude oil from which it is refined cost the refinery. This may well happen when the refiner can get most of his margin out of selling other products, such as gasoline, more remuneratively. But there is no trick in it; the price at which it pays the refiner to sell any given product will depend upon the range of prices at which he can sell the rest. Pricing in the oil industry is dealt with in a later chapter. Suffice it to say here that the relative prices of products, which together make up the return on the refinery investment, will depend largely upon the relative strength of demand for each and the degree of competition in its market, including the cost of entry into each market. Some products are always liable to be sold at low 'by-product' prices to give even a small addition to the refiners' total return on the barrel of crude. Argument about when a product ceases to be a by-product and should be expected to contribute more of the total margin is perfectly legitimate. Argument about 'the cost' of individual refined products is not—except in relation to specialized facilities put in to purify or treat particular products.

The volume of saleable products from an oil refinery is today, though it has not always been, almost as large as the volume of the raw material. This volume of products, moreover, costs rather more to store and to transport than crude does, because it has to be segregated in separate tankage and moved in separate containers, generally smaller and less efficient than the means of transport that crude uses. A refinery need not necessarily be located as close to the source of its raw material, therefore, as for example, an iron and steelworks (into which about six tons of ore, fuel, and scrap have to be transported for every ton of finished steel that goes out). The economies of scale that we have mentioned in refining do in a sense act as location factors favouring refining near the source of crude, simply because nowhere else can one justify refining on a giant scale that may be beyond the capacity of most single markets to absorb. Refining close to the source, again, should theoretically give the greatest

II. REFINED PRODUCTS

flexibility in supplying products to terminals as close to the ultimate market as one can get them.

Originally, refineries were located as a matter of course fairly close to the source of crude, or at least within the producing country. The United States early this century was in any case not only the greatest producer and exporter of oil but also the greatest market. Moreover, when kerosene was the only important product transporting crude would have meant moving a large tonnage of waste; only about 30–40 per cent of the volume of the crude could be sold. But the growth in sales of black oils and of gasoline changed that. Between the wars certain refineries were built in market areas rather than where the oil was produced: a certain volume of crude began to move in seaborne trade, which until then had consisted almost entirely of products. Certain refineries in consuming countries were built for autarchic reasons: others because it was argued that the continuance of crude supplies could be relied on more than that of supplies of refined products. But in general crude was refined as close as could be to where it was produced.

After the war various special factors combined to shift the balance towards refining near the market areas. A number of the European countries' markets for petroleum products had grown to the size and variety that justified a refinery with some minimum economic throughput—say 15,000–20,000 barrels a day. There was a need for rapid expansion of refining capacity after the slowing down of the industry's investment during the wartime years, and there were a number of small specialized refining units in market areas, mainly in Europe, that could be expanded relatively quickly into full-scale refineries. But the influences shifting refining towards market areas were by no means simply economic, or at any rate had little to do with oil economics proper. Europe, a growing market, was short of dollars in that immediate postwar period, and sought to establish 'import-saving' to ease its balance of payments. A variety of currency deals were worked out to facilitate oil imports. But the establishment or expansion of an oil refining industry often with Marshall Aid in most European countries, seemed certain to reduce these costs. Later anxieties after the nationalization of Iranian oil and the growth of nationalist pressure in other host countries may have added reasons of security. And oil companies seeking to secure markets, in developed or underdeveloped areas, have not infrequently found that the price of entry was building a local refinery, whether or not the market really justified it immediately.

OPERATING ECONOMICS

Continued rapid growth of consumption in Western Europe has gradually accumulated the economic justification for the large number of refineries laid down around the coasts of Europe in the immediate postwar years for partly non-economic reasons. Moreover, this growth of markets far inland in Europe has gone far enough to begin to justify the location of refineries inland too, fed by the crude pipelines mentioned in the last chapter. Such refineries are generally built in anticipation of the development of markets for them to serve: one can always bank on some market response to sheer abundant availability. It is possible that the development will be a little slower than the groups investing in pipelines expect; these pipelines and refineries have been projected during a period of intense competition for the European market.

Another justification for locating those postwar refineries in Western Europe has been the rapid development of petroleum chemical production in areas where it was virtually unknown, and in which certain of the world's most advanced chemical industries relying entirely on coal were deprived of the world's most convenient raw material for the synthesis of many organic chemicals. Petrochemicals today form the fastest-growing elements in the world's chemical industry. The ethylene and butylene gases that were at one time 'tail gas' residues of the refining process are now in considerable demand as feedstocks for synthesis. The kind of technology involved in forming many of the products that can be made from them, such as detergents and synthetic rubber, is akin to refinery engineering and can be neatly fitted on to the end of it. Many oil companies have found it more profitable to cross the divide and process these feedstocks at least to the point of making chemical intermediates, if not to go even farther towards the final consumer.

Petrochemical production, in its present stage of rapid product innovation, seems an activity that it might be hard to develop far from large scale markets with high standards of living, fed by highly developed engineering industries on the spot. Innovation in new materials needs to be allied with the development of products one can make out of them. A number of projects for petroleum chemical development near to the oilfields of the Middle East, however, have been put forward in recent years; it can only be a matter of time before one of them breaks through into practicality.

II. REFINED PRODUCTS

The whole object of this industry's elaborate organization is to get petroleum to where the consumer wants it, in the form and the quantities that he is prepared to buy. The distribution and selling of refined products is always a vital element in the industry's operations. At times—and the early sixties seem to be one of those times—access to markets may be the most important asset that any company in the oil business can command. Quite a significant investment, in this final stage of a capital-intensive industry, is always required to gain entry to a market. Once in, a company will have to spend a good deal more money to secure and defend its market position.

In physical terms, marketing is the organization of onward movement, plus the necessary stocks, between the refinery and the consumer; and here many of the same elements enter as are concerned in the transport of crude from well to refinery. Most of the products, being liquids, can physically be moved by any of the means employed in crude transport; but the extent to which marketers can take advantage of the economies of scale inherent in these means depends upon the size and rate of growth of the markets he is serving. An oil marketer is selling and has to move many products, not one, and the nature of his wares, service, and customers varies—even if at any one time one product is likely to dominate his turnover and his profits. He has to move fairly large volumes of products from refineries to storage depots convenient to his various market areas, and often uses coastwise, river, or canal tankers for this medium-scale movement—though rail may offer competitive costs when full trainloads, rather than single truckloads, can be made the unit of movement.

In few countries has the market become large and concentrated enough until very recently to justify the movement of products by pipeline: the United States, as always, proving the exception. Fuel oil, the product for which demand in Western Europe has been growing fastest since the early fifties, is too viscous a liquid to move conveniently by pipeline: it can be done, but it requires heavy insulation of the pipeline, pre-heating of the oil, or the mixture of the oil with water to reduce viscosity. It is only recently that any major centres of consumption in Europe have developed beyond the point of say 5 million tons a year for which it may be economic to build a products pipeline. And geography does not always necessitate it; the London area, for example, is one of the largest centres of consumption of all oil products in Europe, but it is

73

concentrated around one of the continent's largest ports. The first significant development of products pipelines for commercial purposes in Britain, at the end of the fifties, was for certain single points of consumption taking very large amounts of a given product. Gasworks and chemical plant, buying tail gases or chemical feedstock in very large and stable quantities, ensured steady operation of the line at high capacity. Airports are another kind of consumption point that typically require very large supplies of one or two products, high-octane gasolines and the paraffin or 'wide-cut petrol' fuels used as turbine fuels.

Transport fuels, since the development of the internal combustion engine, have become the dominant products of the oil industry, and have supplied most of the return on the range of products it markets. A large proportion of these motor fuels are sold to commercial consumers, in large quantities and by competitive tender, but the dealer gasoline market selling to the motorist forms the most important single element in this business. Motor spirit has to be available in storage, today in perhaps three grades, at a large number of selling points dispersed widely around the main areas of vehicle population and along the main flows of motor traffic (which can alter quite frequently over say ten years). There are about 180,000 filling stations in the United States, and 35,000 in Britain. The motoring customer is highly mobile; and though the oil industry spends a great deal on advertising in an attempt to differentiate companies' own motor spirit, 'brand loyalty' tends to fade when the petrol gauge gets near empty or one has to turn across an oncoming traffic stream in order to get Brand A against Brand B. Price competition in gasoline is discussed later. In general the industry reckons that it gains an individual company little after costing all the companies who engage in it a lot, so it breaks out fairly infrequently in most countries. The economies of scale apply to road tankers as well as to so many other items of equipment in the oil industry; the fewer 'drops' that the driver has to make to empty his tank, the better, so that the marketing company prefers to serve the big stations.

The companies want contracts with garages on the major traffic routes, on which the main volume of occasional sales are made; but to an even larger extent, in most countries the companies seek to sign up those at local points of high density in the automobile population. The companies' usual method of securing a filling station for their brands is to negotiate exclusive dealing contracts for a period of years. During this time, in return for some capital assistance and probably a slightly better margin on his sales, the dealer agrees to sell no other gasoline

II. REFINED PRODUCTS

(and possibly to favour the company's brands of lubricating oils as well). The 'free house' still exists among filling stations, as it does among British public houses. But it is unlikely to get as favourable margins on the petrol it sells as the large garage whose custom offers the companies' tankers much more storage for each grade of gasoline. The more gasoline that can be delivered at one time, the more distribution costs can be reduced. Intense competition to secure the best sites between major companies has at times, in most countries, encouraged the proliferation of filling stations—moderated nowadays by the regulation and zoning which the multiplication of small stations at every cross-roads has provoked. But the volume of motor spirit sales tends to be much more concentrated, even in this dealer market, than the wide spread of filling stations might suggest.

Lubricating oils for automotive transport are sold partly through the same filling station network; but they are also sold widely throughout industry. This is one of the parts of the market in which the specialist blender and marketer tends to buy his base oils from the refiner and to compound and brand his own specialized product. In the general fuel market, particularly where long-term contracts or large single consignments can be gained, the oil companies tend to trade direct. As small-scale domestic central heating business spreads in Western Europe, there is a tendency for the wholesaler, sometimes selling other fuels as well as oil, to include it in his range of wares. Certain products sold primarily to the domestic user, such as kerosene for free standing home heaters, are sold through ordinary retail shops, generally encouraged by the companies to offer delivery. But in the sales of fuel oil, for example, to commercial, institutional and industrial customers, the marketing company tends to supply—and compete—direct.

The pattern of marketing petroleum products is a changing one. The physical organization of distribution tends to change as total oil consumption grows—as it has never yet ceased growing in any country—and as fresh products develop from the sphere of specialized fuels into a wider market. In Europe, at the beginning of the sixties, the liquid petroleum gases, propane and butane from refineries were just graduating from the tiny and specialized markets of heating country cottages and lighting for caravans and cabin boats into significant use as highly convenient and relatively mobile fuels for industrial heating, taking advantage of their relatively high calorific value for a given amount of tankage space in storage tanks. Nor are these the only forms of petroleum gas competing with fuel oil in the European market during the sixties.

75

CHAPTER VI

Operating Economics: III. Natural Gas

Natural gas is one of the forms in which petroleum is found under the earth, and much of the world's output is produced along with oil from the same wells: yet it is not too easy to fit into an economic rationale of the oil industry. It is generally a joint product of the exploration stage of the oil business and sometimes of the production stage, just as most saleable oil products are joint products of the later refining stage. But unlike oil, it is sold almost without processing, as a raw fuel, and it has competed from its early beginnings in the general fuel market, without special advantages in any specialized use. It can be transported long distances overland, though not nearly as cheaply as oil, but it is only just beginning to be moved across the sea. It has entered international trade, therefore, only across certain land frontiers—notably in pipelines from Canada to the United States. But even with that limitation natural gas has developed more rapidly than any other primary fuel since the last war. By 1960, it supplied more than a quarter of all the fuel consumed in the world's richest market, the United States, and in that same year its consumption in the rest of the free world was probably six times as much as it had been in 1950.

Wherever you find worthwhile deposits of oil there is gas too: but the converse does not hold good. Gas exists in an oil reservoir sometimes as 'cap gas' compressed between the top level of the crude oil and the sealing 'caprock' above it, but also, nearly always, dissolved in the crude oil. At a given temperature and pressure, oil will dissolve a given volume of gas. If it contains more, this will tend to come out of solution into a gas cap: if it has less, the gas does not help much in bringing the oil to the surface. When gas is stripped out of the oil at the surface it may be put down the well again for 'repressuring' (providing this is not 'unsaturated' oil that would simply dissolve it) or for 'gas lift' to keep the oil coming. Gas, however, may exist in reservoirs on its own. Its main constituent is methane, a rich hydro-carbon gaseous at any but very low temperatures, but it usually contains some 'natural gas liquids'. Exploration for petroleum is virtually indivisible: when you drill a wildcat well you are looking for 'oil and/or gas', and glad to find either. Until recently, moreover, the discovery of gas could be considered largely as a by-product of drilling for oil. Gas alone was hardly worth the high cost and risk of wildcatting, though once located, even alone, it could justify development provided it was within practicable reach of a market. In the United States—partly, perhaps, for somewhat special reasons—drilling for gas alone is now becoming a more reasonable commercial proposition. Where encouraging geological indications occur in the midst of industrialized areas that could offer ready markets, they may justify quite a systematic drilling programme. (Between 1956 and 1961, for example, the British gas industry, which was then making its gas largely out of coals that were becoming steadily more expensive, spent £5 million on exploring for natural gas in several promising areas of Britain; it found some caverns in which gas could be stored, but almost no gas.)

But over a large part of the world petroleum exploration is a gamble on the discovery of oil, in which finds of gas alone provide no pay-off whatever. And in many others, exploration and much of the development of any given field is counted as a joint preliminary cost against the oil and gas that may be produced together, presuming that the gas finds a separate market and is not used merely as an agent to assist extraction of the oil. Traditionally, in this joint accounting one would charge the costs against oil as the main product and throw in as a credit whatever one managed to get for the gas; this is now becoming an inadequate formula. The costs of development drilling, in some cases, can be divided more accurately between gas and oil; and those of production, in most cases, can be partly distinguished once the oil and gas pass the separating equipment at the top of the well. One American consultant reckons typical well costs as say 30 per cent for exploration, 40 per cent for development and 30 per cent for actual production, but reckons that at best only half the development and production costs —i.e., one-third of the whole—could be identified as between oil and gas.

Gas can only reach the final consumer along a pipe (a point that is recognized in the nationalization statutes of certain state-owned gas industries, which are given a monopoly of 'piped public supply', not of gas manufacture or production). Its first large-scale development, in the Appalachian fields of the United States in the eighteen-eighties, awaited the advent of the iron pipeline—one that served Pittsburgh from Murrysville, Pennsylvania, was perhaps the first of real importance. The first high-pressure pipeline, serving Chicago from the very large gas fields discovered in Ohio and Indiana, came before the turn of the century. But it was not really until after the thirties that the long-distance welded pipeline came into its own—and transformed natural gas, across the vast overland expanse of the United States, from a localized to a nationally available fuel. During the war the United States government financed the construction of two large oil pipelines, the 'Big Inch' (a 24-inch line running 1,250 miles) and the 'Little Big Inch' (a 20-inch line running 1,475 miles) from Texas to the Atlantic Coast states, to economize in the use of tankers. After the war these lines were taken over by the natural gas industry; successful experience with them was followed by the laying of a network of large-diameter lines across the continent. By the middle fifties almost all of the states in the Union, except one or two in its north-eastern and north-western corners, had a supply of natural gas and plans were in existence to pipe gas to some of these from Canada. Across the border in Canada, even in spite of administrative delays over the laying of pipelines, consumption rose about sixfold during the fifties, to make it the free world's second largest consumer and producer of utilized gas. (Consumption in the U.S.S.R. with its far larger area and population, was much larger than in Canada, but less than 15 per cent of the United States consumption.)

When you move gas along a pipeline under high pressure, you move fewer heat units for a given diameter of pipe than in pumping oil along the same line. All the same economic peculiarities of any pipeline apply—the high investment in an immovably fixed asset, the need for very high utilization of capacity to achieve economical transport, the transport costs varying only very little with distance. But the gas line needs to move 170 cubic metres of natural gas (at atmospheric pressure) to equal one barrel of oil; and the eventual cost of transporting energy may work out at twice to three times as much as for oil. On the other hand, gas is in some applications an even more convenient general fuel than the oil products with which it competes; and industrial demand, which makes up a half to two-thirds of the sales in the U.S., is very responsive to the low prices charged for 'off-peak' supplies. Gas is clean, and the consumer requires no storage, though the retailer needs a rather high-cost network of distribution mains, often utilized below capacity. Its first competitive impact was on an inconvenient solid fuel, coal, and on the gas made, by techniques becoming obsolescent, from that coal.

78

III. NATURAL GAS

It was mainly later that it made inroads in the United States upon fuel oil's share of the general fuel market. It was made available around the United States at prices which were particularly low for industrial consumers who could take large quantities outside the periods of peak consumption, and its sales multiplied enormously. And the business yielded a return to the distributors, the pipeline companies and the gas producers that may have been low in unit terms but grew impressively in aggregate.

None of this was of any consolation to oil producers who could not help raising huge quantities of gas to the surface, but had no markets within reach of a pipeline where they could sell it. In Venezuela and the Middle East the gas produced with oil was originally flared off to waste as the cheapest way of getting rid of it. More recently, it became of use in many Venezuelan fields for maintaining the flow of oil wells where underground pressure was falling; and large volumes were also pumped back underground in the Middle East, though in most fields there pressures seemed adequate to keep the oil flowing on natural drive for many years. The amounts being flared in both of these oil-exporting areas, it was estimated in 1960, had been reduced to about 100 million cubic metres a day, the equivalent of 600,000 barrels of oil a day. But even this was a frustrating reminder of the industry's inability to make use of a rich fuel that it could not help producing, and of rich gasfields that had been discovered in these areas only to be shut in. Projects for pipelines running miles from the Middle East to Europe were studied: the political complications of crossing a dozen or more borders, apart from the economics, put them out of court.

But during the middle fifties there came a chance—and for Western Europe an added incentive—to move natural gas across the sea to market. Methane can be liquefied at a temperature of minus 260 degrees Fahrenheit, which is nearly half-way down towards absolute zero. The technique of liquefaction offers no particular problems; but though the use of liquefied methane had been discussed several times before the war, technical problems concerned with the storage and transport of a liquid refrigerated to such a degree had deterred experiment.

In 1950, however, through the initiative of a Midwest stockyard and cold storage company that felt it was paying too much for its locally-produced fuel, experiments were begun again with refrigerated barges designed to move natural gas liquefied near its source up the Mississippi to Chicago. The liquefaction plant was built; barges were insulated in a new way to carry the liquid methane. But the river authorities and insurance companies raised difficulties about this new and seemingly dangerous form of transport up the Mississippi; and in the meantime the Chicago stockyards managed to get a better price out of their local fuel suppliers. The project might have foundered at that point, which had little to do with the technique or the economics of the actual transport of liquid methane. But its proponents managed to get in touch with a customer of a much larger magnitude, to which liquid methane, providing it could be had economically, offered powerful attractions—the British gas industry. This nationalized industry is the largest manufacturer of coal gas 'for its own sake' in the world: the United States and Germany make a greater volume of gas, but make most of it primarily as a by-product of carbonization industries of which the main product is metallurgical coke. The British industry was experiencing severe competition from oil and electricity; in a growing market for fuels of convenience in Britain, it was failing to hold its own.

The British gas industry had turned to various ways of making gas out of oil to relieve some of its problems; but to import gas direct, perhaps much cheaper than it could make gas from new equipment, seemed an opportunity not to be missed. The Gas Council put up capital, jointly with the Americans who had originated the idea for the conversion of a small tanker to carry liquefied methane (using specialized insulation made of balsa wood); the existing barge liquefaction plant was used; and the *Methane Pioneer* carried through a series of experimental voyages carrying frozen natural gas from the Texas Gulf to the banks of the Thames, apparently with complete technical success. The gas was first stored in a refrigerated gasholder and later 're-formed' to town gas of standard British calorific value.

The economics of this technical innovation in petroleum transport were not fully revealed, though the sponsors declared themselves satisfied that natural gas could be landed in Southern England more cheaply than it could be made from British coal. The coal would have had to travel from the Midlands. The natural gas, originally, was to have come from Venezuela, where supplies were offered cheaply on a long-term contract. But when the project began to be discussed more seriously in Britain at the beginning of the sixties, the source that its sponsors had in mind had changed, not surprisingly. Their attention had shifted—as had most of Western Europe's—to the Sahara.

Development of the Saharan gasfields during the late fifties was providing the nations of Western Europe with a powerful added incen-

III. NATURAL GAS

tive to devise some way of moving gas across the sea. Within Europe, the economy of Northern Italy had gained a powerful impetus from development of natural gas in the Po Valley; France was fitting gas from its Lacq deposits into its pattern of fuel consumption; and France again, as a leader in the European Common Market, was anxious to get both liquid and gaseous petroleum from its 'franc zone' widely accepted within its partners' economies. Elaborate studies were made for under-sea pipelines, following various alternative routes across the Mediter-ranean, to Spain or Italy, from which the gas could be piped north to north-western and central Europe. These, at the time of writing, are still projects under study. But a pipeline is in existence from the Hassi R'Mel gasfields to the Algerian coast; and a long-term contract has been made between the French nationalized companies exploiting this natural gas, a company formed to develop ocean transport of methane in refrigerated tankers, and the British Gas Council. Since it was made Algeria has become independent, and its politics, though more peaceful, remain none too stable: but the commitment to export its gas, liquid in special tankers, remains.

In regions where natural gas has been the first large-scale source of gas available, it is consumed virtually raw, after separation of liquids and in some cases after removal of troublesome impurities. This is un-doubtedly the ideal way to use it; it is a rich gas and cheaper to transport along pipelines (though liable to somewhat greater losses of heat value through leakage) than town gas mixtures of lower calorific value. But when it is introduced, initially perhaps in relatively small quantities, into an existing supply of gas of lower heat value, it presents a dilemma. The equipment with which a consumer burns gas is not flexible enough to accommodate gases of such different qualities. To switch over all the burners in a house carcassed for town gas of European quality to methane gas, in the renewal of burners, might cost some £5–£10 per consumer; and even if the gas supplier were prepared to accept this high capital cost, it would not necessarily be able to guarantee any such consumer the whole of his supplies in the form of natural gas for quite a long time. In such circumstances, when introducing natural gas initially as a supplement to existing gas supplies, the authorities may opt to sell it only to major consumers who can afford to convert their equipment; but even this involves separate supply mains. More often they may choose, as the British Gas Council is choosing, the alternative of reforming the methane into lower-value gas.

Discovery of further really large deposits of natural gas in the industrial areas of north-west Europe—and during 1960–61 it became clear that huge discoveries had been made in Holland—may possibly slow the pace of development of either kind of ocean transport for Saharan gas. But these would simply be alternative ways of supplying natural gas in these areas. It seemed fairly certain, given the current state of the technology of moving natural gas and current attitudes towards the economics of doing so, that natural gas from one source or another would make deeper inroads into this rich market. If this happens, one possible and significant result might be to reduce the divergence of the pattern of demand for oil products in Western Europe from that of the United States, a divergence that was so marked a feature of these two oil markets in the fifties.

The main reason why the United States still refines a much larger proportion of gasoline out of its crude oil and a considerably smaller proportion of fuel oil is not that its demand for motor spirit in road transport is still expanding much faster than its demand for energy in other sectors of the economy, or that American coal is able to stand up to oil competition so much better than coal elsewhere. The reason is that natural gas has accounted for much of petroleum's advance in the general fuel market of the United States. If one adds together the growth of consumption of fuel oil plus natural gas in both areas, the totals are more in line than their consumption of fuel oil alone. To the extent that supplies of natural gas become available in very large quantities in Western Europe, one might expect the pattern of oil product demand in this region to shift back more towards that of the United States. But it would be unwise to exaggerate the speed of any such swing back towards common refining patterns. There remain considerable uncertainties about the trans-oceanic transport, at any rate, of natural gas; and while some of these are political, others are economic.

To say that demand for petroleum, both liquid and gaseous, over the medium run at least, will be increasingly for consumption as a convenient general fuel implies that demand for the petroleum products which serve specialized uses will not rise as fast as total demand for petroleum. These specialized products command a premium for their peculiar value in particular applications—which in some cases amounts to irreplaceability. If demand for these products rises less rapidly than demand for oil products that have to meet competition in the general fuel market, one would expect the revenue from a given quantity of petroleum products used to fall.

III. NATURAL GAS

This point is generally acknowledged when people discuss the effect on refining margins of more rapid growth in demand for fuel oils than for gasolines. At first sight, the introduction of natural gas into the general fuel market beside fuel oil might seem to assist matters, by allowing the refiner to adjust his balance of products towards a more traditional pattern. But when one realizes that this is simply achieved by bringing the rate of growth of demand for fuel oil down more into line with that for gasoline, it is clear that the net effect must reduce the rate of growth for all oil products. And in terms of return on capital, the natural gas that one sells instead may rank as a poor relation even of the fuel oil. If one considers gas and oil as products of a single industry—and they are, at the least, nearly always joint products of petroleum exploration—then the traditional pattern of prices of this industry may seem a mixed blessing.

This is a problem that has not yet been resolved in the world's greatest market both for oil and for gas, the United States. Gas, originally, was sold there for whatever it would fetch in whatever markets it could reach. Its wellhead price therefore reflected a highly competitive price for general fuels in the distant market less the cost of transporting the gas by pipeline. Originally, this meant extremely low prices at the wellhead; but the producer was glad to take whatever he could get. This was a perfectly reasonable policy to adopt in fostering a market for a new product that commanded no particular area of monopoly value except rather more convenience than some of the competition. But external influences operated to freeze this approach to the market into a permanent stance.

Long-distance pipelines gave natural gas distribution throughout the nation; they also made it a product moving in inter-state commerce, subject to rate regulation of its transport charges. And the products with which American natural gas naturally competed were produced by public utilities. Gas, too, began to be regulated as a public utility, in the states where it was finally sold, early in its history, and since the fifties its wellhead prices too have been subject to general supervision by the Federal Power Commission. None of the traditional criteria used in the regulation of public utility prices—ascertained costs, the capital employed as a 'rate base', or a stable rate of return on capital—can easily be applied to the wellhead price of gas. This is a fuel most of the costs of which are joint costs, in which some elements of the 'capital' invested are customarily written off in the same year as they are spent, and in which the rate of return expected customarily reflects a habit of self-financing plus a very high degree of risk upon one's initial invest-ment. One can forgive the administrative authorities concerned for some uncertainty in seeking for reasonable criteria in regulating prices; the accounting methods used by the gas producers also reflect a certain intellectual disarray of attitudes towards this fuel.

The petroleum industry in the United States, therefore, is its own best competitor. In the market, its prices have to be broadly com-petitive; and though wellhead prices have been rising in recent years, the higher cost of transporting gas to market generally has meant that in terms of heat content, at the wellhead, the price one can get for gas is only about a quarter to a third of the price of crude oil. So every time that gas displaces oil in consumption, or even captures a market from coal that fuel oil might without it have gained, the eventual revenue of the petroleum industry goes down.

This does not necessarily imply that investment in the natural gas business, in its current expanding circumstances, is unattractive. In American wildcatting, the discovery ratio of gas is significantly higher than that of drilling for oil, and the reserves-production ratio for gas is higher than that for oil. Replacing the cubic metre of gas one has just sold with another cubic metre of reserves, that is to say, does not cost as much as finding the next barrel of oil to replace the one that you have just sold. Moreover, though it is subject to regulation of its charges, gas is not subject to any control over the volume of production, as oil production is in some of the United States. Producing more gas, even with a low return, may well suit the particular circumstances of par-ticular companies. One should never, in a free economy, assume that 'the industry' is a single thing with a single set of interests and responses. In spite of much overlapping in operations and ownership, the gas producer and the oil producer in the United States do not always speak with quite the same voice, and the short-term decisions of one cannot always be expected to take account of the longer-term interests of the other.

What this rather complex interaction of gas and oil upon one another in the United States may imply for the development of natural gas consumption in the rest of the world, and now in international trade, is that the balance of advantage in such developments may not be as simple as it seems at first sight. When gas that has been moved long dis-tances expensively is sold cheap enough to supplant one of the joint products of crude oil that itself was a joint product with the gas, which could have been moved more cheaply to the same market, is the original

III. NATURAL GAS

allocation of costs blurring the producer's commercial judgment? When there is a surplus of crude oil, traditionally the main product of petroleum exploration and production, should the other product still be sold at give-away prices that will enable it to be transported to new markets and to seize business that fuel oil, which might offer at least a slightly better return, may already have been in the process of capturing?

One developed economy confronted almost overnight with the opportunity of becoming a large-scale natural gas producer, Holland, has chosen a quite different way of marketing it from this traditional American way. In marketing gas from deposits in Northern Holland which are now known to be clearly the largest in Europe, the Dutch government, Shell and Esso have decided to sell it at home and for export as a 'premium fuel'—i.e. at prices suited to a rather cheap manufactured or by-product gas, but not in cut-price competition with the cheapest coal and fuel oil. This may mean a relatively slow and controlled growth of the natural gas market, though higher unit returns on the gas sold. It will not displace fuel oil and coal in the general industrial fuel market or in power generation or chemical manufacture as widely as it might otherwise have done.

One may criticize this policy for not giving Holland the cheapest possible energy immediately, or for taking too much care of established fuels, both home-produced and imported. On the other hand, the Dutch government is treating this gas bonanza as a rich windfall, but one that in the history of the country may be counted as short-lived. It thinks the developers should get the best possible return out of this windfall without dislocating its basic, less rapidly-changing, energy supply pattern. For gas development in an already industrialized country—without the same need as remote sources have to quote rockbottom prices in order to gain the gas any market at all—this method of exploitation has its logic. For the petroleum industry as a whole, considering reserves of natural gas which are universally much smaller and shorter-lived in relation to consumption than oil, it might seem a logical method too. But how much chance oil and gas suppliers in other countries have of switching to this system is another matter.

Much depends, obviously, on how much business there remains in any given market that either fuel might capture from coal in its raw form or from its secondary fuels, manufactured gas and electricity. And much also depends, as always in this industry, upon the business situation of the particular petroleum producers concerned. But the outside observer

85

of this industry is sometimes tempted to feel that the peculiar history of the natural gas business in the United States, and the sheer inability to sell it, until recently, in most other producing countries, have absolved the petroleum industry from ever fully thinking through the economics of developing natural gas in a competitive market for energy.

CHAPTER VII

Investment and Returns

Reckoned in terms of what was originally spent to bring it into being, the free world's petroleum industry, at the beginning of the sixties, may have had a gross book value of about $105 billion; written down, the 'net investment' involved in it was of the order of $60 billion, or well over twenty thousand million pounds. A comprehensive analysis of the industry's capital investment made by the Chase Manhattan Bank of New York suggested that at the end of 1960, the industry's gross investment in the United States was $57,800 million against a 'free foreign' total of $46,750 million. American oil thus represented about 55 per cent of the whole, though ever since 1955 oil investment outside the United States has grown faster than inside it, and since 1958, the amounts invested annually outside America have been larger than those inside.

A word, first, about what 'investment' means in oil. Very large amounts of money have to be spent to find and develop oil reserves: these do not always produce 'fixed assets' for the industry, nor in accounting terms are they always treated as are the sums invested in productive facilities for other industries. When an oil company surveys a fresh section of a concession area in which it already has production and income, it customarily writes off the whole cost of its preliminary search, such as geophysical work, against current income in that year, as one of its current costs: it usually does the same with the current cost of drilling operations. If the well it sinks discovers oil and this is developed into production, it takes the actual cost of the tangible assets involved—casing in the hole, Christmas tree of valves at the top, gas separation equipment, pipe for gathering, storage tanks, and the like—on to its books as an investment, capitalizing them and writing them down over an agreed period of depreciation like any other fixed assets. The whole cost of drilling development wells in areas after oil is discovered, by contrast, may have to be capitalized and written

87

down, not partly expensed: practice differs between countries and companies.

If the well does not find oil, and is abandoned as a 'dry hole', the whole cost of it can usually be written off as a current cost against the company's other income in the producing country. But if the company has no other income in that country, there is nothing to write it off against. It may be that in an integrated group the tax authorities in its parent country will allow it to be charged against current income from other areas, but that may depend upon the institutional structure of the group. If the company finds oil after a period of unsuccessful exploration, it is usual for the cost of its exploration up to the point of success to be written off against the income that eventually arises—in one way or another, generally by instalments. The same may be done for rents paid during the period of exploration before oil is found—'dead rents'—and on occasion for bonuses and premiums paid to get a concession, though less often. The precise rules settling which items in oil operations can be written off as expenses in the same year, which 'expensed' by instalments, and which capitalized with amortization according to a depreciation formula, vary as between countries, companies and concessions. American tax rules are fairly generous here, and have often been taken as a model overseas, but in recent years countries granting new concessions have become tougher about what they concede in these parts of the 'fine print' of the concessions.

These preliminary costs certainly represent money that has to be spent to find oil, or to go on developing reserves. Are they capital investment? It is a nice conceptual point. Is an array of dry holes abandoned all over the world—and for every successful exploratory well, there will be a number of dry holes—part of the 'fixed assets' of the oil industry? Are the 'intangible' costs of geophysical survey and drilling, written off against current income in the year they were incurred, part of the 'book value' of the industry? In accounting terms, few companies would show them as such in the books. Yet if you look for oil anywhere, these form a large part of the initial stake you will have to put up; and if you do not find oil and have no other income against which to offset them, they are lost even more irretrievably than any clear 'capital' elements in any unproductive investment. You can adopt any convention that you (or the tax authorities you are currently dealing with) choose: what is important to realize is that the convention will be arbitrary, and that the net cost to you of searching for and developing oil may depend to a considerable extent upon it. This becomes a significant factor when one considers rates of return on investment in this industry, particularly in production: what 'investment' is one talking about? The conventions adopted in the totals we are now considering, those compiled by the Chase Manhattan Bank, exclude the costs of geophysical search and the amounts paid for leases from the figures for 'capital investment'; but they do include the whole cost of drilling.

Technologically, as well as geographically, a 'map' of this global valuation emphasizes the spread of the industry's commitments. About 45 per cent of the net value of assets was in production facilities (including exploration and development); about 18 per cent in pipelines and tankers; 20 per cent in refining and petrochemical plant; 15 per cent in marketing facilities. But the United States alone accounted for about 70 per cent of assets in the production stage, a far larger proportion than its share of assets in any other stage of the industry; outside the United States, the distribution of assets was oriented considerably less towards the countries that produce and export oil than the total breakdown by 'departmental' figures might suggest. The big investment in refining and marketing oil in Western Europe makes this area the second largest geographical concentration of fixed investment in oil in the world: and an even larger technological concentration was the world's ocean-going tanker fleet, with a net book value of $6,365 million in 1960. In terms of the net value of fixed assets, there was said in 1960 to be more oil investment in Canada than in the Middle East or Venezuela at that time. These book values obviously do not include the oil in the ground, which indeed the oil industry outside the United States normally does not own, but works under leases or concessions.

Gross or net 'investment values', at any one time, lump together an assortment of expenditures made at times when the price levels may have varied considerably: it is as well to supplement them with figures of new expenditure by the industry over recent periods. Between 1950 and 1960, the Chase Manhattan Bank estimates, the oil industry spent $90 billion on developing its capacity. In the United States oil investment over this period represented about a sixth of total fixed capital formation by business: in the 'free foreign' world as a whole the proportion was probably nearer a third, though in Western Europe, the biggest consuming area relying on imports, such investment in oil as had to be made within its borders probably represented no more than 5 per cent of fixed capital formation by all business there. About two-thirds of what the bank counted as capital expenditure in the oil industry of the United States during these years, went into exploration, development, and production, about 13 per cent into refineries and petrochemicals, about 6 per cent into transport and another 6 per cent into marketing facilities. But in the 'free foreign' world outside the proportions were very different: only just over a third into exploration and production, nearly a quarter into transport, another quarter into refining and petro-chemicals, and about 13 per cent into marketing.

Oil is clearly, as the outline of its technology and commercial arrange-ments in previous chapters has suggested, a highly-capitalized industry though not an evenly-capitalized one in all areas of the world. It may not be much more heavily-capitalized, to be sure, than some of the other energy industries, and particularly those that supply energy processed into highly convenient forms. Comparisons of capital requirements in all these industries are highly debatable, whatever yardstick one chooses; but some of the most recent suggest that outside the United States, at any rate, the investment required to expand oil production by a ton a year is no more than is required to increase coal capacity by an equivalent amount (say $1\frac{1}{2}$ tons a year, as the oil has a higher calorific value). The oil is almost never used raw, while large tonnages of coal still are; transport, processing and marketing may add twice as much again to the investment required to bring oil products to the consumer. But if the coal has to be processed into fuels of a convenience to com-pete with petroleum products, substantial further investment has to be put into power stations or gas-making equipment (coke ovens, for example, are as capital-intensive items of plant as oil refineries). Hydro-electricity and, so far, nuclear power stations are indeed even more capital-intensive than oil, gas or thermal electricity.

Petroleum, however, has for some decades achieved a faster rate of expansion than any other fuel industry except electricity; and it has an element of specialized long-distance transport built into its capital requirements that is unknown in most other energy industries. Its pro-cessing plant and specialized storage and distribution facilities cannot be dispensed with. And it is mainly a privately-owned industry, whereas other highly-capitalized energy industries tend to be public utilities, regulated and often owned by local or national governments. These are often guaranteed some degree at least of monopoly: they are not ex-pected to earn much more than a low and stabilized rate of return; and some in practice fail to earn even that and at the same time to maintain the value of their assets intact. Among privately-owned industries that are expected to earn a commercial rate of return, oil is by any measure one of the most highly-capitalized as well as one of the most rapidly growing. Moreover, its initial investment is often peculiarly risky.

During the fifties various rules of thumb were worked out about 'capital requirements per annual ton of additional capacity' for use in long-term forecasting in the oil industry. In 1956, an OEEC commission quoted a figure, apparently derived from some earlier Chase Manhattan estimates, of $60 for exploration and production, $30 for transport and distribution, $30 for refining—a total of $120 per annual additional ton of oil. Whatever the validity of this as an average for 'free world' figuring, it seemed too high for anywhere outside the United States, where the incentives to drill for new oil are peculiarly high and hence the investment in exploration and other drilling tends to be exceptionally high. A later commission, covering much the same ground in 1959, put the total capital required for an extra annual ton of oil at $50-75: it was apparently drawing upon unpublished European estimates of about $6 a ton for exploration and production, $20 a ton for refining, and $28 a ton for transport. A 1961 study for the World Bank put the total capital requirement throughout at $5,000 for a barrel a day, or $100 for a ton a year.

Such figures are estimates that mask a wide range of values for different circumstances. One has only to recall the millions spent in Nigeria before payable oil was proved and the Japanese success with their first well off the Saudi-Kuwait Neutral Zone; the contrast between rates of production per well in the United States and in the Middle East; the sharp difference in cost between a refinery incorporating all the techniques such as catalytic cracking and 'platforming' to increase its yield of light products, and of a topping unit that merely strips out the heavy products and may simply re-cycle the surplus light fractions back down the well. It may be rather more meaningful to talk of average capital requirements for tankers. Though the cost per dead-weight ton of an 80,000-ton tanker may be 10-15 per cent below that of a 20,000 tonner, over any given period the sizes of tankers actually ordered do tend to cluster within one or two 'bands' of the range. But the capital required to expand production—even in a period of apparent shortage where it can be assumed that most kinds of capacity have to be pushed up in step—will always vary enormously in practice.

When there is a world surplus of oil-producing capacity, however, the capital cost of an extra barrel of oil from some well somewhere will be nil. And at any time it is unlikely that all of the capacity of the industry or of any single company will be precisely in balance. Some of the extra capacity through which extra supplies have to be processed or handled will at any given time be available free, already 'sunk' into existing facilities: it is only over a period, as the various units have to be supplemented in discontinuous increments, that any averaged 'capital requirement' can be attributed to extra throughput.

In the long run, the capital that will have to go into finding and developing any wasting natural resource may be expected to rise; but with oil that can be a very long run. Drilling technology, in particular, seems to be developing fast enough to offset much of the greater physical effort involved in going steadily deeper. But unless we also postulate capital-saving development, technical advances usually increase capital costs. In some countries finding oil is probably becoming on the average a steadily more expensive gamble: but there are probably many bonanzas to be happened upon still, and there is also a lot more cheap oil already located than anybody has ever yet cared to produce to its full capacity. Nor is capital intensity in transport and refining as certain to rise as seemed likely ten to fifteen years ago. Larger tankers cost less per ton to build, and larger diameter pipelines take less steel per ton of oil moved. A switch from the one to the other, as in the new pattern of supplies to North-West Europe, means substitution with a slightly more capital-intensive form of transport; but the saving in distance involved tends to offset this. In refining, because demand for products that require less specialized treatment, or for natural gas, is rising faster in many markets than demand for the specialized fuels, the industry is now building considerably less complicated and expensive refineries, requiring somewhat less investment for a given increase in petroleum consumption. But one must expect continued pressure for purification of the less specialized products; treatment to reduce the sulphur in fuel and diesel oils, for example, may soon be a legal requirement in many countries. And factors that are not wholly economic may mean that more separate refineries, and smaller ones, are built than economics alone would suggest.

Two elements in the capital investment of this industry that lie slightly off the track beaten from well head to petrol pump deserve special note. Technical research and development in this industry are somewhat analogous to exploration for oil, in seeking fresh opportunities for successful investment, and offer a roughly similar chance of success. The oil industry ranks as a fairly heavy spender on research and development among those industries that pay for their own, though it does not compare with the heaviest spenders of all such as aircraft and electronics, industries that can usually get the government to finance most of their technical endeavours on defence grounds. This is an element of investment that seems likely to go on rising, perhaps particularly during a régime of cost-cutting. Any industry with so diverse an array of expensive techniques must offer a myriad of opportunities for improvements, from the well-drilling equipment that automatically erects itself from a lorry once it reaches the site to the computer that works out all the possible programmes of operation for a refinery and 'optimizes' its production of a given range of joint products. And there is always commercial pressure to diversify the range of products further. The oil industry cannot guarantee a steady flow of the best ideas by employing an army of trained men to consider technical problems: but it can ensure that the possible innovators learn what its problems really are, and increase the likelihood that good ideas from outside the industry (which have offered many of its basic improvements in technique) are picked up and assessed without delay.

Petroleum chemicals, the most rapidly developing part of the world's chemical industries, is a manufacture born from research into refining technique and into the properties of petroleum hydro-carbons. It is incidentally, in the sixties, the most rapidly growing part of the petroleum industry. In tonnage, it is still small: in 1960 in Britain, for example, it accounted for no more than $2\frac{1}{2}$ million tons, or 5 per cent of total refinery throughputs. For the Shell group in 1959–60, however, it represented about 9 per cent of turnover, 5 per cent of profits, and 25–30 per cent of expenditure on research. Petroleum chemicals are usually extensions of refining technology, with a similarly capital-intensive array of plant. Oil companies have varying policies as to the extent that they process and re-process these chemical intermediates towards the finished product. But in general they have recently tended to move farther into this growing branch of chemicals at a time when profits are less easily come by in their basic business of producing fuels. This may mean a continued increase in 'processing' investment to offset any moderation in the rate of investment for refining actual fuels.

Some of the forecasts of capital requirements produced for this industry in the middle fifties, before the fact of surplus was made plain, will probably have been as exaggerated in parts as much other fuel forecasting was then; but the rate of capital expenditure in the oil industry in the sixties is still likely to be prodigious. The Chase Manhattan Bank estimates referred to above were made as the basis of forecasts of capital requirements in the future. The bank's petroleum department has calculated that between 1960 and 1970 the industry would probably have to invest about $140 billion (much more than the gross value of all its assets today) in order to provide the facilities necessary to meet demand for oil in the free world, which certainly continues to rise steadily.

If one thinks in terms of a notional 'world oil industry', there is quite a large part of the 'investment required' in such an estimate, during the sixties, which might not in any real sense be 'required' at all. Everybody postulates a continued growth in world demand for petroleum. Physical facilities will have to be provided to refine and to distribute the growing volume of products. Refinery capacity was not, at the beginning of the sixties, in practice, much larger than total demand: so one must postulate an investment in new refineries roughly in line with market development. Distribution and retail selling capacity is more difficult to assess. In the dealer gasoline market, for example, many countries have a large amount of apparent excess capacity and a very low throughput per pump. Some part of the new gasoline marketing capacity has to be geared to the shifts in traffic flows, and in particular to the building of new motor roads, rather than to the rise in total demand for gasoline: but elsewhere larger throughputs at existing stations could in theory mean rather better utilization of the capital equipment there and of the distribution organization that supplies them. How far the distribution of other petroleum products may require new capital investment—for example, in terminals and storage—is not easy to judge. But the development of products pipelines in Europe certainly will, and one must expect the disproportionate growth of demand for the black oils, and for liquid petroleum gases, to demand new facilities.

In exploration and development, however, it is difficult to argue that any given amount of capital investment will be absolutely 'required' to meet the continuing increase in world demand for crude oil; nor is it easy to guess when market demand need begin to exert pressure on the world's 'fleet in being' of tankers. If oil were free to move around the world simply in accordance with the arithmetic of how much is required at given places at a given cost, there might not need to be much further investment at all, for some time at least, in the oil industry of the United States. The same reasoning, in the circumstances of the early sixties in which this book is being written, might apply to Venezuela—where indeed, by today, exploration is almost at a standstill, with much capacity shut in and few major fields being significantly developed. A number of major fields in the Middle East, again, could physically sustain the current rate of increase in world demand for quite a period of years, given some continued investment in development wells, pressure maintenance, and loading facilities, without enough depletion of their reserves to worry the 'world oil business'—if such a business, single-minded and monopolistic, were to exist.

It does not: so the forecasts of capital expenditure made in the mid-fifties may not turn out to have been as wrong as theoretically they might be argued to be. The minimum capital that would unavoidably have to be invested in physical facilities to supply the amounts of oil that the world will need in the sixties is an interesting subject for speculation. What will be invested while doing so is another thing. 'Capital requirements' as the Chase Manhattan Bank hardheadedly reckons them are its best guess at what the institutions in the oil industry, as actually organized, will choose to invest in doing so. Their national circumstances will affect this: those are political factors dealt with later in this book. So will their institutional circumstances. This is an industry organized in different units, which are differently placed in terms of commercial advantage; and the men running many of those units cannot think in terms of one decade only, but are concerned with the long-run advantage of their organizations. The high and continuing rate of exploration for new reserves of oil at a time when existing output is still far below potential capacity and total reserves are immense, for example, arises from the pattern of location and producing cost of those reserves, and of the amount of cheaply-developable reserves of crude, and power to sell oil, that particular companies command. The government of Kuwait, to take an example, awarded a major concession to Shell at the end of 1960 not primarily because of the generous terms it was offered, but because Shell wanted new supplies of cheap crude oil, and had not only the marketing capacity but the will to market products made from it. Some other companies who had bid, it was wickedly said in the industry, were not after a concession to produce oil: they were after a concession not to produce oil.

However much capital the oil industry of the free world requires or decides to invest in the sixties, the chances are that it will generate a large proportion of the money from within. This has always been *par excellence* an industry of self-financing, accumulating most of what it invests from earnings. Between 1951 and 1960 for example, one representative selection of major companies—mainly American, plus Shell and BP—is reckoned to have provided 94 per cent of the $62,000 million that it put into fixed investment and working capital from internal resources. This means, essentially, getting the wherewithal to expand from one's customers, through price, rather than by asking one's shareholders or other investors to invest it in oil: shifting the decision, that is to say, from the plane of the individual investor to that of the collective management. The proportion of self-financing in oil has since the war been considerably higher than in most other industries in the United States or Britain. The industry is inclined to say that this was inevitable because it would have been quite impossible to raise such sums from the capital markets of the world. It is certain that in the postwar era, while those capital markets were restoring themselves painfully, this would have been so. At the same time, the reverse of the medal has to be considered: such amounts of money did not become free for investment partly because the oil companies did not pay out to their shareholders what they could have done. The argument is circular, and partly affected by the general business climate of the period. Capital appreciation was more palatable to many shareholders than income on which they were heavily taxed, and most industries tended to adopt cautious dividend policies—though not many, considering what was being earned, as cautious policies as the oil industry. In this industry as in others, there developed and remains some tension between the prerogatives of management and shareholders. Managers find it difficult to be sure that shareholders, or the investor at large, can decide as sensibly as they where capital ought to be ploughed in to sow future benefits. They think it safer not to give him the option.

Towards the end of the fifties, there were signs of some change in this attitude within the management of the privately-owned oil industry. Various of the major international companies, for example, had more recourse to the outside capital market for new finance. But most investment decisions in this industry are still taken largely in terms of the cash flow generated in its international operations, of the investment opportunities it sees open within its own spheres or others into which its experience may make 'diversification' worth while, and—in many cases but not all—of its long-run prospects in the oil business. A company that is 'long' on marketing facilities, such as Shell, is prepared to invest heavily in finding new crude however long on crude others may be; one without sufficient market power to dispose of its supplies, such as the French *Compagnie Française des Pétroles*, is investing more heavily than others need to in gaining entry to new markets.

What rate of return does the oil industry expect and obtain on the vast capital that it employs? There are a number of statistical series relating to oil company earnings; but it is not too easy to arrive at meaningful comparisons with other industries. In the middle fifties earnings in the whole of the free world's petroleum industry indicated a net return on capital after tax of the order of 15 per cent on the shareholders' equity in 1951, falling to some 12 per cent by 1954. One run of figures calculated recently by the National City Bank of New York for the major international oil companies runs over a very long period. It shows a net return on the 'net worth' of these companies of about 10–11 per cent in the late twenties, falling drastically in the thirties (though only in 1931, on the average across the industry, showing a loss). Returns were stabilized at about 7–9 per cent in the war years (partly by wartime taxation): but the average jumped up to 15 per cent or more for the early postwar years. Since 1951, the bank's figures show the average return running down slowly, from nearly 17 per cent in 1951 to about 10 per cent in 1958 and 1959, and 11–12 per cent in 1960.

The slight improvement occurred mainly among American companies, among which some have no operations outside the United States, and many no operations outside the Western hemisphere. The same bank, in 1959 and 1961, did produce some calculations relating to the profits of the major international companies that operate outside the United States, attempting to separate out the part of their profits attributable to operations in the Eastern hemisphere.

Such a separation must at best be rather rough and ready. Very large quantities of oil are still traded between the Western and Eastern hemispheres, and the profits shown on refining and marketing in either hemisphere may relate partly to the processing or sale of oil from the other. Many of the tankers that move crude from or around the Eastern hemisphere, once again, are owned by companies that have their head-quarters and show their profits in the Western hemisphere (more often in Panama, Honduras, or Bermuda, the havens of 'fleets of convenience', than in the United States where the final owners may be).

The bank, in this calculation, extracted, from published reports of the seven major international companies, what it was satisfied were the net profits of these companies in the Eastern hemisphere. It combined these with a kind of figuring that is nowadays becoming more common, somewhat to the embarrassment of the oil industry. This is to take the revenue paid to each host government in the exporting countries in any given year, and to reckon that according to the 50–50 formula the total oil company profit from production in these territories ought to be exactly the same. Compare these calculated 'production profits' with estimates of Eastern hemisphere profits on all operations, and the difference should show the return on non-producing 'downstream operations'. The answers this exercise produced were that while in 1954 'non-producing profits' amounted to about 27 per cent of the profits shown on production, by 1957 they had dropped to almost nil, and that during 1958, 1959, and 1960 these 'downstream' activities had been conducted at very substantial losses. The companies' total net return on Eastern hemisphere operations, that is to say, fell some $250–315 million short each year of the amounts paid to producer governments.

During 1961–62, considerable further talent was bent upon the task of calculating just how much the return on investment in production really was and should be. At its second meeting in Caracas in January, 1961, OPEC decided to make such a study, and later in the year it commissioned professional economic consultants in America, Britain and Italy to carry out different aspects of this. These consultants did not need to rely wholly on published sources. They sought information, via OPEC, from the companies operating and represented in their countries.

It was more easy, no doubt, to assess the profits earned than the investment involved. Valuing this is conceptually difficult as well as politically sensitive, though nothing that can clarify the finances of this industry in host governments' minds is anything but desirable. Whether it is economically to the point is another matter. As we saw at the beginning of this chapter, it is not easy to decide how much of the preliminary expenditure required in oil development can be called capital investment. One has to be arbitrary: and an organization of governments anxious to show that the return on investment is high might well choose accounting conventions that show less of this early expenditure as capital than some companies would (equally arbitrarily).

In its own first study, the First National City Bank had reckoned that at the end of 1958, the net fixed investment of these companies in 'non-producing' operations in the Eastern hemisphere was of the order of $4·4 billion, and that the operations tied up half as much again in working capital. On its showing these non-producing operations, on balance, were conducted at a loss. A much more interesting comparison, of course, would be with the total capital employed in Eastern hemisphere operations, on which the total return was shown: of this the First National City Bank made no estimate. One estimate of net fixed assets in petroleum facilities in this hemisphere (by its colleague, the Chase Manhattan Bank of New York), valued them at $5,525 million for 1955 and $12,475 million for 1960, for all companies. A very rough allocation of that might credit the seven major companies, which with the French company CFP control practically all Eastern hemisphere oil production outside the Soviet orbit, with say $4,000 million in 1955 and $10,000 million in 1960. The 'Eastern hemisphere profits' of the seven major companies, according to the First National City Bank, amounted to some $950 million for 1955 and $1,102 million for 1960. This would imply a net return on integrated operations in the Eastern hemisphere of the order of 20–25 per cent in the mid-fifties; but perhaps not much more than half of that by the end of the decade.

By the same token, if practically all this net profit was shown on the production of oil, with practically none on 'non-producing activities', then the percentage return on production would be very much higher. The Chase Manhattan Bank's estimates of capital employed in this industry suggest that of the total net investment in oil facilities in the Eastern hemisphere only between a quarter and a third consisted of production facilities, or were invested in producing countries. So the assumption that all the industry's profits in this hemisphere were earned in production—which is an assumption which can, as we have seen, be drawn from the companies' prized formula of 50–50 'profit-sharing'— would imply that in the mid-fifties the major international companies operating in the Middle and Far East were earning net profits of the order of 60–90 per cent on the net capital employed in production there, after paying like sums to the host governments that shared these profits equally. But these rates, again, would have been cut by nearly half by the early sixties.

A United States Department of Commerce survey of American investment abroad, in mid-1961, put the book value of capital investment in the American petroleum business in the Middle East for 1960 at $1,195,000,000, the turnover of these businesses at $1,745,000,000, and their profits after tax at $610,000,000: for Venezuela the book value of investments was estimated at $2,071,000,000, the turnover at $1,902,000,000, and the profits at $595,000,000. This figuring suggested rates of return for American oil companies on the book value of their investment as about 50 per cent in the Middle East and 29 per cent in Venezuela. These figures were not altogether easy to link with those of the First National City Bank, which however was concerned purely with the largest international groups; nor with the figures of total asset values made by the Chase Manhattan Bank. But the answers they suggest are of the same order.

The Department of Commerce study, however, provided some high figures for critics of the international companies to brandish in argument: they were indeed adduced at the third Arab Petroleum Congress in October, 1961, by a representative of the Russian oil export organization, which as usual had done its homework quickly. Few people in the Middle East oil business doubted that the notional rates of return on the book values of assets of the operating companies there were at least as high as these governmental estimates. One American company with interests in the Iran Consortium—where all presumably fare alike—has published figures suggesting a net return of about 100 per cent on its net assets after depreciation: Aramco has recently shown profits of the order of 45–72 per cent. Informed guesses at the rate of net profits achieved in Iraq (by trading companies rather than the IPC group itself) put this in between Aramco and Iran; and most oilmen in other companies will argue that net profits on the comparatively modest investment in Kuwait, by the various companies who gain a direct or indirect share of these, must be higher than in any of the other oil-producing territories of the Middle East.

Is this 'where' the profits on oil are really 'earned'? It is certainly where the major companies show these profits to the many governments to which they pay taxes. Can it be rationalized in economic terms? It might, certainly, be possible to argue that once an entrepreneur has located cheap oil he could acquire the capital required for some if not all the later stages in the oil business—tankers, pipelines, refining, at any rate—for no more than the long-term cost of borrowing, which for a major oil company can be very low indeed. Certainly most people would agree that the main elements of risk in this business are concentrated at the earliest stages of exploration and production. On such an analysis you might argue that the later stages of an integrated operation 'need' no more than some riskless 'public utility' return on the capital employed, after depreciation but before tax; i.e., that the capital would be forthcoming on these terms to anybody, and more particularly to any big company, that had found cheap new oil. You cannot argue rationally that capital in these later stages needs no return at all, or can be run at a loss, which is what some of the integrated companies have found themselves doing in recent years through this kind of accounting. Moreover, in practice the capital requirements of these later stages are in aggregate very high; whether or not these stages of the business incur much risk, they do pose the newcomer a very high 'cost of entry'. Probably 65-75 per cent of the fixed capital employed in this business, outside the United States, appears to be in stages later than production. A company that was earning 20-25 per cent on its total integrated operation, as in the mid-fifties most of the majors probably were in the Eastern hemisphere, and the most efficient might be still, could on this argument allocate a considerable proportion of his net profits to the early stages. If he accepted a return that covered no more than the net cost of borrowing, which would be of the order of 2-3 per cent, allowing for the charging of interest against tax, on 65-75 per cent of his capital employed, it would leave net profits of 60-80 per cent for the capital employed on his smaller but much riskier investment in exploration and production. Alternatively, an Italian estimate prepared for OPEC in 1962 reckoned that allowing a return of say 10 per cent for 'downstream' investments, production in the Middle East would have yielded the companies operating there a return of only 22 per cent.

In practice, according to the figures of the First National City Bank, the major international companies have in recent years been accepting even lower rates of return than this net cost of borrowing on the vast amount of capital employed in the later stages of their business; and at times, in some areas, may have shown even larger returns on their productive activities than the figures above. It is possible to rationalize these differences, too, according to the argument that suggests the profits should be where the risks are. For the even higher rates of return on countries such as Kuwait are in places where the risky gamble of exploration has paid off most handsomely. For each of these several exploration enterprises may have had to be abandoned in other countries. The average return on exploration that an entrepreneur might require to put his capital into oil exploration and development would be lower than this; but the entrepreneur takes higher returns than average out of his bonanzas to go on exploring in other places. At any one time the oil industry, or an integrated company, is exploring for oil in a number of countries. In some this is paying off already; in others it has not yet; in some it never will. You can quibble about the actual rate of exploration that the industry need be engaging in at any one time; but even to keep pace with the normal growth of oil consumption during a period of surplus some substantial rate would certainly be required. And in practice the industry tends to finance all of this from profits on the most successful ventures.

This question of the 'proper' rate of return on risk capital in the oil business is crucial in the relations between oil companies and governments. It is one in which the governments both of countries where the major companies produce oil and those where they process and sell it take a growing interest. But in economic terms it may be useful here to enter the caveat that much of the argument about 'where' the profits are made in the oil business can only be regarded as notional. A possibly plausible case for argument that the bulk of the profits 'needs' to be made on production has been set out above. But it might be as easy to produce an argument that at least 65–75 per cent of the profits ought to be made on stages following production. Would allocation of profit according to the investment involved at each stage be any less logical than the allocation of it according to the degree of risk involved, which is anyway not easy to 'quantify' in any real sense?

In reality this is a profit on an integrated operation—the whole investment in exploration, development, production, transport, refining and marketing is required to give crude oil in the ground any value at all. Most of the oil is not sold until after it has been refined into products and distributed to final markets; it moves to that point under the same ownership. And where the major companies do sell large quantities of crude, they do so at prices differing from the posted prices that can be used in exercises such as the above to show 'where' profits are made in the oil business. To say that there is a large profit on the production of crude oil and none on say, refining in Europe—as has purported to be the case in recent years—is a matter largely of accounting practice, rather than of the actual occurrence of profit at different stages of the business.

This is not to argue, as some critics of this industry would argue, that the integrated company is at all times free to choose where it shall take its profits. The profits shown at different stages at any given time will represent the result of decisions taken at different times in the past, many of which an integrated company cannot easily reverse. Moreover, the integrated company is subject at certain stages of its business to differing degrees of competition on price. It will ordinarily be under some pressure to set its transfer prices from one department to another, and hence the profits it can allocate to any stage, broadly in accordance with competitive rates in the general market for that stage of the business—if significant competition exists there. Up to the mid-fifties, in some stages, there was little, and the major companies were free to set transfer prices as they chose. Since then, competition has returned, and they have lost most of this freedom.

Whatever other critics of the companies would argue, the consumer may be inclined to feel that in the past the companies decided to take a high and disproportionate share of their profits at the stage of production, or at any rate to 'post' prices at this stage that offered the host governments a large revenue from tax which it was convenient to call a half-share in the profits. This formula has been of tremendous advantage to the oil-producing countries in the past, in terms of revenue, and not too inconvenient for the companies, which could set off taxes there against tax liabilities on foreign income elsewhere. But it is now causing them considerable difficulty. The Middle East governments' understandable opposition to any reduction in the posted price, because this would automatically reduce the 'profit-sharing' revenue they receive, has come into play as a 'ratchet' preventing the integrated companies from reducing their transfer prices, and hence from adjusting their departmental profits, in the opposite direction.

An international oil company concerns itself primarily, however, with its rate of net return on capital as a whole, not with the rate of return that may be attributed to any particular part of it. There is such flexible and continuing movement of resources between parts of the world in this industry, for companies that have a really wide spread of business, as largely to blur the geographical analysis of oil profits.

Two interlocking factors that affect capital investment in this industry have had considerable significance in the structure of organization that it has in fact assumed. The first, as we have seen in the discussion of operating economics in oil, is that at most stages in its operations there are significant technical economies to be gained by operating on a large scale, and that with continued growth of the total market these tend to be offset by commercial limitations on local markets in fewer and fewer places. A second factor, allied with the first, is that in most parts of this industry the cost of entry for a newcomer is very high. To secure concessions over the very large areas that have until recently been characteristic of oil exploration in most countries except the United States, for example, or equally to establish oneself to sell petroleum products in any of the developed markets of the world, very large initial investments are generally required. These factors militate against entry into this industry, today, on anything but a very large scale, unless one can gain some political privilege in entry; and perhaps even then. This large entrance fee to the industry, moreover, constitutes a stake that one may find it advisable or imperative to protect by gaining control of other stages in operations—integrating backwards and forwards. The integrated company is in part a product of the characteristic high cost of entry into oil operations. And the dominance of integrated companies in the international industry tends, in its turn, to perpetuate and even to raise the cost of entry for newcomers.

CHAPTER VIII

Bigness in the Oil Business

In glancing at the operating economics of the petroleum industry in the last few chapters, we have seen various factors that make it convenient to have big units of ownership. Many of its operations are highly-capitalized, and in some there are considerable economies of scale. Moreover, the large areas over which rights to explore for oil have become available, in many parts of the world outside the United States, have raised the cost of entry into this one stage of the industry where one might expect to find adventurous individual businessmen—though one sometimes still does. These elements make for big units of ownership at particular stages of the industry's operations—that is, for 'horizontal integration'. They may also, indirectly, make for 'vertical integration', or the ownership of more than one stage of oil operations. In practice, oil companies frequently own or directly control almost all the operations that are applied to petroleum, from exploration right down to selling the processed products. There is still great diversity in the company structure of this industry; many small units or largish non-integrated units survive and flourish. But integration does dominate at most levels in the structure; and whether or not one regards it as an inevitability in the development of such an industry, it certainly has played a logical part in the way this industry has developed in practice.

First, the facts. Here, as in other ways, there are marked differences between oil in the United States and in the rest of the free world, even though many of the same companies are involved in both, and American companies own a majority of the privately-owned oil industry outside their borders. In particular, the share of vertically-integrated oil companies, and of the seven great 'international majors', is much greater outside the United States. Here the oil industry developed later than inside America, and the shape that it adopted, historically, was in some ways a reaction to the structure and strength of American oil companies at the time.

105

In the oil industry of the United States bigness is too common for even any giant, nowadays, to dominate ownership of the industry. In 1954, the four biggest companies in American oil refining accounted for about a third of total deliveries, which was rather less than the average 'concentration ratio' for American manufacturing industry; the share of the top twenty companies in oil, on the other hand, was much larger than the average for other manufacturing industries. These top twenty producing companies, in 1955, produced probably 55 per cent of the crude oil produced in the United States. Twenty companies accounted for 85–90 per cent of the crude oil moved through pipelines; and about the same proportion of refinery throughput was in the hands of a similar number. The top twenty marketers were responsible for about 80 per cent of all sales of gasoline, though for only about 55 per cent of service station sales. There were two fields of operations in which ownership by large companies was fairly insignificant: small companies or specialists drilled three-quarters of all new wells, and very few service stations nowadays are actually owned by big companies. But a large proportion of the drilling was done by specialists under various risk-sharing arrangements with the largest companies. And practically all the service stations through which these companies sold gasoline, though no longer owned by the largest refining and marketing companies, were tied by exclusive dealing contracts to them, or leased by them.

Those estimates, properly, are measures of concentration—that is, of the share controlled by the largest units in particular stages of the industry—not of the share controlled by vertically integrated companies. But in practice, there happens to be not much difference. Among the top twenty companies in American crude oil production, refining, gasoline sales, and the top twenty in terms of total asset value, in 1958, there were only twenty-four different names. In 1950, there were 50 fully integrated companies in American oil (while many others had interests in more than one stage of operations). These accounted for just on 60 per cent of crude production in the United States and for 99·6 per cent of crude produced by American companies abroad; for about 90 per cent of American refinery capacity and a fractionally higher percentage of actual refinery runs; for 60 per cent of bulk sales of products and 58 per cent of gasoline sales at service stations. These 50 companies engaged in all stages of the industry's operations; there were about 2,700 non-integrated drilling companies and perhaps 6,600 in production, 28,000 marketing organizations of all types and sizes and

250 refining companies. Bigness, in the world's largest oil industry, is therefore cheek by jowl with smallness amounting at some stages almost to fragmentation of ownership. And integration co-exists with large numbers of non-integrated companies at each stage, in many cases highly prosperous ones. The Texas millionaires, for example, are generally independent explorers, producers, and dealers in oil leases: selling to the majors, but not within them. But for the most part bigness and integration coincide.

In the free world outside the United States, oil ownership is far more concentrated into the hands of a few fully integrated companies, some of which are the biggest of the American integrated companies. A 1956 estimate showed that 99 per cent of crude production outside the United States and the Soviet orbit was in the hands of fully integrated companies; 90 per cent of refining; and about the same proportion of marketing. The international integrated companies owned a notably smaller share of the world's tankers—some 34 per cent in 1956—but of the nearly 60 per cent owned by independent tanker operators, they had on charter a large part, so that perhaps three-quarters of the operating tanker fleet sailed on their account. Ownership of service stations by major companies has not developed as much outside the United States as it did there during some periods of the industry's history; but a similar network of leases and contracts ties the owners of most service stations to their suppliers of gasoline. Since 1956, the share of these companies in all these departments of the oil business may have shrunk somewhat; but they retain their dominance.

Essentially, this oil industry outside the United States is overwhelmingly dominated by seven of these fully-integrated majors—Standard Oil of New Jersey, Royal-Dutch/Shell, British Petroleum Company, Gulf Oil Corporation, the Texas Company, Standard Oil of California, and Socony Mobil Oil Company (to rank them in order of crude production). The French *Compagnie Française des Pétroles* ranks as an eighth of these majors, less in terms of sheer size than because it shares their joint operating companies in parts of the Middle East.

The extent of control of oil operations by these international majors, however, varies a good deal between different countries. Of late, moreover, some sizeable newcomers have begun operating in the world oil trade, without as yet commanding any very large share of it. Some hundreds of American companies have re-entered international operations, or entered them for the first time since the Second World War; the most important of these are themselves fully integrated companies too. Certain nationalized or semi-nationalized companies, previously in the industry only as refiners or marketers, have been extending their operations backwards and outside their own borders into exploration and now into production of crude oil. In the refining and marketing stages, there are a significant sprinkling of independent refiners around Western Europe and many independent marketers of particular products.

Bigness and integration developed differently in oil inside and outside the United States because of geography, history and the different social and legal systems concerned. In its beginnings in the United States this industry had to be fitted into a settled pattern of land ownership that was perfectly well suited to the mining of coal and other solid minerals. The owner of the land on the surface was held to own whatever might be found under it; he was prepared to lease exploration and development rights in his subsoil for petroleum as for other minerals. This pattern of ownership, however, did not suit a mineral that might not stay where it happened to be found. If another driller on somebody else's land nearby penetrated through to the same oil reservoir, he could begin emptying it out of the porous strata beneath your property as well as beneath your neighbour's. The law that applied here was the 'rule of capture'—that regardless of where the oil may have been *in situ* it belonged to the owner of the land where it was actually brought to the surface.

In wildcatting for oil, this rule of capture was an incentive to proliferate small units, not to create big ones. Nor did the simple techniques of early refining demand organization in large units, though they did require rather more capital and commercial acumen than drilling did. But the incentive not to let one's oil be sucked away by another driller, or alternatively to join in wherever someone had struck it rich, led to wasteful over-drilling, followed in some cases by the collapse of output in what had seemed tremendously rich fields. Refining capacity, similarly, was expanded as each rich new field was discovered and then hastened into over-production. Fears of scarcity of oil were regularly followed by the fact of surplus and severe price competition, particularly for refined products. Since cutting the price did not increase demand much, these price wars left most refiners with much the same share of the market as before, only poorer. With small-scale refining capacity duplicated to a point where in the eighteen-seventies it could have handled three times as much oil as was produced, the need for rationalization was obvious. The general desire for stability offered Rockefeller the chance to begin combination in refining. The strategic role of the transport that carried oil to market, first exploited by the railroads competing to secure large-scale oil traffic, offered him the chance to oust his competitors, and to secure virtual control of the market for crude. Development of the pipeline, where his large-scale organization could not only secure transport rebates but actually own the means of transport, sealed his control over the movements of oil from well to refinery.

Control of the transport of crude to the refinery, by owning part of the means of transport and contracting with the owners of the rest, was Standard Oil's first step backwards into vertical integration from the refining stage. Integration forward into the marketing of kerosene, once again seeking economies of larger scale through bulk delivery and local storage, was a logical sequel, securing Standard's grip on the market for what was then the key product of oil refining. The original combine did not buy its way into the ownership of actual crude production to anything like the extent that it bought up transportation and refining, and developed marketing; at no time did it own more than a third of American crude production. Its control was adequately exerted by transporting and processing the crude oil. The behaviour of this dominant combine, however, left room for other major entrepreneurs to enter crude production, the one point of entry then open to large-scale new independents, and to grow with the discovery of rich new oilfields. 'To avoid becoming in effect a part of Standard Oil Company's production department,' as W. L. Mellon once said of the beginnings of the Gulf Oil Corporation, it became essential for such companies to integrate forward into pipelines, refining and marketing.

Bigness as well as vertical integration thus proceeded largely from economic factors in this industry. When the first was checked by social attitudes embodied in American law, the other continued. The thirty-three separate corporations into which the Standard Oil group was dissolved by an anti-trust judgment in 1911 were not all balanced as oil businesses. Moreover, the dissolution came at a time when the rapid emergence of gasoline as the industry's new main product was beginning to overturn established patterns in the industry. Most of the former Standard affiliates tended to integrate backwards or forwards to complete their own vertical structures. At the same time other vertical combines in the business grew with the rapid development both of the new gasoline market and of rich sources of crude.

The largest of the American major companies, along with two or at the most three groups based in Europe, also dominate the privately-owned oil industry outside the United States. The structure of the international industry bears the stamp of the men who created it, at a time when the American oil industry was already in being and crystallizing in its ownership structure. But it also reflects the economic consequences of oil geography—and the social and legal attitudes towards business development both in the countries from which these creators came and in those where they developed the oil.

In the oil producing areas outside the United States the pattern of land ownership has led directly, not indirectly, to bigness. The only European petroleum industry that was of comparable size to the American by the turn of the century, that of Russia, was locked within the economic stagnation of a feudal state; it never experienced the stimulus of America's automotive revolution, and the First World War removed it from private ownership (though not, for very long, from the world oil trade). No other European power found enough oil within its borders for its needs. European enterprise had to enter the oil business by way of oil exploration in countries where often no settled pattern of land tenure existed and where legal rights in the subsoil were not firmly vested in any surface landlord. Explorers for oil in these colonial and semi-colonial areas had to deal with rulers whose ownership of territory and subsoil was absolute (or was promptly presumed to be). The early concessions granted comprehensive rights to exploration and development over very large areas, and in some cases over whole countries. In the Middle East, the reservoirs developed have been huge, and it has certainly made for technical efficiency that they should have been developed under single managements. Moreover, the high costs of exploration and development in these under-developed countries required very heavy investment, which only big companies could afford, initially, to risk there.

European attitudes towards oil abroad, on the part both of entrepreneurs and of governments, moreover reflected their lack of oil at home. The Royal Dutch/Shell grouping, which came together to compete with Standard Oil for kerosene and later gasoline markets outside the United States, was always concerned with finding the crude as well as moving it to market. It could not rely, as could Rockefeller, upon gaining control of the means of transport in the certainty that enough crude (or even more than enough) would be forthcoming. Its sources of oil were across the seas from its markets: this put the emphasis upon the development of the tanker, which originated in the European companies operating internationally as logically as the overland pipeline originated in the American. European pioneers in the oil business did not have to worry as much as American about social or political attitudes to the growth of their enterprises. European governments were less concerned with the ideology of small business and much more concerned with laying hands on the oil.

Governmental reactions to the combine of Shell and Royal Dutch before the First World War, therefore, were not to try to divide it up but to get into the oil business themselves. This, as well as securing oil for the Royal Navy, was a reason for the British government's investment in Anglo-Persian (later Anglo-Iranian, and today British Petroleum). German enterprise, private or governmental, was shut out of world oil by defeat in that First World War; the French government secured its share of right to oil development in Iraq and gave private enterprise, within the *Compagnie Française des Pétroles*, a share in exploiting this. After the Second World War France increased its own state and private participation in oil through the development of Algerian oil and gas; Italy, developing local gas through a state enterprise, began to market and refine oil and then sought with this state company to integrate backwards into oil production abroad. All of these were consumer countries putting capital into the development of oil sources; their logical course was integration, and with national backing they attained bigness.

Wherever the oil industry has grown to prominence you find bigness and vertical integration; the one, indeed, makes the other advisable. Operating units are big and heavily capitalized, with comparatively low running costs; either low or unstable rates of operation, therefore would raise their total operating costs. At the level of production, where each well for a time is in a situation of increasing rather than diminishing returns, the owner whose investment is already sunk is tempted to maintain output at almost any cost. Yet reductions in price for crude or products do not, in general, significantly widen demand from the final consumer, and price wars may serve only to reduce everyone's return on capital. So the incentive to secure a share of the market by integrating forward is stronger than the pressures in the opposite direction. From time to time the need to command extra supplies of crude—particularly cheap crude—may dictate backward integration by companies strong in refining and marketing. But more often than not in the history of this industry, such companies have had the upper hand in bargaining with those that are 'long on crude'. Vertical integration seldom leaves a company completely in balance. There is still such a large element of luck in exploration that continued heavy expenditure on searching for oil may still leave the largest of companies short of low-cost oil reserves in the places that it would like. Shell had many years of poor luck, for example. But even a large integrated company happening upon exceptionally rich oilfields may be hard put to find a market for its new and abundant potential supplies of crude: and not infrequently marriages or less regular liaisons between differently-placed groups can be arranged.

Bigness may make it easier to finance expansion—either by the market power to obtain margins that allow for self-financing, or in this industry's infrequent recourse to finance from outside. Size and solidity have their attractions for the investor outside: so may an integrated situation even when the market prospects are not buoyant. And the very large company in an industry growing at the rate that oil is has a built-in pressure to expand. Its expenditure on exploration, for example, will be related not merely to its forward estimates of demand, its present reserve-production ratio, and its views of the chances in possible new areas. There remains, even after so many years of search throughout the world, a strong element of pre-emptive bidding. If one company does not look for oil in even an unlikely place, the next one may find it there; geology is not an exact science. The largest international oil companies are concerned with maintaining their own positions in the world oil business. These are entities imbued with the intention of permanence; and they are in business to stay, and ideally to stay with as big a share as they have today, if not bigger. The majors in this industry almost always prefer a continued steady return over a long period to the maximum advantage in the short run. And wherever oil is found, they prefer it to be in strong hands.

When one looks at the historical development of that structure, inside or outside the United States, it is hard to distinguish many points at which one can say that the economic advantages alone of bigness or vertical integration need have been overwhelming. In each stage of the American industry, some independents have survived and thrived; nor has the independent ever been for very long shut out of the international oil trade. It is sometimes said that bigness is essential to research on the scale that the petroleum industry needs it. But in the United States, at least, many 'small' oil companies are large enough to carry on research on a scale that European firms in other businesses would find impressive. Independents and plant engineers have made vital and continuing contributions to progress in the technology of the oil industry. The record of every major company, in spite of the impressive contributions to technology reaped from the vast amounts of money and effort it will have harnessed to research and development, is still studded with innovations adopted from outside.

Of late, indeed, the major companies have been tending to bring the independent operator back into various stages of the business, under their own wings. More and more of the exploration done on behalf of the major companies is in fact carried out by small individual specialist companies. In transport, the majors have been content to charter a large part of the extra capacity required to meet growing demand from independent owners—who have, indeed, led the way in innovation in each successive size group up the super-tanker scale. In research, again, the big company often puts specific investigations in the hands of the plant engineer or the sponsored research institute. This readiness to let specialists do the actual job displays a sensible apprehension about possible diseconomies of scale, in the sphere of management and of communication. Decentralization of operating management becomes essential for enterprises spread as widely as these (though the amount of real decentralization sought and achieved in practice differs quite considerably between the major international groups). And they do not find it easy to measure their performance against what others achieve—let alone to achieve optimum performance.

One notable disadvantage of bigness in any business is that people, rightly or wrongly, distrust it. Ever since Rockefeller hired Ivy Lee, the large oil companies have recognized that their growth and accumulating power breeds suspicion, even apart from envy. This is not confined to countries with an ideological attachment to small, competitive business, such as the United States. In countries where the oil industry is present only as a foreign capitalist, bigness serves to strengthen the feeling that the country is being unfairly exploited. And even in European countries with less emotional attachment to the ideal of competition than the United States, public attitudes towards the great oil companies that work from headquarters within their borders are often somewhat mixed. Their very international sphere of operations is in a sense suspect; it may give the impression of being always able to remove any issue from the context in which it is raised, and of taking decisions for reasons that are never wholly explained. Quite a significant element in oil's overhead costs goes into public relations departments in these companies, which have the task of explaining the companies' behaviour. Whether or not this task is ever adequately discharged, it is certainly never completed. The policies change with the years; so do the kind of people one has to explain them to. The responsibility for explaining themselves lies primarily with managers at the top, not with the expert practitioners in communication whom they have assembled to present however much they are willing to tell.

Such disadvantages of bigness, however, do not stop newcomers seeking to achieve it, and certainly seeking to achieve vertical integration. From the host countries to the countries that lack oil, all recent new entrants to this industry on any substantial scale have sought to integrate forward or backward: Signor Mattei back to the oil well, Kuwait and Saudi Arabia, perhaps, forward to the foreign market. Vertical integration may not be the only 'organic' structure that the oil industry could have assumed, though some integrated companies would probably have been important in any practical structure that did emerge. But there has been as much logic as accident in the way that vertical integration has predominated in the structure of the world's oil business. This integrated structure largely determines the amount of competition in this business and the way it occurs; and it largely though not wholly determines the level of prices at which the industry has delivered, over its history, so vast a volume of the goods.

CHAPTER IX

Pricing: I. The American Market

In 1960, you could buy a gallon of regular-grade gasoline at any service station in the United States for about 30 cents, which included about 9 cents of state and federal taxes: the average retail price excluding tax, in that year, was 21·47 cents. Forty years before it would have cost a motorist about the same, with practically no tax at all: the price excluding tax was 29·74 cents a gallon. In Britain, regular grade petrol cost 4s. 10½d. an imperial gallon (which is a fifth over an American gallon) in 1960, including 2s. 6d. tax; in 1920, this spirit (which like the 1920 gasoline in the United States would have been a distinctly lower-grade product) cost about 4s. a gallon, including only 3d. tax. Those prices relate to the main petroleum product of the 'gasoline era', which hardly dates back beyond the First World War. As to the raw material, crude oil sold in the United States averaged about 94 cents a barrel (of 42 U.S. gallons) in 1880; $1·19 a barrel in 1900; $3·07 a barrel in 1960. (Here again, over the years, the quality of the many crudes whose prices make up the average will have changed considerably.)

Comparisons over the forty years of the gasoline era are perhaps rather unduly favourable for the prices of crude oil and what has become the main product made from it; the base date was a year of pretty high prices. Oil prices had risen sharply immediately following the First World War reflecting an apparent shortage (they did the same, after some years of price controls, immediately following the second). Reckoned against general wholesale or retail price indices, indices for petroleum and its products have risen somewhat less since 1947 than those of the other things a dollar could buy, but in the inter-war period often stood much higher and never came down as far. Comparison with some other fuels is perhaps more meaningful. Bituminous coal in the United States cost $1·25 a ton in 1880; $1·04 a ton in 1900; $1·12 a ton in 1910; $3·75 a ton in 1920; $1·91 a ton in

115

PRICING

1940; and $4·50 a ton in 1960. In Britain, where coal came on to the defensive against oil much later than in the United States, its price has risen six times since 1920—and has not yet stopped rising. Natural gas in the United States, in 1960, was sold at about 10 cents a cubic foot, much the same as forty years before; it had cost 7 cents a cubic foot at the turn of the century. But that was a controlled (and controversial) price; so were the prices that utilities charged for electricity, another fuel that could beat even oil for price stability.

The oil industry, therefore, can fairly describe its products as cheap fuels with a quite impressive record of price stability. It repeatedly does: but that is almost all it has to say about the matter. Even inside the American oil industry, which is the most mature and urbanely informative to outside inquirers of any oil business in the world, it is not too easy to get rational discussion of the way in which these prices are in fact formed. In the United States, the spectre of anti-trust proceedings broods over any such discussion, and its shadow extends wherever in the world American companies operate. Even so, it is notable and unfortunate that of late the international oil companies, in particular, have left almost all the serious discussion of price formation in the international oil business to their critics—contenting themselves with the claim that oil pricing is the result of 'competition', naïvely defined.

The 'literature' on this subject consists largely of discussions by outside investigatory bodies, such as the Federal Trade Commission of the United States or the Economic Commission for Europe; or by independent students of the oil industry, such as Messrs Walter Levy, Paul Frankel, and David Ovens, or by academic economists such as Professors Cassady, de Chazeau and Kahn, and Leeman. Published contributions to the discussion of prices from people actually within the industry have been infrequent and unfortunately rather often anodyne, though when anyone else discusses prices there have always been spokesmen of the companies to emphasize how distorted a picture you can get from outside. (This was, predictably but unfortunately, the line that the company spokesmen took towards one of the few Arab contributions to public discussion of oil pricing, the paper presented by Shaikh Abdullah Tariki at the Beirut oil conference in 1960, which was briefly mentioned at the opening of this book. There the companies gave the same impression that their contribution to arguments about world oil pricing have given before—that they are more concerned to show that other people have the wrong ideas about it than to help them to get the right ones.)

116

THE AMERICAN MARKET

In their own few positive contributions to discussion of the subject, company spokesmen have usually been hampered by having to postulate that prices in this industry are formed by the processes of perfect competition. This seems to be partly because the anti-trust laws require the pretence that this is how modern American industry actually behaves; but also partly because big oil companies, English as well as American, seemed to feel that this copybook economics was about as complicated an explanation as they can expect anyone outside the industry to understand without stirring up further embarrassments for themselves later on. To the interested outsider, this explanation may seem no more realistic than the opposite assumption from which some of their critics begin—that oil prices are fixed by an all-powerful and largely sinister cartel. Many people in the industry will agree, in conversation, that they ought to change their attitude, and discuss their pricing in more sophisticated and realistic terms. But the attitude has not changed yet. This has made it no easier for an inquiring reporter like myself—whose only partialities, I hope, are those of an oil consumer—to offer more than a sketchy outline of this complex and somewhat controversial question.

Most of the factual information on record, as I have said, is American. In theory, since oil moves fairly freely in international trade, and in larger volumes than any other commodity, one could say that until recently at least in the free world it was traded in a fairly unified market, and that logically the prices of crude oil and products at any point in this market should bear some relation to prices in this dominant market, the United States. And in practice, they still do: though whether the market is now unified, or the relation logical, are separate questions. In theory, again, in such a single market, the basic elements affecting the price or series of prices at which oil changes hands on its way to the consumer will be the final demand for petroleum products and the cost of obtaining the crude oil from which they are made; and the relation between the two should perform the function of bringing demand and supply into balance. In practice, oil is a business in which neither demand nor supply is particularly responsive to the 'price mechanism' in petroleum. Moreover, the remoteness of the consumer from the source of oil, economically as well as geographically, and the important role played by integrated companies throughout each stage of the oil business introduce further complications into its pricing.

Discussion of oil pricing in the United States, as elsewhere, is generally in terms of 'posted prices' for crude oil and petroleum products. It is useful to get clear what the term means—and to bear in mind that it is often not representative of the terms at which oil is transferred or traded in petroleum markets. A 'posted' price for crude or products is a statement of the price at which a buyer or seller of oil is ready to do business with all comers prepared to buy in the quantities of oil specified: it is in practice, if not quite in principle, a guarantee to do business on those terms with anyone. Who does the posting? In the United States, it tends ordinarily to be the refiners. These post the prices that they are willing to pay for crude oil at the wellhead from producers connected to their pipeline gathering systems. And these prices set the figures at which oil is held to have changed hands at any given time, though the actual purchases may take place continuously, without any re-negotiation in respect of a price change, under long-term 'open division' contracts between refiner and producers. This advertising of crude prices by the buyer and not by the seller, in the United States, reflects the structure of the American oil industry, where most of even the largest integrated companies produce much less oil than they refine, and are accustomed to making up their requirements by buying from a wide variety of independent producers. Outside the United States, where most of the world's production is in the hands of very large-scale producers, integrated to varying degrees, and where the crude-buying outside refiner is of limited (though growing) importance, the seller posts the price of crude, and in certain major 'export refining' areas the prices of products, at which he is prepared to sell to all comers in cargo lots.

Postings thus set the prices at which business is publicly on offer: and they have a major influence, at least, on the frequently different prices at which individual bargains are made in particular circumstances. Posted prices are often taken as a benchmark for continuing business, even if the bargain is done at a discount: long-term contracts, for example, may be set at posted prices less a given percentage or number of cents per barrel. Apart from their purchases from independent producers, most integrated companies in the United States are constantly involved in 'trading' crude and products with one another, to adjust the amounts and qualities of oil they have available at particular points into line with their pattern of requirements in different markets. Posted prices will form a basis for much of this trading, though very often the actual bargains will involve barrel-for-barrel exchanges of crude at different points rather than money sales.

Posted prices, again, may be used for internal accounting purposes in an integrated company where the crude oil only formally changes ownership, when it is transferred from the producing department, or affiliate, to the refining affiliate: and even if the internal transfer prices used differ from posted prices, they may often be altered broadly in line with changes in them. These transfer prices, as distinct from posted prices or individual bargains, may be simply book-keeping transactions: but they apply to most of the crude oil that moves to market in the United States—or anywhere else.

Prices for some of the main products, also, are 'posted' by certain refiners in most of the main producing and refining centres of the United States, and published daily by a number of specialized price-reporting agencies such as Platt's Oilgram Price Service. These agencies show a range of prices at which they learn that business has been done in these centres, or at least offered. (Even in the most active 'spot' markets for American oil, such as the Gulf Coast market, there are times when comparatively little business may actually be transacted.) Such reported prices, again, appear to affect a very large number of transactions throughout the United States, in that contracts are often made with the prices agreed to fluctuate say, with 'the low of the Oilgram Gulf Coast range' for a given gravity and quality of oil. They also record the prices in what could theoretically be, whether or not at any given time they are, 'marginal' markets for the whole United States. Crude oil and products from the Texas Gulf can be moved to almost anywhere in the United States, by tanker. Texas, as the largest producing area with the most spare capacity, could in theory at least always act as the marginal supplier.

So prices of crude and products at different points in the United States, regardless of their precise relation one to another, do tend broadly to move in step. (California and other Far Western States form a market for oil products physically rather insulated from the rest of the United States, of late consuming more than they produce and hence as an area a net importer: but prices there are not wholly insulated from price changes at the U.S. Gulf.) The United States is too big to be a single market for oil. It is a series of regional markets, of which few are self-sufficient and some of the largest are entirely dependent on 'importing' from producing areas of the United States—or actually importing crude and products from abroad. The patterns of demand in these regional markets vary sharply: so does the degree of competition for the general heating range of oil products, for example from coal or natural gas: so do the transport costs inherent in the location of fields and refineries near to or remote from their centres of demand. But these regional markets are interconnected, and much oil can and does move between them; and this interconnexion is reflected by broadly congruent movements in posted prices.

However, more than 60 per cent of the crude moving to market in the United States is never actually sold, at posted or any other price: it is simply transferred to a refining department or affiliate of the same integrated group. The first point of actual sale of such oil, where its ownership passes at a price paid in money, may be at the refinery, where there are some sales to independent oil terminal operators; at the company's own terminal, where quite a large proportion is sold to independents owning 'bulk plants'; or at its own bulk plant, to retailers with service stations. (The pattern of distribution, and the degree to which independents are concerned at each stage, varies between products and kinds of customers.)

'Tank wagon prices,' at which sales are made from bulk plants to service stations and certain large scale consumers, are in the United States the most representative and important quotations for products. In practice, these may often be the first point at which oil is actually sold in an 'arm's length deal'—i.e. in which ownership actually changes. And they also mark the points where the elements of cost in supply—crude, transport, processing, storage and delivery—are measured against the actual pressure of final demand in any given regional market. It is possible to trace a broad correspondence between tank wagon prices in major centres and the 'cargo lot' prices posted for products by export refineries in spot markets such as that of the U.S. Gulf Coast. Which set of prices influences which is another question. The spot market prices certainly signal price fluctuations in a large number of transactions. But whether they can affect the general level of product prices in the regional markets dominated by integrated companies, or merely act as barometers recording the general climate of business in certain parts of the industry, is a matter of somewhat esoteric argument among experts on American oil pricing.

At many of these points of sale where prices are posted in the American oil business the actual prices paid in many transactions differ quite significantly from posted prices. Large customers can exact discounts for the volume or regularity of their orders: where refineries have particular surpluses of certain products, they may be ready to dispose of them at distress prices; and in the commercial consumer markets for products, particularly those such as fuel oil in competition with other general fuels, it is the rule rather than the exception for marketers to accommodate their prices to the circumstances of any particular deal. In the nature of this business, these discounts off posted prices are hardly ever published, though the expert buyers of large-scale consuming businesses, who buy on specification and put their requirements out to tender, know the state of the market as well as the seller. These are products for which the demand is fairly elastic to price, since there are usually direct substitutes on offer. In many parts of the United States, the price of residual fuel oil used to be set basically by the price of coal. It now has to be aligned with the lower prices of natural gas (which are generally controlled by state or federal authorities).

Gasoline, however, is a product for which demand is generally considered to be inelastic to moderate movements in price; and most of it is sold retail, at openly published prices, to motoring consumers. Moreover, the amount of it that customers require, particularly in the American market, is what mainly determines the level of general refining activity—and hence may largely determine whether the market for oil products as a whole, in any given region at least, is in a state of surplus or scarcity. Price inelasticity is a phenomenon that tends to hamper the traditional function of 'the price mechanism' in bringing demand and supply into balance. Where it exists, a moderate cut in prices will generally bring about less than a proportionate increase in demand, and much less than a proportionate reduction in supplies. This is generally taken to be true of motor fuels and lubricants. The amount consumed depends on the volume of motor transport and the degree of activity of a vast range of different machines. In the long run, the retail price of gasoline certainly affects the type and size of engine designers put into cars; and in countries where large numbers of motorists are only just over the 'threshold' of owning a small car or a scooter, the price of gasoline can affect the amount of pleasure motoring that they can afford. But this price of gasoline is ordinarily a small element in the total cost of motor transport, and the price of lubrication an insignificant one. Motor transport itself, too, often represents a 'derived demand', being dependent on business decisions to which the transport involved is ancillary. Even in pleasure motoring the high initial cost of a car and its rapid depreciation in value give the owner a certain economic incentive to get as much use out of his investment as soon as he can; the price of gasoline would seldom deter him.

The high taxes on gasoline often levied by governments, moreover, tend to reduce the effect that small changes in net prices by the supplier can make to the total retail price at the pump. One of the few recent cases where any significant increase in gasoline consumption does seem to have occurred *post* if not wholly *propter* a cut in prices was in Italy in 1960–61. But there a cut in net prices was backed up by a large cut in tax and the retail price fell by no less than 25 per cent (more, indeed, than the total net price of the gasoline). And governments seldom reduce a tax that is so dependable a source of revenue: no product seems to them more suitable for indirect taxation than one for which they can assume that demand is inelastic to price. American taxes on gasoline would seem mild to any European motorist; even so, they are currently adding about 40 per cent to the price before tax.

The inelasticity of supply, on the other hand, stems largely from the high capital-intensity that we have seen is characteristic of most stages in the supply of oil. In refining, even when prices are weak, any competitive operator is always under the temptation to go for 'incremental throughput'. The next barrel of crude oil he puts through his processing spreads his heavy overhead costs a shade more, and appears to improve his margin (unless or until he finds he cannot sell the products made). At the level of crude oil production, the point where oil supplies are ultimately determined, a similar weight of overhead cost, already sunk with the well, makes output inelastic to price. One would have to push prices down a very long way before it would not pay to produce more oil: the marginal cost of production, for most producers, is much lower than the average cost (however calculated). That extra barrel, once again, costs little or nothing to produce and should reduce unit overheads; and there are other pressures of various kinds, from competitors in the field and from landlords who want their royalty incomes maintained, to keep the rate of production up.

The independent oil producer, indeed, may act like the smallholder in a plantation economy: when his price goes down, he may be inclined to push *up* production, to maintain his total income. In the few countries where reserve-production ratios are tending to fall because additions to reserves are hard to come by, a producer may consider the cost of 'replacing' the oil he takes out of the ground as a consequential 'running cost' of marginal production. This might in theory make him more ready to reduce output when prices fall: but there is little sign that it ever effectively did in the United States, until the state governments went into output regulation.

If total demand for gasoline is fairly inelastic, demand for any particular brand of gasoline is a lot more elastic than marketers would like. Brand loyalty, much as the advertising departments strive to inculcate it, is evanescent (there is far more loyalty to a given service station than to the brand it sells). For any given grade of gasoline, therefore, an established marketer cannot afford to charge any more than the next brand is sold for. In theory, every major competitive marketer has to match whatever cuts are made, and knows his competitors must too. In theory, therefore, to initiate a price war is likely to be not only costly, but relatively ineffective in increasing one's share of the market. For the established marketer, therefore, competitive activity may take the form of financial help for the retailer in rebuilding, advertising, and real estate operations: getting the best located stations and helping them build up their service, rather than price cutting.

Such theoretical reasoning offers plausible reasons why gasoline price wars should never break out. But as in the United States they pretty often do, it is somewhat inadequate as a rationale of gasoline pricing. Not every established marketer has the same degree of influence on the final selling price of gasoline at stations selling his brand; and on occasion a particular station owner may feel that while prices will eventually be cut everywhere to match a reduction he initiates, a cut may in the meantime pick him up some extra business that he can retain. Nor are all the established marketers equally established everywhere, or always equally in balance in their producing and refining activities. The most statesmanlike of major companies, on occasion, may want to expand its sales in a market where it feels underrepresented. And companies below the major level—which in the United States may still be pretty big oil companies—are usually seeking to penetrate some new market somewhere with lesser-known brands or 'unbranded' gasoline. In certain cities in the United States, such as Los Angeles, Chicago, St. Louis, and Milwaukee, gasoline price-cutting seems endemic: but it happens in most large cities there from time to time.

In the American market 'unbranded' gasoline can generally sell at one or two cents a gallon less than branded gasoline of the same grade without generating retaliation from the majors. Certain major companies will argue, on the basis of market research, that these two levels of price often reflect a division between two largely separate markets, hardly overlapping or competitive in price, even in the same town; one set of customers who buy simply on price, and another who patronize a given station for all kinds of automotive service. But once the prices begin to differ by more than an accepted, conventional margin, even regular customers will begin to transfer their allegiance, and competitive price-cutting may begin. And once started, this may go on until the level of prices has been forced down well below costs. The retail dealers involved take the brunt of such price wars, though their suppliers will usually make some kind of arrangement to share the cost of price-cutting, and sometimes guarantee their margins regardless of the levels to which prices are cut. Such price wars occasionally appear to end in covert agreements not to go on cutting each other's prices and throats. More often, however, one leading marketer in the field will take a stand, when margins all round have been pushed too low, and persuade his dealers to stabilize or even to increase prices at all their stations. Providing he has picked the psychological moment when most other suppliers are sick of the price war too, his move is often successful in snuffing out further price-cutting. But it may take quite a time before prices can be edged up to the earlier levels, restoring everybody's margins. And the eventual pattern of shares in the market, contrary to the theoretical arguments against price-cutting, may have altered quite significantly.

Only a few major integrated companies—Standard Oil of California, on the West Coast, is a salient example—still own large numbers of service stations and operate them through salaried managers. Nor are there many states in the Union where 'fair trading'—resale price maintenance, as we should call it in Britain—is legal. Even so, the influence of the gasoline supplier over the prices at which his product is sold, exercised in many ways, is considerable; and it is the suppliers who ordinarily take the initiative in starting, or trying to stop, price wars. Ordinarily the major companies would be expected to play only the latter role. But there have been several instances in recent years where major companies, purchasing sizeable 'unbranded' marketers in areas new to them, have gone on selling aggressively at lower than branded prices; or where they have introduced separate 'unbranded' gasoline into areas where they are selling already, in order to take the competition to independent marketers who are selling unbranded gasoline already. The introduction of 'dispenser' pumps, which can blend and supply a wide variety of ranges of gasoline from the same tank by 'spiking' the regular grade with measured proportions of high-octane additives, has given some American majors the opportunity to introduce new grades with octane ratings other than those usually sold. Their competitors have argued that this also enables them to go in for a disguised form of price-cutting.

Open and unbridled price competition, therefore, quite often breaks out in the gasoline market of the United States; but sooner or later it tends to be snuffed out, if only temporarily, and replaced by a general identity—and fixity—of price. This is not evidence of collusion; on the other hand, in many areas it is connected with the market power of some particular large-scale supplier who is generally able to take and sustain the initiative, either to cut or to hold prices. These gasoline prices, stable or fluctuating, are published to all comers. For other petroleum products, there are published list prices too, generally quoted for delivery within geographical marketing zones in what economists would call a 'zone-delivered price system'. But these prices, as we have seen, are subject to discounts, privately quoted to particular customers. Outside the 'dealer gasoline' market and the sale of other products such as lubricating oil, kerosene and heating oils to the domestic consumer, price discrimination between customers is the rule in the marketing of petroleum products.

Product prices in the United States are thus determined in markets that have little in common with the 'perfectly competitive' commodity markets beloved of nineteenth-century economic theory, where no single buyer or seller is assumed to be able to affect the level of the whole market, and in which information on all deals is assumed to be instantaneous, complete, and universal. In that, the market for petroleum is not unique. Whether or not competitive conditions satis-fying those theoretical criteria ever existed in real business anywhere, they certainly exist very seldom in the markets for products of large-scale industry today. The prices of petroleum products do not arise as the resultant of a myriad minor deals in some idealized commodity market, or through the operation of some hidden hand. They are the result of rational business decisions, often more or less identifiable, and these decisions succeed or fail according to the market power and the judgment of the companies concerned. But most economists who have examined American oil markets closely in recent years have concluded that 'workable competition' does exist in them, and that consumers have considerable choice and some degree of countervailing power. Until a few years ago such students were wont to point out that in these markets, as would be expected, 'price leadership' often occurred—i.e. one major marketer could often take the initiative in moving a price, taking into account in advance his judgment that all other established marketers in the area would follow suit.

At that time, indeed, this piece of economic jargon was used quite widely in the oil industry's discussion of its own pricing behaviour; it had the technical and quite neutral economist's meaning of a particular kind of behaviour to be expected in markets where much of the business would be in the hands of a few very large competitors. The businessmen, admittedly, would also point out that the 'price leader' in any market did not always remain the same company, and that if he judged the mood of the market wrongly, even an established leader might soon find out how limited his powers of leadership really were: but the label was not worrying in itself. Of late, however, 'price leadership' has turned into two very dirty words in the American business vocabulary. It has been argued by the anti-trust authorities that 'conscious parallelism' in market behaviour—i.e. setting your prices with a fairly clear assumption of what your competitors are liable to do in reaction to your move—may amount to some reprehensible form of collusion, even though you may never have discussed the move with any of them.

'Price leadership,' on such an interpretation of the law, would obviously be suspect. Naturally enough, in recent years American major companies have eschewed the phrase, and they now tend to jump down the throat of any innocent bystander who uses it to describe what appears to him, for perfectly understandable reasons, to be likely to go on in parts of their market. At the most, American oil companies are now prepared to talk about 'the reference marketer' in any area: so far, no anti-trust decision has outlawed this phrase.

A similar sensitivity related to the folklore of anti-trust applies to discussion of the market power of the major companies in the American oil trade. Any large American oil company, conscious of the not altogether loving care lavished by the lawyers of the anti-trust division of the Department of Justice on any description of its business behaviour published anywhere, becomes hyper-sensitive to objective analysis of what is admittedly a complex economic pattern with many intangible elements in it. The relation between prices in a home market where integrated companies occupy so large a role at every point, and where the tendency appears to be for integration to extend its scope, and the thin 'spot' markets where American oil prices are sometimes alleged to be set, is not easy to assess. One may feel, however, that some of the immobilities in price relationships that are often attributed to the structure of this industry, and to the power of the major companies, arise in part at least from some of the legislation and regulation that states and the federal government apply to the American oil business. It is often argued that in the American part of the world oil business— as elsewhere—there is a tendency to take most of the profit at the producing stage, on crude. Indeed, many oilmen will tell you that 'crude production is where the money is made' almost as a law of nature. Since the bulk of the crude moves within integrated channels, this contention is not easy for the outsider to test beyond cavil. But if it is taken as true, has not the fact that tax allowances are particularly favourable towards oil-producing income something to do with it?

The tendency towards bigness in American oil companies that was checked in 1911, again, can in one sense be regarded as an attempt, deliberate and in a sense organic, to reduce the instability in price to which an atomistic market in oil may be inherently liable. This attempt was checked and reversed by government action; and it was not until the middle thirties, when governmental regulation of much crude oil output in the United States began to become effective, that some degree of price stability over time was indirectly restored. This stability, of late, has been further reinforced by restrictions on imports of foreign oil, of which the production could not, by the same mechanism, be controlled. These legislative and regulatory processes fall into the category of governmental influence on this industry, which is examined in more detail in the second half of this book; suffice it to say that they may now, indirectly, if not directly, provide more support than any market power that the integrated major companies can bring to bear for oil prices inside the United States. (It should be added, however, that this element at least of government interference is not one about which the American oil industry is apt to complain!)

For many years the 'spot' market at the United States Gulf was not only the nearest thing to an atomistically 'free' market in the oil business anywhere, thin market though it was. It was also the market that set the price at which American products or crude oil became available to the rest of the world, and set a ceiling to the prices at which producers or refiners anywhere else could sell oil to the United

States: the point of commercial contact between the world's largest oil producing area, and market, and the rest of the world oil business. Up to the late twenties the United States was, moreover, the main 'marginal supplier' of crude or products. As such, the prices ruling in it were logically used to set a ceiling over the world price of crude oil and of products. It was not possible to sell oil to anybody anywhere in the world for more than the price at the United States Gulf plus the cost of moving it to the market concerned, which there were independent buyers and sellers ready to do. Texas has a large surplus of oil for export: whether or not it was the cheapest supplier of a single cargo at any one time, it tended until the thirties at least to be the cheapest dependable supplier from which buyers anywhere in the world could count on large and continuing supplies.

How long it would in practice have remained so is a matter of argument. From the late twenties to the mid-thirties the world oil market was in a state of surplus, with large amounts of existing capacity 'shut in' for lack of buyers, and prolific new fields such as East Texas and eastern Venezuela coming in to swell potential supplies. By the mid-thirties Venezuela was producing about 9 per cent of world oil output and exporting virtually the whole of this, supplying perhaps 40 per cent of the world export trade in oil, only slightly less than the United States. The major oil groups, at this time, were attempting to consolidate agreements to control most current production, to keep the development of new oil areas such as the Middle East 'orderly', and to limit price competition in many markets throughout the world, with varying degrees of success. (The thirties in oil, indeed, had much in common with the sixties. And much of what the major companies tried, not altogether successfully, to achieve by agreement was not dissimilar to what some oil-producing 'host governments' would like to have happen today.)

One thing these agreements did achieve, however, was generally to maintain 'Gulf plus' as the basis for the delivered price of oil almost everywhere in the world. No marketer, regardless of any agreements, could have got more for his oil than the c.i.f. price at which comparable oil could have been delivered from Texas. The question as the thirties wore on was whether in circumstances of unbridled competition buyers everywhere need have paid as much as 'Gulf plus'. At the beginning of the thirties, with oil running to waste in East Texas at ten cents a barrel, this was a very low price indeed, but by the late thirties it had become a fairly high one in relation to the cost of oil from, say,

Venezuela or Rumania. The development of conservation in Texas and other parts of the United States, 'pro-rationing' output in most cases into line with 'market demand' as well as with efficient production of the oilfields concerned, tended even if only incidentally to stabilize American oil prices at a pretty respectable level compared with the giveaway prices of a few years before. As the major international groups, in setting prices abroad according to the 'Gulf plus' principle, used freight rates reckoned according to long-term averages, rather than the often wildly fluctuating spot rates for single voyages, this element in world oil prices too became relatively stable. (Moreover, by the mid-thirties international tanker schemes were in operation which also tended to keep freight rates fairly steady.) The general world price level for oil, though here and there discounts or price-cutting could make it cheaper, was thus set on a relatively high and stable basis in relation to the potential surplus overhanging the world oil market at the time (which was proportionately greater than anything we have seen since the war).

Rearmament and war supervened before that world price structure was put to the tests that might have come inevitably from the more rapid development of oil sources outside the United States. The agreements which had had much to do with strengthening it became largely inoperative and were eventually, in large degree, abrogated. Since the war 'Gulf plus' has lost this decisive significance for world oil pricing, though it still has some indirect influence on, in particular, the prices of oil products in certain foreign markets. But first Venezuela and then the Middle East rose to oust Texas from the role of the world's marginal supplier of oil. Secondly, the development of refining in consuming areas has levelled off the growth of international trade in products and vastly developed the volume of crude oil movement. The United States, with its internal demand outstripping the pace at which production could be raised, became a net importer of oil by 1948—yet within a few years it was restricting these imports by quota and largely cutting itself off from the growth of the international oil trade. But the effect of these fundamental changes on oil prices in the world market has to be considered also in the light of the institutional structure of the world oil business during the period that these changes were taking place.

CHAPTER X

Pricing—II. The World Market

Oil supplies in the free world outside the United States, at the end of the thirties, were almost entirely in the hands of the seven great international majors with whom we have become already so familiar—Jersey, Shell, Texaco, Socony, Gulf, Standard of California (later allied with Texaco in refining and marketing abroad as Caltex) and British Petroleum (then Anglo-Iranian). All were integrated companies, though not equally so: each had its own refining capacity and marketed oil in certain areas, though not all of them sold oil products on the really world-wide scale that the Jersey and Shell groups did. It follows that most of the transactions by which they moved oil towards the final markets of the world were effected at internal 'transfer' prices—between different 'affiliates' or even between departments of the same company. They made some sales and exchanges of crude to each other, at prices settled by direct bargaining. They sold large quantities of products and some crude oil to independent buyers—local marketers, some state import monopolies, the few independent refiners in market areas (generally protected by discriminatory tariffs)—also in direct bargains. But the bulk of their supplies in the international market was moved within each group, right to the point where they sold it wholesale to dealers and service stations.

Now within an integrated company, producing and refining oil in more areas than one and selling it in many, the logistic decisions about which sector of demand shall be supplied from which source via which route are taken not according to prices but according to the 'net integrated return' gained by the group in following alternative courses of supply. That net integrated return may not necessarily depend at all upon the transfer prices that the company chooses to show in its internal accounting. It may, certainly, be affected by the value declared to landlords or to tax authorities at various points in the oil's journey to market—where royalties or tax payments vary according to this value, however defined. The declaration of these values, in such circumstances, does affect the net integrated cost to the company. But this has not always been the case for the international majors. In the Middle East from the early thirties to the end of the forties, for example, a fixed money royalty per ton or barrel of oil was their 'rent for the lease', regardless of the value, or income eventually gained from, the oil when processed, moved, and marketed. A company operating on its own, as Anglo-Iranian was in Persia, would have had to declare a value for products from Abadan when it landed these in Britain and other markets. But unless duty was chargeable on the oil (and until currencies began to become less than freely convertible) the transfer prices that it recorded between departments or affiliates in different stages were of secondary importance.

Among the figures that mattered to an internationally integrated company were, first, the 'laid-down cost' of getting its oil products to any given market, and secondly what it could get for them from buyers there. It could minimize the first by acumen in selecting the cheapest routes for its oil to market (or even by managing convenient exchanges with other people's oil that could get there more cheaply). The second figure, the final price, depended on what consumers had to pay there to get oil from anyone or anywhere else. Logically, for many years, the only place where consumers could get large-scale continuing supplies was the Gulf of Mexico. Up to the end of the thirties, even if the strict logic was perhaps wearing a little thin, the fact remained that buyers had to pay prices roughly corresponding to the value of products or crude delivered from the U.S. Gulf, adjusted for quality according to standard formulae. An international marketer, wherever he delivered oil from and to, could not hope to get more than this, but need not ask less. For many European markets, moreover, the potential suppliers from Texas or the Caribbean would have been some of the same international companies: these had no incentive to undercut themselves.

Moreover, the international groups had even less incentive than integrated companies operating in the United States to compete in ways that would push down the general level of prices in final markets. They were, clearly, in a situation of 'oligopoly'—that is, of competition between a few sellers, as distinct on the one hand from single-firm monopoly and on the other from the 'perfect competition' of many sellers in the market. Smaller independent operators existed; but at no stage of the integrated world oil trade were these as important as they were in the oil industry of the United States. Each major group, moreover, sold oil in many places; could press, but equally was vulnerable, on many fronts. Under conditions of oligopoly, action to alter price or rates of output by any one of them was certain to affect the general balance of the market for all the others. Each international group had to consider that if it cut the price of oil, its competitors would almost certainly match the cut and possibly cut further; so its initial decisions involved deciding how to react to the reactions that its move would be likely to provoke. This situation of oligopoly is frequently present in oil marketing. But for the international companies it existed on a wider than national scale. Price cutting to put pressure on a competitor in one market might bring pressure in return in some other part of the world where that competitor happened to be better placed.

Like marketers in the United States, the international groups were occasionally disposed to embark on price competition to enter some new market: but the thirties had seen a series of truces to some extremely painful price wars in international oil, which those remaining in the trade were not anxious to renew. They were not quite universally able to get landed prices for all products corresponding to the delivered price from the Gulf of Texas. But the prices of oil products from export refineries throughout the world, in general, did correspond after allowing for the costs of transport, with the cost of supplies laid down from the United States Gulf; and later, as the main source of exports shifted to Venezuela, from the Caribbean. The companies supplied each market throughout the world from the source that gave them the best net return, considering local production and refining costs, the cost of transport and insurance to market areas, and their tax situations at all points. But consumers at any one place in the world paid the same wherever the oil came from. This 'single basing point system' of pricing meant that suppliers from elsewhere got different 'netbacks', or proceeds at source, according to where they sold the oil.

Up to the Second World War, it should be noted, world trade in oil was basically a trade in petroleum products. Comparatively little crude oil was shipped across oceans: it was generally accepted as more economical to process oil near its source in big refineries, and to ship the products, which were higher in value, had less waste in them and did not necessitate the later 'cross-hauling' of products that local refineries' markets might not be able to consume. The only really large-scale movement of crude by sea was originally not international but coastwise. This was from the producing areas bounding the U.S. Gulf to the great market-oriented refining centres in the north-east United States such as New Jersey.

During the thirties there was a shift in this Western hemisphere pattern of trade, through considerations of integrated return rather than of availability or of open price competition. Oil was in surplus and cheap in Texas: but output of crude and refined products was mounting in the Caribbean, with a much higher output per well and hence lower incremental costs of production than in the United States. The Caribbean crude terminals and export refineries are somewhat nearer by sea to the north-east seaboard of the United States than those on the U.S. Gulf. (Eventually, too, the fact that coastwise shipping around the U.S.A. has to pay U.S. maritime labour rates became a considerable factor in comparative transport costs.) American companies with access to their own oil at cost in Venezuela, but which were for various reasons obliged to purchase a good deal of any supplies they used inside the United States at posted prices from other producers, began to use this alternative source of supply to serve markets to which Venezuelan oil involved lower transport costs and a better profit margin than they could get from the same delivered price by moving more Texan oil. These markets included Western Europe and Latin America, served almost entirely with refined products: but also the north-east United States, where Venezuelan crude began to be supplied to the main refining centres.

A $10\frac{1}{2}$ cent duty was imposed on crude imported into the United States in the early thirties: this did not limit the flow of oil from the Caribbean, but it did slightly reduce the price that the supplier could realize for his oil there. The netback value of Caribbean crude oil could be no higher than the price of comparable oil shipped from the U.S. Gulf to eastern seaboard refineries, less the duty, and less the freight from the Caribbean to the same refineries. Effectively, when prices began to be posted at ports in the Caribbean, these differed from U.S. Gulf prices by virtually the amount of the American duty. Higher duties on products such as gasoline confined the trade in products from the Caribbean to the United States to fuel oil, which it did not pay American refiners to manufacture and for which some Venezuelan heavy crudes were particularly suitable.

While the United States was ready to absorb all the crude oil on offer at prices based on delivery from the Texas Gulf, there was no reason for any international marketer to accept less than a corresponding 'netback' price anywhere in the world. During and after the war, at the same time as certain European and other consuming countries were founding or enlarging their own local refining industries, United States imports (also mainly of crude for 'market-centred' refining there) began to increase. In spite of a considerable and continuing export of particular oil products, the United States demand for crude rose faster than the capacity of its facilities for moving crude to refining centres, and there were indeed scares about a shortage of production capacity. The world's largest producer of and market for oil swung over in the late forties from being a net exporter to a net importer of oil. And a new source of cheap crude was now growing in importance on the world oil map. At the end of the forties, the United States as well as Europe began to import growing quantities of crude oil from the Middle East.

The Middle East countries had been the scene of many years' political and commercial bargaining and intrigue over oil concessions. But in most cases, oil did not take as long to find as the concession had taken to secure: most of the fields found were exceptionally prolific, and some were fortunately located near the sea. Oil had been developed, or at least located, in each of the main present producing countries before the Second World War. But that war made it hard to secure an outlet for their potential supplies: production and exploration there was deliberately slowed by the Allied governments during the war years, and only by the end of the war was it possible to tap the vast 'producibility' and the extremely low marginal costs of output that these new oilfields offered—provided that very large volumes of the oil could be marketed. And after the Second World War the international majors, which in one grouping or another controlled all oil development in the Middle East, began to move this low-cost oil to market.

The major international companies after the war faced a rapidly rising demand for oil products in Western Europe, which was unable to pay in dollars. They were short of refining capacity anywhere to meet the postwar growth in demand, and particularly of conveniently-located capacity. They were also short of tankers—and the growth of domestic demand in the United States was beginning to make larger demands on the tanker tonnage available. In terms of supply possibilities, political expediency and of dollar shortage, at the time, the solution chosen was logical: to supply Western markets with Middle East oil, and to supply it as crude for refining in Europe, not as products.

Before the war Persian oil had been exported, mainly to Near and

Far Eastern markets, as products from Abadan: Iraq oil, piped to the Mediterranean and Persian Gulf, partly as products from coastal refinery-loading terminals, and partly as crude to certain countries in Europe such as Italy and France that had already developed some local refineries, with a certain amount of tariff protection against imported products. Oil had still to be exported in significant commercial quantities from Saudi Arabia or Kuwait. It was not until after the war that two of the largest American majors, Standard Oil of New Jersey and Socony-Vacuum (as it was then) bought their way into Aramco, enhancing the financial resources available for development of Saudi Arabian oil and giving it access to considerably more widespread markets than its original owners, Standard Oil of California and the Texas Company, possessed outside the United States. Large-scale purchasing contracts between Standard Oil of New Jersey and Socony-Vacuum respectively and B.P., and between Royal Dutch/Shell and Gulf, similarly offered Kuwait oil access to world markets. The massive movement of Middle East oil to which this re-organization of financial and technical resources gave rise was to become the largest flow of crude oil across the seas in the industry's history.

Before the war, no prices had ever been posted at export terminals in the Middle East, for products or for crude oil. Purchasers of oil from this region, even when they were located close to the Persian Gulf itself, paid the same landed price that they would have done for oil from the United States. This meant that the effective values obtained for any given oil at Middle East terminals varied according to how far away the customers who bought particular shipments were. If the distance to a given market from the Middle East was less than the distance from the U.S. Gulf to the same point, a 'Gulf plus freight' price to the customer charged him a margin of 'phantom freight', and gave the Middle East supplier a higher realized value at source than the Gulf price. If oil from the Middle East were moved farther to supply any given market than oil from the U.S. Gulf would have had to have been, the Middle East supplier had to 'absorb freight' and accept a lower netback value than the Gulf f.o.b. level. Given the pattern of the world oil markets and of ownership among the international suppliers this system was logical: it bore rather hard upon customers geographically located near, say, Abadan, but these had a low demand and little bargaining power. It can be argued that the international majors, within this basing point system, were prolonging the 'tenure' of the U.S. Gulf as the basing point—though the Middle East, up to the beginning of the war, was

135

supplying under five per cent of world exports and was hardly significant enough to form the nucleus of any new pricing pattern. They certainly had a number of interlocking agreements designed to reduce the likelihood of price competition and to stabilize market shares. But it is fair to say that it was output regulation in the United States, rather than any influence these major companies could bring to bear, that had kept this American base price, to which world delivered prices were related, relatively high in the late thirties.

During the Second World War, however, Middle East oil deliveries to Europe were cut for lack of tanker tonnage, and though deliveries east of Suez rose in volume, total sales were held down. Moreover, suppliers in the Persian Gulf had to deal on a very large scale with two 'nearby' customers of very considerable bargaining power, the British and United States navies. The British Treasury, it turned out, was not prepared to pay for bunker supplies at Abadan what it would have had to pay for fuel oil shipped from refineries in Texas: after much argument it agreed to pay prices in the Persian Gulf at the same level as the prices published in the Gulf of Mexico. The United States Navy, buying products (and later crude for lend-lease purposes) from Bahrein and Saudi Arabia, was indeed none too satisfied with an f.o.b. price identical to that in the U.S. Gulf; but it did eventually accept this level. During 1945–46, quotations for crude oil and products in the Persian Gulf became broadly aligned to the comparable American levels, allowing for differences in quality.

The quotation of specific prices to customers, at Persian Gulf terminals, as against identical delivered prices in every market regardless of where the oil came from, altered the pattern of delivered prices and established a 'natural' market area for Middle East oil—the area to which at prevailing freight rates Middle East crude and products could be delivered more cheaply than oil from the Gulf of Mexico. The westward limit of that area, a 'watershed' between the markets to which it paid the supplier best to ship Middle East as against Western hemisphere oil, at the level of freights then ruling, was in the region of Italy. With prices equal at each source or 'basing point', it would not theoretically have paid to ship Middle East oil farther west into Europe. But the net cost of this oil, as distinct from its price, was potentially very low providing output could be stepped up: the world was short of crude oil: Europe was short of dollars and was building market-oriented refineries in order to reduce the dollar outgoings on its growing oil imports.

As the European affiliates of international oil companies began to bring these local refineries into commission, their parent companies began to ship large volumes of crude from the Middle East for the first time. On the bulk of their transactions the quotations in the Persian Gulf were no more than transfer prices to these major groups. While the price at source was identical with Western hemisphere oil, the net integrated cost of moving this Middle East oil to Western Europe was lower, and the dollar element in it—which mattered a lot then to European customers—could be held down. So the majors delivered the Middle East oil as far as it paid them, well beyond the 'watershed' of the market area based on those Persian Gulf quotations, and customers were glad to have it.

This was a period when posted prices in the United States were rising rapidly in a period of shortage after the removal of OPA price controls, and Venezuelan postings were being increased in line with them. The Middle East quotations—which were not, in the earliest postwar years, 'posted prices' offered to all comers, but notifications by telegram to existing customers—were raised several times too, but rather less than proportionately. This made the quoted prices of Middle East crude and products steadily cheaper in relation to prices in the Caribbean. The prices quoted in the Persian Gulf were then not necessarily set at the same levels by all companies, or changed simultaneously. But as these prices generally became cheaper in relation to those in the Western hemisphere, the 'watershed' where delivered prices became equal moved westward across Europe.

By 1948, the point of equalization of delivered prices from the two hemispheres was the United Kingdom. During that year the Middle East quotations were cut somewhat, taking into account the lower freight rates from Venezuela than from the U.S. Gulf, which when equalized at the U.K. 'netted back' a rather lower price to the Persian Gulf. But by the end of that year certain majors were in fact moving large volumes of Middle East crude into the United States: once again they were 'absorbing freight' on a significant scale, and selling farther west than their Middle East quotations plus freights would in theory have permitted. The European Co-operation Administration at this time was zealous in its determination not to pay higher prices for the crude oil that it was often financing for West European countries than any other substantial buyer was effectively obtaining for regular supplies. Partly perhaps to satisfy representations from this agency, Middle East prices were again reduced during 1949, in two steps; by September, 1949, the equalization point for 'delivered price competition' between

Middle East and Caribbean crude had become the eastern seaboard of the United States.

Middle East prices did not begin to be formally 'posted' for deliveries to all comers until 1950, when Socony began posting prices for 'free on board' sales of oil from Ras Tanura in Arabia, Qatar and Tripoli (terminal of one of the larger Iraq pipelines, then not long completed). Within a short time all the other major companies were doing the same. This shift to publicly posted prices coincided with, and eventually became linked with, a shift in the financial arrangements between these companies and the host governments of the Middle East: the replacement of fixed royalties per ton or barrel of oil by income taxes which were set to give the host governments 50 per cent of the profit shown on Middle East oil. For the first time in most of these countries, the governments acquired a direct interest in Middle East oil prices.

At first, certain of these '50:50' agreements were based upon transfer prices, not postings or quoted prices. In Saudi Arabia, and later in Kuwait, the profits of which tax and royalties were set to take half were based upon unpublished transfer prices from Aramco to its parent companies not on posted prices, and in Kuwait, in part upon the initial prices at which Gulf and BP transferred crude oil under their long-term contracts with other major companies. For sales to independent buyers the prices actually realized were taken as the basis of income and profit. But in revising the Iraq concession to an income tax basis in 1951, the Iraq government, very reasonably, was wary of transfer prices to parent companies and their affiliates as a basis for income: it insisted that the prices must be published and must be available to buyers generally. The companies accepted these prices—i.e. posted prices—as the basis for reckoning income and tax, though stipulating that they did not always promise to sell at such prices (even in 1951, certain customers were getting discounts).

The posted prices in which these governments became newly interested, during the fifties, moved parallel with, though below those in the Western hemisphere. American crude prices rose in 1953, and the international companies increased Venezuelan and Middle East posted prices in line with them. There were rises in American and Venezuelan prices in 1956–57, owing to the Suez crisis, when deliveries of Middle East oil were sharply reduced because the Canal was cut; and when supplies were resumed, Middle East crude was put up too. This increase, once again, was less than proportionate to the increases that had taken place for Western hemisphere crudes. If you still wanted to use the netback pricing formula to explain this in terms of a unified oil market in the free world, you could argue that the 'equalization point' of delivered prices was being pushed still farther westwards, and that Middle East oil was competing inland, within the oil market of the United States mid-continent. But in practice 'nobody figures it that close'. Oil demand and supply, and the facilities required, were roughly in balance by the mid-fifties, apart from interruptions such as the Suez incident, and it was no longer advisable to push up posted prices upon which there was growing pressure for discounts strictly in accordance with any theoretical formula. The next rise, in Venezuela in late 1957, was not matched in the United States or the Middle East.

In 1959, a cut in prices was initiated in West Texas and followed first in Venezuela and later in the Middle East; then there was a further adjustment in Venezuela. At the beginning of 1960, another small cut in Texas was not followed elsewhere, though discounts on posted prices for crude were becoming general in independent deals in the world market. And on 9th August, 1960, a unilateral cut in Middle East prices was made, and followed nowhere else. International oil prices were ceasing to be explainable in terms of netback pricing formulae linking the prices in different producing centres. A growing amount of oil was being moved at discounts off the prices formally 'posted'; and as experience in 1960 showed, the international companies seemed uneasy about adjusting posted prices on which government tax revenues depended according to the real circumstances of the world market. It was growing more and more doubtful, indeed, whether the concept of a unified world market for crude oil still had any meaning.

It is difficult for the outside observer to know quite what to make of these 'netback' formulae in oil pricing. They have been critically questioned by both oil consumers and oil-producing governments; nor have the major companies that first advanced them in order to explain the common factors that affect and link up oil prices around the world recently been keen to discuss them in great detail. Originally these formulae were offered to various investigating committees as *post-hoc* rationalizations of the companies' pricing behaviour, rather than as specific explanations of how decisions about prices were in fact made as market conditions changed. Obviously in setting a price any marketer has to consider the cost of supplies from other sources. But posted prices in the world oil market, until recently, were seldom prices set by arm's-length bargaining in openly competitive markets. They were prices set in markets where such arm's-length deals were the exception: and though offered to all comers, in practice they served mainly to set transfer prices between producing and refining affiliates of the same international groups. They were not simply matters of book-keeping, in the postwar era: they determined the amounts of particular currencies that had to be transferred between affiliates of the groups in different countries, and later they became the determinants of taxable income in producing countries. But they were 'administered prices' set by corporate decisions in circumstances of oligopolistic competition, rather than prices emerging from market bargaining: and not the prices that might have emerged from competition between many less powerful producers and purchasers.

When these formulae have been quoted at them by outside critics such as the Economic Commission for Europe, or Shaikh Abdullah Tariki, the companies have been anxious to emphasize the significant part of their business, at least, that is done in bargains where posted prices are largely irrelevant and their own bargaining power far from absolute. Shaikh Abdullah complained in 1960 that the international companies, over the decade from 1949 to 1959, had posted Middle East crude prices lower than was necessary, so that the host countries' share of profits from those prices was unnecessarily depressed. He proceeded from the point that while the Middle East postings for crude were being brought down, in stages, by comparison with the Western hemisphere, product prices in Western Europe and other major markets were not. This was broadly true: the list prices for products in Europe until say the mid-fifties did remain approximately in line with 'Caribbean parity' —i.e., what it would have cost to import them from export refineries in the Caribbean—and discounts off list prices, in circumstances of shortage, were not granted at all generally. When crude postings were brought down in the Middle East, therefore, the refinery margins available to the major's European affiliates—and to independent refiners there—must have widened. Western consumer countries welcomed this because it cut import costs and saved foreign exchange, and gave them a better return on the very heavy investment in new refineries in their countries. To the representative of a Middle East producer government such as Shaikh Abdullah, however, the process appeared as one of siphoning off profits into tanker or refining companies at the expense of profits on Middle East production—in which profits, once the tax basis was linked with posted prices in the mid-fifties, host governments had a vital financial interest.

During the years of postwar fuel shortage, while posted prices served mainly as transfer prices to affiliates and independent bargaining power in crude buying was fairly limited, it seemed to observers outside the industry that the major integrated companies were largely free to set these transfer prices, and hence allocate their profits, as they chose, up to whatever point an actual sale to an outside buyer, usually of products, took place. The companies could reply that they were under considerable pressure, at least, from European governments, to reduce import costs and disbursements of convertible foreign currencies by their refining affiliates. But bargaining power in the ordinary market sense, at any rate, was weak on the consumers' side. However, after taxes were adjusted to posted price, the companies became somewhat less free to set these prices as they chose—at least, to cut them. From the West, indeed, it would appear that from about 1954 onwards, as supply and demand came more into balance, the companies were taking the bulk of their profits, and paying practically all their income taxes on international oil, in the host countries. This was partly involuntary. Consumers were becoming more able to exact discounts off the list prices for products, and in arm's-length deals for Middle East crude; but with host countries' revenue at stake, the companies became reluctant to push posted prices for crude down in line with the growing pressure of market forces.

There were also limits, no doubt, to the level of refining and marketing profits that any integrated international company wanted to demonstrate: it might encourage competition in this later stage of the business. So they were probably not anxious to push crude posted prices down too far, even for commercial reasons: much contract business with other majors and large scale customers was done at fixed discounts off the posted price, so that cuts in this did cost money. There had always been large-scale transfers of crude between major companies (in respect of which tax is normally now paid to host governments as if the oil had passed at posted prices even if it actually passes at heavy discounts). Apart from these contract deals between majors, the proportion of Middle East crude moving in arm's length transactions was then said to be of the order of 10 per cent for the larger companies. It will always have been higher than this for certain among the seven majors, who happen to be long on cheap crude but short of marketing facilities; and lately, as surplus developed, the proportion has probably risen for all companies.

Shaikh Abdullah's main argument about the netback formula was that the equalization point for delivered prices of Eastern and Western hemisphere crude should never have been changed from London to the United States in 1949. This shift, certainly, was used to explain lower Middle East postings for crude—and to widen markets for this crude. Shaikh Abdullah felt it was never justified, since the American market was absorbing no more, in 1949, than 10 per cent of Middle East crude exports. To the impartial observer, the American market, from 1949 until, say, 1958, may nevertheless be argued to have been—at that time—clearly the marginal market for crude from any source in the world. These formulae, after all, were used to 'simulate' the conditions that would have applied in a freely competitive market, in order to assist the sensible allocation of resources between 'departments' of large international companies in conditions where such competition was largely lacking. To bring published prices into line with a sensible resource allocation in such circumstances—i.e., the movement of oil as far as it paid the companies in terms of 'net integrated cost'—it would be logical to set them in terms of the marginal market that would accept additional crude, even if it was not already taking vast amounts from any given source. So according to the netback pricing formulae, which Shaikh Abdullah accepted and used, equalization at the eastern seaboard of the United States may have been rational enough.

The United States is still, today, the largest single importer of crude oil and the only one still importing large quantities from both Venezuela and the Middle East. But it is no longer possible to suggest that it remains the marginal market for imported crude, from anywhere except perhaps Canada and Mexico; no other crude is imported freely. For since 1958, the informal American restrictions on oil imports have been made statutory, limiting imports to quotas determined by administrative decision regardless of price (however formed and however competitive). It is effectively insulated from the effects of price in the world market. In these deliberately altered circumstances, Shaikh Abdullah's contention that Western Europe ought to be taken as the marginal market for Middle East crude for pricing purposes may now seem more justified to the consumer in Europe. But the Western consumer of oil could draw some very different conclusions about the 'right price' of oil from this same set of premises.

For Shaikh Abdullah, in late 1960, suggested that the price to use in London, if this were re-adopted as an equalization point, ought to be the delivered price at which oil from the Caribbean (he said the Texas Gulf, but his figuring suggested he was basing the argument on Venezuelan crude) could be delivered there. The posted price that he would have suggested for the Middle East would be such a price in London less freights from the Persian Gulf—in practice some 60 cents more than the posted prices ruling there at the time he spoke. A consumer's reaction in Western Europe might be to ask, 'Why base the price on Western hemisphere crude oil at all? The chance of importing it might set a ceiling to crude prices here. But why should we accept it as a floor?' For by 1960, not much Venezuelan crude, apart from cargoes of a few grades specially imported for lubricating oils and bitumen, was reaching the European market. And independent buyers there could get petroleum products and crude, from the Middle East and elsewhere, at bargain prices quite unrelated to 'Caribbean parity'.

Consumers' criticism of the prices they have had to pay for Middle East crude oil and the products refined from it in the largest market for both of these, Western Europe, have always harked back upon an element that is generally missing from any discussion of these prices among producing interests—the cost of the crude oil. There has been a good deal of argument in the past about what this cost is. As we have seen, estimates of the average cost of oil from any field depend on assumptions about the working life of it and the reserves *in situ* beneath it. But what is relevant in oil—relevant anyway for the producer deciding whether to take oil from one point in his world-wide operations or another, is the comparative incremental cost of the next barrel of it, the profit he can make on this, and the amount he will retain of that profit after tax. Naturally the companies do not publish cost figures; informed estimates of the producing cost of supplying different Middle East crude oils have varied, in the past, from about 8 cents a barrel to about 45 cents a barrel. But the kind of calculation that can be used to give an indication of profits on production, mentioned in the chapter on 'Investment and Returns', can also be taken a little further to give estimates of costs. Within these countries, obviously, there will be large differences between costs at different fields; production in the Mosul field, in Iraq, for example, appears actually to be carried on at a loss. But in general the range of production costs shown above seems a reasonable one, so far as averages in the Middle East countries are concerned. And consumers, criticizing Middle East prices, have generally fastened on the fact that these actual costs of producing oil in these countries may be no more than 5–20 per cent of the prices that are posted f.o.b. terminals there.

One consumer government, that of West Germany, indeed had a set of independent estimates of crude costs prepared on its behalf in 1962. These suggested that costs up to the ocean terminal averaged about 33 cents a barrel in the Persian Gulf in 1959, as against an average f.o.b. price of about $1.76 cents a barrel (from which the host governments' take of some 70 cents a barrel, and any discounts that the producing companies might concede to independent buyers, would of course have to be deducted). It compared this estimated average cost with similar estimates of about 90 cents a barrel for Venezuela, $2.40 a barrel for the United States, and $1.60 cents a barrel for Russia. These figures of cost, depending on the accounting used, may or may not have included another set of comparative figures that are significant for any international company that can supply crude from a variety of sources. These are the varying amounts of money that companies think it necessary or advisable to spend on replacing the crude taken out or at any rate developing the reserves of each area. Such figures, calculated each year by the Chase Manhattan Bank, need to be interpreted with caution—as indeed do most figures in this shadowy area of estimating production costs. But they show a similarly wide variation, from about 16 cents per barrel of current crude production in the Middle East to about 50 cents in Venezuela, and nearly $1.75 a barrel in the United States (these are averages for the period 1951–60). And this 'unit cost of maintaining and expanding production', as the Chase Manhattan Bank calls it, is a significant one for consumers and producers alike.

Oil industry spokesmen, quite reasonably, have generally objected to calculations of cost from published figures of posted prices, of the volume of exports, and of government revenues, when these are put forward by consumers as the basis from which the final price of oil products 'ought' to be built up—and to the assumptions about profits on production that are drawn from it. They point out that the host government's royalty and tax, from their point of view, rank as elements of cost.

Mr. R. A. R. Pattman of Shell once described suggestions that the 'right price' for Middle East oil ought to be based on production cost plus some 'fair and reasonable' profit figure as comparable with 'one of those fantastic arithmetical problems ending with "What was the name of the engine driver?" ' Obviously, consumers cannot expect prices to be set in that way in the circumstances of this industry. In any business transaction, prices depend upon the balance of bargaining power on each side of the table, which depends mainly on the alternative supplies or markets open to the buyer and seller.

In the immediate postwar years oil supplies hardly kept pace with growing demand; and during the whole period up to the placing of statutory restrictions on oil imports into the United States it could be argued reasonably that if the buyer in Europe did not want to pay the posted prices that the majors asked for Middle East crude and the products refined from it, there were customers in the United States (mainly company affiliates but also independent refiners) who would. And the customer in Europe, be he one of the few independent refiners in business or, farther removed, the ultimate consumer, could not then get large and continuing supplies any cheaper from elsewhere. The alternative source for large-scale imports was the Caribbean; here costs were higher. The customer was in fact dealing there largely with the same set of international suppliers, who had no reason to undercut themselves and logical reasons, set out before, for not undercutting each other. But while the market was tight, independent suppliers from Venezuela would not have supplied oil to Europe any cheaper, either, than they could sell it in the United States—where the level of prices was supported largely by pro-rationing by state authorities.

There is nothing sinister about such a market situation as this, though consumers may not enjoy it. Nor does it wholly arise out of conditions of oligopoly among suppliers, though these conditions probably did tend to delay adjustments of price to changing market circumstances. In any market, however atomistically competitive, a supplier whose costs are particularly low, and whose circumstances are immune from being matched by competitors, is likely to reap the 'economic rent' of his specially advantageous circumstances. His costs will not set the ruling price, unless other additional supplies can be had elsewhere at such a cost. For a time he will obtain whatever price the total supplies available in the market can be sold for. He can reduce his price to increase his share of the market, but would be unwise to do this faster than he can build up output to supply the increase his reduced prices can capture. Middle East crude supplies to the world market expanded very rapidly in the postwar decade—as fast, perhaps, as refineries could be built to process the oil. Even so, this area took several years to become the dominant supplier in world trade, and it was not until the late fifties that the world oil market moved into surplus. The few major international companies largely controlled the total supplies becoming available in the market, during the forties and early fifties. Independent supplies of oil were not abundant enough in the market to push the reigning level of world prices down below those ultimately bolstered by the American proration system.

As the supply of Middle East oil was expanded, bringing its marginal costs down, its prices, in relation to those of higher-cost areas, came down too—but more slowly and less far than competition between many smaller operators in the market would perhaps have brought them. So Middle East producers earned an economic rent—indeed, what might be called the richest economic rent of all time. And by the time the 50:50 deals were finally completed and adjusted, the companies were committed to share the main benefits from this economic rent with the host governments, which gave the landlords an equally strong interest in maintaining the ruling prices of oil. Within a few years, however, surplus in the market was removing the opportunity to go on obtaining that economic rent. The very comfortable return earned at this time on integrated oil operations as a whole, though shown mainly at the production stage, had tempted various newcomers to try to break into the enclave of special advantage enjoyed in the original concessions. And this competition made itself felt in the late fifties at the point where all oil finally changes hands, in real rather than notional sales—in the market for products.

Ultimately, this is where the price of oil is set: the effective value of crude can be no more than whatever can be realized for the range of products refined from it, less the cost and return on capital required for distribution, refining, and transport from the source. The Western consumer may agree with the Arab 'technocrat' that Western Europe has become for the present the world's most important market for internationally traded oil—though Latin America, Canada, and of late Japan, are perhaps challenging it in importance. But the European consumer looks at pricing at the other end of the telescope from the Middle Eastern producing government.

Product prices, in theory, bear a similar relationship to one another in the different regions of the world market to those of crude; but they are not all quoted in the same way. Refineries in the United States, the Caribbean, the Middle East and the Far East post prices ex-refinery, as well as tank-wagon prices for products delivered to major market zones. In Western Europe, almost without exception, the only prices quoted are delivered zonal prices; ex-refinery prices are not posted. Relatively and now in absolute volume, the amounts of refined products actually imported in Europe have dropped since the war, as the continent has switched over to local refineries. The schedules of wholesale prices are still set broadly in accordance with the level of products delivered from export refineries in the Caribbean (or for some countries from the United States Gulf). But there were no European markets left by the end of the fifties where such prices could in practice be realized for all products from all customers.

The Caribbean certainly remains the world's largest exporter of refined products; and quite a large quantity of products, even after the very low levels of freight in the late fifties had reduced Venezuela's advantage over the Middle East in distance, continue to be moved across the Atlantic to Europe. Middle East refineries, such as Abadan, sent some products, though in much smaller quantities, through the Suez Canal to Europe; but their main markets are in the countries bordering on the Indian Ocean. The Far Eastern refineries in Borneo and Indonesia supplied mainly nearby markets; some of the larger Far Eastern markets, notably Japan, had become large customers for Middle East crude after the war, and by the beginning of the sixties oil was beginning to be shipped from new Japanese-developed wells in the off-shore areas of the Persian Gulf. In almost all markets, however—sometimes in anticipation of rather than in response to the growth of market demand—refineries were being erected. The long-distance movement of products, except to balance demand and supply for particular products or to suit the circumstances of particular companies, was in relative decline.

It was still possible to argue that the Caribbean was the marginal source of supply for refined products, even to areas as well supplied with refining capacity as Western Europe—though at the beginning of the sixties some people feared or hoped that Russia might later take its place. So the possibility of importing more products from the Caribbean, if necessary, did set a ceiling to the prices that could be charged for all products. But in practice the pattern of market demand upon Caribbean refineries was very different from the pattern of demand in Europe. And product prices related to each other roughly in accordance with what would give a refiner in the Caribbean a reasonable margin did not necessarily do so for the refiner in an area with a different pattern of demand. After about 1955, in Western Europe, demand for oil had begun to rise rather less rapidly; and the growth slackened off most for gasoline—which in accordance with Western hemisphere rules was the high-priced product marking the largest contribution to refining margins. These margins, in parts of Europe, were further squeezed because price competition in 'dealer gasoline', as well as in all other products, began soon after 1955 and after the Suez interruption became quite bitter. There were many suppliers ready to offer crude at bargain prices to such independent refiners as existed; and in some markets, though not all, these independent refiners could get fairly ready access to the final consumer with products cheaper than affiliates of the majors liked to sell them.

The effect of this widespread discounting was that in Western Europe, regardless of the official delivered prices reflecting roughly the Caribbean or United States Gulf prices plus freights, the actual level of product prices reflected the pattern and strength of actual demand and the extent to which suppliers other than the established marketers could penetrate any given markets. The 'cost of entry'—investment in terminals, storage and the building of stations or financial inducements to dealers—was high in many markets; but some major companies themselves were determinedly giving bigger and bigger rebates, either to get a bigger share of the business or to make the competition too hot for smaller fry. The pattern that emerged reflected European demand better, perhaps, than prices related according to Caribbean formulae might have done; but it was far more erosive of refining margins for any refiner who had to pay posted prices for crude. The wholesale price of gasoline was pushed down in all European markets, though in some more than others; this one might have expected in a region where demand for gasoline was weaker, relative to other products, than in the Western hemisphere. But the price of fuel oil, for which demand was rising so much more strongly, did not harden as independent refiners might have wished; for this happened to be the main form in which large imports of petroleum, at distress prices, were available from other regions, such as the Caribbean and the U.S.S.R. The strongest prices in Europe, at the end of the fifties, were for the middle distillates. It took about three years from the sharp decline in the market during 1957–58, for any corrective measure, such as the slowdown in European refining expansion, to restore even slight signs of stability to some of the 'free prices' in Europe.

Whether any logically unified pattern of actual prices for petroleum products would emerge in Western Europe, and if so what it would be, was a matter of major controversy inside and to some extent outside the oil industry from the early fifties onwards. The number of people inside the industry who were prepared to agree that 'Caribbean plus' or 'United States Gulf plus' no longer made much sense in Europe grew as the years went by. But even those most anxious to get rid of this formula differed about what kind of price structure should replace it.

There was a growing body of opinion in Europe, among the better-informed representatives of oil consumers, in favour of a structure of published prices in Europe related to actual demand there—as the actual prices paid were perforce becoming related in most European markets. This might imply the posting of prices at actual refineries in Europe reflecting the kind of realistically discounted price for Middle East crude that large-scale buyers (for example the Japanese) could regularly get and were regularly publishing; spot market freight; and some reasonable margin for a European refiner producing the yield of products that European consumers actually want. Caribbean prices for certain products might certainly continue to set a ceiling; but the 'low' of the range should come from some such new formula. Whether one structure of prices would do for the whole of Europe, or whether it might really need more than one, remains to be argued. Would one set of prices do for south-east and north-west Europe at once? And how far should Russian prices—for politics apart Russia would be a logical and inevitable supplier of oil for certain parts of Europe—affect European patterns of pricing? Western Europe is now the dominant market for Middle East oil and likely to remain so for many years so long as the volume of imports into the United States, even if it grows, remains politically rather than commercially determined. And European demand for petroleum products is exerted upon European refineries processing imported crude. The prices set by demand, supply and bargaining power in these local markets seem to the consumer more logical than any price reflecting conditions in distant markets, even if all the regional markets in the world oil trade continue to overlap at the fringes.

The acceptance of product prices geared to European market conditions, however, would necessarily reflect back upon the prices of the crude oil from which those products are processed. And in mid-1961, for the first time, one official price was posted for crude, at a new source of supplies for Europe, which did take realistic note of the pattern of European demand. The Jersey group, which more than any other international major had shown itself inclined towards bringing posted prices for Middle East crude closer to the discounted prices at which independent business in this crude was actually done, posted the first price for supplies of Libyan oil. In terms of the conventional netback arithmetic, the price it set was low in relation to those in the Middle East. One could rationalize it either in terms of discounted prices there,

149

or in terms of the fact that it ignored the traditional 'quality differential' of two cents per API degree of specific gravity. Libyan oil is a light crude, yielding a lot of gasoline and comparatively little fuel oil: according to the traditional valuations of the industry, worth much more than heavier oils offering less of the industry's traditional 'premium product'. But it had to be sold in Europe, a market for which Libya has considerable geographical advantages; and in Europe the most rapidly rising demand was for fuel oil. So the Jersey group posted a price for it that largely ignored the traditional value of this light quality, and suited the conditions of refineries in which such a crude would be far from ideal.

In practice, the price posted in Libya was still higher than the company would be able to get from independent buyers, though Jersey could probably charge it to the affiliate refineries to which it began to move this new crude. But whatever happened to this Libyan price, it was a significant move: the first, by any major international company, to break out of the unrealistic tangle of political and traditional factors, growing less and less related to the real pattern of the market, in which most oil prices published internationally remained caught. For the European observer, again, it was the first crude price bearing some relation to the demand for products in the European market, even if it was not as low a price as he might secure with his free bargaining power.

It goes without saying that the majority of European consumers were not concerned with analysing oil prices in this or any other way; they simply wanted the prices down, and in many parts of Europe they had enough bargaining power to get them down. To them, unlike Shaikh Abdullah Tariki, the profits apparently earned from the posted prices of Middle East crude had seemed too high over the years, not too low: the oil companies and the Arab countries for years seemed to them indeed to have shared something of a killing. That the posted prices of Middle East crude, which of late have become simply a matter of tax convenience to the host governments and of tax inconvenience to the companies, tended to include practically the whole return on the highly-capitalized business of getting oil to the consumer in the forms that he wanted it was lost on most consumers—though it was not lost on the tax authorities of consumer governments. Between the prices that consumers in one part of the world wanted to pay and the rents that landlords in another wanted to charge, the international oil companies have been finding it difficult, in recent years, to maintain a balance and earn an integrated return nearly as good as they did in that halcyon postwar decade. Nor can it be said that these companies, any longer, retain nearly as much power as they once had to administer prices according to their own judgment. At both ends of their business, the pressures exerted have become more and more political; and in the meantime, commercial competition in the world oil market has become more real and bitter than it had been for many years.

CHAPTER XI

Orderly Competition: As Was

I f you ask a chemist to tell you something of the essential nature of petroleum, he is apt to begin drawing a number of diagrams in which a large number of capital Cs and Hs are joined by lines in criss-cross and latticework patterns are varied by hexagonal 'rings', and sometimes by a few Ss. If the interest that you hasten to express betrays a continuing incomprehension, he may show you the same thing done rather more elegantly with a number of white, red and black plastic balls that can be linked together by springs, or segments of which can be fitted together into variegated clusters, also joined together by these flexible steel linkages. These 'solid diagrams' of the petroleum molecule are of almost unending complexity; any given crude oil contains a mixture of many. The connexions are hard to trace through; the segmented clusters join each other and their 'parent' atoms at many points, but remain a mixture rather than a rigidly connected structure. It was a senior executive of one of the seven major international companies who first pointed out to me how closely this organic mixture resembles the interlinked structure of the privately-owned oil industry outside the United States.

Take these seven companies—or eight with the *Compagnie Française des Pétroles*—which own some 90 per cent, as we have seen, of production, refining and marketing in that industry. They control perhaps the most important segment of it, Middle East oil, almost entirely through joint producing companies in which all or some of them are associated. All the major companies, together with a band of smaller American companies, are shareholders in the consortium that manages and operates the Iranian oil industry, though actual ownership is vested in the National Iranian Oil Company. Five are shareholders in the Iraq operating companies; four in Saudi Arabia; two—with special contracts involving three of the others—in Kuwait. These are the most important joint operations in producing oil in the Middle East, though there are many others in the area. Quite a number of independent 'newcomers' to the Middle Eastern scene have secured concessions on their own (or in partnership with governments); but Shell's Kuwait offshore concession at the end of 1960 was the first that any of the majors had secured on its own in the region since 1950. The same is not as true of Venezuela—or indeed of new producing areas such as Libya. In these areas the major companies such as Esso, Shell, Texas, Gulf and Mobil operate mainly through separate, single-company concessions or licences in smaller areas than those in the Middle East, and it is the smaller American groups that in some cases operate on a joint basis. In Europe, and 'the franc zone', however, the majors often prospect and produce together or jointly with local companies: for instance, it was a company owned by Jersey and Shell that recently discovered big natural gas deposits in Holland and is developing it with the Dutch state as a major partner, while the major companies have concessions in the Sahara in partnership with semi-nationalized French firms.

Joint producing companies, then, are the first clusters linked to the primary 'atoms' of the oil industry: once one goes further into refining and marketing, other sets of cross-linkages, formal and informal, appear. In the United Kingdom, Eire, the Near East, many African territories, and Ceylon, Shell and BP engage in joint marketing operations and occasionally in joint refining as Shell-Mex and BP; Standard of California and the Texas Company do so in most countries of the Eastern hemisphere as Caltex. Until the end of 1960, Jersey and Mobil worked together in Africa and most countries East of Suez as Stanvac; though this partnership is being largely dissolved, some vestigial joint operations continue. At this stage of operations, the links may be a matter of contracts rather than of joint ownership. Shell buys much of its Middle East crude supplies from Gulf in Kuwait, and shares the eventual proceeds of marketing, wherever and under whatever brand the oil is finally sold; Jersey and Mobil, similarly, have long-term purchase contracts with BP in Kuwait. Gulf, BP and some others have long-term contracts with a number of so-called independent refineries in Italy and other parts of Europe to refine crude for them (which is one way that companies short of marketing facilities can get their oil to the final consumer). Moreover, outside the United States as well as inside it, substantial exchanges of crude and products take place between the major companies as a matter of business convenience. The majors sell crude to their biggest competitors, such as ENI in Italy; their European refineries, again, often supply products to some of their most thrusting independent competitors.

In the ocean transport of oil, joint operation is much less frequent, though the majors, owning large fleets of tankers and controlling the operations of yet larger fleets, sometimes charter out their tankers to other oil companies; and one or two joint delivery arrangements exist. But in pipeline ownership in Western Europe, as it began to develop at the end of the fifties, joint ownership by the companies' marketing affiliates was the rule: the line from Lavera near Marseilles up to Mulhouse, Strasbourg and Karlsruhe, for example, is owned by no less than 16 major and minor companies.

Any outside observer—particularly the private motorist who is used to buying his gasoline from these companies, in spite of their strongly competitive advertising, at identical prices—may be forgiven for not quite managing to sort them out, and for wondering whether they really are as separate as all that. Most people are vaguely aware that at times in the past, if not today, the major international companies have joined in various business agreements, tending to limit competition. Italy's Signor Mattei, who admittedly gets few kind words from the major companies himself, seldom refers to the majors as anything but 'the cartel'. The French, and officials in the European communities, have a rather more temperate habit of calling them 'le club'.

Yet in the original home of the oil industry and of several of these major companies, the pressure of anti-trust legislation and investigation is constant and powerful. Any form of consultation or concerted action between the companies, even in such emergencies as the shortage of tankers after the Suez incident, requires clearing by the United States Department of Justice—which clearing usually tends to reduce or delay the flexibility in logistics that the companies can manage. At any time since the Second World War, there has usually been one kind of investigation or another going on into the American oil industry, whether it be the Federal Trade Commission, a Senate committee, or the judge in an actual anti-trust suit who has been doing the inquiring. The very European officials who call the majors 'le club' are aware that the local *groupements* and oil trade associations with which they broadly prefer to do business are a source of constant anxiety to the headquarters of the American companies represented in them. More than once since the war these headquarters have sent high-level emissaries throughout their European subsidiaries, impressing upon them the undesirability of engaging in just the kind of joint action, for example on fuel oil prices, in which European governments have simultaneously been pressing them to engage.

Oil companies with headquarters in Europe do not live under nearly the same pressure always to be seen to be competing. But nobody in the oil business, especially after the bitter marketing experience of the last few years, would take kindly to the implication that he or it is insulated from competition, or comfortably free to rig prices in some form of conspiratorial international cartel of the type that used to be caricatured by the industry's more sensational critics. Even the domestic consumer in Western Europe, during recent years, is becoming faintly aware that the members of *le club* are beset by some complete outsiders, and are not even behaving in a wholly clubbable manner towards each other.

Nobody would suggest that business behaviour in the oil trade is governed by 'perfect competition' in the 'ideal' copybook sense. Even in the United States, which as we have seen, has a far larger number of much smaller independent operators at each stage of the oil business than there are abroad, the market power of the larger companies makes competition distinctly 'imperfect'; and competition in the international market is even more 'oligopolistic'. These are quite real forms of competition, at most times; but as we have seen in the preceding chapters, they are not generally conducive to price competition. Published prices tend to be identical—though with a large amount of discounting off these prices in the myriad separate deals of the commercial and industrial markets. Oligopoly is not infrequent in the industrial world today, particularly where very large amounts of capital are required for anyone starting up in business. And in other industries, as well as in oil, it is characterized by what is called 'non-price' competition.

'Non-price' competition between oil companies, major or independent, for the favour of the private motorist is usually concentrated on the dealer, not the motorist. The main competition occurs in seeking supply contracts with the favourably-placed service station. The dealer gets special rebates for exclusive dealing; he may get capital assistance when a contract comes up for renewal, or assistance in the re-equipment of his station. Alternatively, the supplying companies may bid up strategic sites to a real estate value well above anything that the site could fetch for any other purpose; make their stations more and more lavish and attentive; and engage in the duplication of their main rivals' stations wherever these are particularly well-placed.

ORDERLY COMPETITION

At times this has led to the building of far too many service stations,
and the reduction of average throughput to an uneconomically low level;
but in most countries today some form of licensing has been imposed
to limit the number of service stations built.

Though some marketing men in oil profess considerable scepticism
about it, the companies spend heavily on another form of non-price
competition—with advertising and to some extent with research. They
spend very heavily on attempts to implant the brand name in motorists'
minds; sometimes mainly through general advertising designed to inculcate goodwill, but often through the steady refinement of claims for
new and specialized additives to give improved qualities to the petrol.
Over the last thirty years or so, there has been a very marked improvement in the purity and the general fuel qualities of the gasolines sold.
Many consumers and some oilmen, however, express more scepticism
about particular 'new additives', and about the 'octane race' that has
steadily raised the anti-knock quality of gasolines. This has been partly
engendered by the motor industry's search for more efficient engines:
but it may also by now have outstripped the compression ratios of the
engines fitted into many customers' cars.

Quality competition of this kind is one of the characteristic forms
of non-price competition. It steadily helps to increase the technical
efficiency with which the consumer can use the fuel, though sometimes
at a significant cost in the technical efficiency with which the refinery
that produces the fuel is run. It gives the consumer higher quality
at the same price without offering him the choice of the same quality
at lower price, which sets up a kind of technocratic criterion, and tells
the customer what is best for him. Wholesale distribution of gasoline
and lubricants has probably become a good deal more efficient since
the growth of exclusive dealing and one-brand stations increased the
amount of gasoline 'dropped' by the road oil tankers of any one company at each of its filling stations. But this has been at some limited
cost in the reduction of consumers' choice, and there may have been a
tendency towards building too many unnecessarily lavish stations. Non-
price competition is real—though it is a good deal more convenient for
established producers than the other kind. But whether it brings the
consumer as much benefit as price competition is debatable.

This kind of competition in marketing is backed by a considerable amount of non-price competition farther back in the integrated
operations of the industry. Quality competition postulates a steady
effort in product development; the competitive development of refining

techniques to serve fresh markets, or to increase the proportion of the more lucrative products, and to branch out into new fields such as petroleum chemicals, requires an even larger effort in competitive research. Back at the level of production, the major companies are constantly engaged in the exploration of fresh areas, seeking to maintain or increase their share of the business of the future. And the absence of open competition in published prices, again, does not preclude very real price competition with discounts and rebates, open and hidden in parts of the international market. Independent customers for crude have for a long time now been able to get significant discounts off Middle East and even larger ones off Venezuelan posted prices, but in addition they have been able to secure less obvious advantages. Finance has been forthcoming from the majors for local refineries; tanker companies who are linked with significant buyers of crude have found steadier employment, at better than rock bottom rates for their vessels. Many forms of special inducement have been devised—for customers with bargaining power.

Conditions of sharpened competition such as these, which recurred quite often in the American oil industry up to the mid-thirties, have since been moderated to some degree by state regulation on crude oil production there. They have returned to the international oil market only in the last three or four years, after about a quarter of a century, during which the majors were largely immune from any significant outside competition. Competition since the mid-fifties, however, has not yet reached the degree of severity of the really bitter international competition of the twenties—in which the attitudes of the majors towards really severe price competition were decisively tested. During the twenties, a number of other American companies, plus the Russians, were also active in the world oil market, while the rivalry of the American and British/Dutch groups for leadership was somewhat accentuated by diplomatic backing for both sides. Many of the other American companies eventually 'retired hurt', selling off their interests to one or another of the few remaining in the world market. The Russians had patched up an armistice with the remaining majors at the end of the twenties, and though this truce was not without its frontier incidents of further dumping at cut prices, development of their own economy during the thirties reduced Soviet interest in the world oil market. The main American and British/Dutch groups, in 1928, reached agreements, which came to be known as the 'As Is' agreements, on the stabilization of company shares in the world market and some stabilization of prices. These arrangements were later paralleled by the 'Red Line' agreements between the main groups in the Middle East for the co-operative development of existing oil-producing areas and controlled development of new ones. The As Is agreements were to be abandoned on American initiative at the beginning of the Second World War, partly in deference to growing public and governmental suspicion towards cartels (though they were echoed by a curious 'take-over bid' by governments for the whole pattern of regulation they implied, in the form of the abortive Anglo-American petroleum agreement of 1944). But one has dispassionately to recognize how logical the agreements were for the major oil companies that engaged in them after almost a decade of potentially ruinous price wars. It was no accident that this attempt to regulate prices in a seemingly bottomless market paralleled the development of plans for state regulation of output in the United States. Both were reactions to aspects of essentially the same situation.

Joint operating companies in Iraq preceded the Red Line agreements of the thirties: but these agreements would have stamped the pattern on each new concession and in fact, though not simply as a result, most Middle East concessions are jointly owned. These agreements too were abandoned after the war (causing some litigation between certain of the American companies that were withdrawing and European companies that did not want to lose benefits from the 'Red Line'), but the pattern of joint ownership persisted and was indeed developed. Standard Oil of New Jersey and Socony Mobil bought their way into Aramco, for example, after the war. For about ten years after the war the international majors were largely without effective competitors in the Middle East, though during the fifties a large number of other concerns had begun to seek concessions in Venezuela and in the Middle East. This was a period of rapidly rising demand for energy, with little expansion in supply of primary fuels. Demand for oil products was rising as fast as the major companies could build tankers, refining and marketing facilities to meet them.

No formal agreements governed the market behaviour of the international majors during this period, and the American companies were particularly uneasy even about the informal arrangements that had to be reached from time to time to deal with political emergencies. But no agreements were needed during such a period to persuade most of them to desist from price competition. There were other, less potentially double-edged ways of raising total revenue and, for some, of increasing one's share of the business. Certain of the relative newcomers to these rich supplies of cheap crude and to the European market, such as Caltex, offered very advantageous terms for products and occasionally crude to independent buyers during this period, to gain footholds in parts of Europe; but the established marketers had no need to match them. What some of these majors approvingly christened 'orderly competition' was the rule. And though it has been largely disrupted by the advent of newcomers, both from private enterprise and from nationalized or semi-nationalized oil companies, during the fifties, orderly competition is what many in the major companies still think can and should be restored. This aim, it may be noted, is shared by some of the newcomers and by many of the governments seeking nowadays to influence the world oil business. These have different ideas, however, about who is going to do the ordering of the competition.

How real was that orderly competition, and is its equilibrium likely to be restored? These are obvious questions for the sixties. It has been noted here that orderly competition did not preclude shifts in market shares. Indeed, the forbearance involved in retaining relative stability in the market probably meant that the largest and most powerful companies exerted less than their full strength, and that 'juniors' among the seven obtained a share in the international market more easily than they might otherwise have done. This orderly development of low-cost Middle East oil, and the huge shift in the pattern of world oil movement that it involved, occupied a decade in which the growth of the total market and the high rates of profit available from oil produced in the Middle East, were more important to the biggest of the established companies than maintaining their share of the market. Since the growth of oil demand began to slacken, and thrusting newcomers have arrived on the scene to challenge all established marketers, this forbearance has been largely discarded. But it might not have lasted much longer anyway.

Some people at the top of the major companies, at any rate, argue that these external influences—the slackening of world demand, plus the restriction of imports into the United States, the intrusion of Russian competition, and the arrival of the newcomers—did no more than hasten the time at which competition even among the few would have begun to become less orderly. The interests of the seven or eight great international groups had lain broadly parallel during the first postwar decade, through common interest rather than through any compact, formal or informal. There had been too much work to do profitably for anyone to wish to rock the boat. But any period of forbearance from competition, in any industry, generally tends to be at the expense of the most efficient. And there were signs that these most efficient groups were becoming restive, even apart from the other influences leading towards more competition in the market. As one man at the top of one of the large groups said late in 1960, 'I am not sure that we all still live in quite the same world.'

It has to be remembered that the geographical dispersion of interests of these eight major groups around the world, and their relative strength at different stages of the oil business, differs considerably. So does their pattern of net profitability after tax. What on balance may be advantageous to one may not suit another at all.

Ordinarily, this does not matter; there is no reason why their operational behaviour, for example which markets they decide to supply from which source, need be more than coincidentally uniform, or remain so. But as we have seen, in this pattern of 'competition among the few' there is one point on which their policies cannot differ for long—published prices. If one alters his price, the others may or may not match the new figure; but if they do not, he is unlikely to be able to make it stick.

While one accepts a particular price level as given, the essential art of efficient management of an international oil company becomes primarily logistic—the art of arranging one's disposition of supplies among markets to give the best possible net return right across the business. If one were to accept a particular pattern of supply as given, the art would presumably lie in getting the price at each point in the business that offered, similarly, this best return—remembering the significance of tax at so many points in this world-wide pattern. In practice, of course, the two are indivisible: one is the mirror-image of the other. In practice, the major oil companies have always chosen to change published prices relatively seldom. So over long periods the logistic art, the ability to keep a vast and interlocked network of production, movement, processing and marketing flexibly deployed, and to seek out every advantage that can be sought from shifts in the pattern of return here and there, will predominate. But the balance of advantage and cost, for any single company, changes over time. And from time to time the point will be reached, for that single company, when this balance—which reflects trends of advantage at different points—has shifted so much from what it was when prices were last posted that the company feels the time has come for a change. But this time—and the extent of the change this company would like—will not necessarily suit some other major companies.

One should not under-estimate the powerful common interests of these major international companies. They are all in the business to stay, and they may well regard the competitive activity of newcomers, who may take shorter views, with common alarm. They have had bitter experience of competitive price-cutting across the world. They co-exist in many countries in not altogether easy relationships with the same governments. Nevertheless, their interests, ultimately, may diverge. It may be that the periods when their common interests are so predominant—as for example the decade or so after the war when they were developing the vast potential of the Middle East, to their own and that region's joint and great profit—are exceptional. It can be argued, on the other hand, that this decade of parallel policies on price and on profit-sharing with governments demonstrates the extent to which genuine common interests will generally govern the conduct of this industry whenever it is in the hands of those who want to stay in it. But that may not be inconsistent with the proposition that at times this common interest is more manifest than at others. Even the prewar period of agreement to limit competition in various ways did not always or universally hold very firm.

The companies' common interest in bringing Middle East oil on to the world scene in a controlled and orderly fashion was one of the main positive elements in that period of agreement. This long out-lasted the formal agreements: it became, indeed, the majors' main task during the postwar years. But it is broadly complete. The companies jointly entrenched in this fabulous area for oil mostly have substantial interests elsewhere. In some areas, their advantage is declining, leading them towards greater dependence upon this region of common interest! Shell, for example, is clearly in a period when its interests in Venezuela may be declining and its direct commitment in the Middle East increasing. But it is also concerned in the newly-developing areas of North Africa, as is Jersey Standard in Libya. No one company's balance of interests, over the years, is likely to remain the same, if it is managing to hold its share of the business. Like the resources that it develops and exhausts, an oil company has always to move on.

No cartel agreements survived to clamp conformity on to the business behaviour of the major groups after the war. None was needed, during that first fabulous decade. But the joint operating companies did and do survive; in Iran, indeed, another was added. And clearly these partnerships, plus the major shareholders' interlocking interests within them, do serve generally to restrain severe internecine competition in terms of development. Elaborate rules for the forward planning of production and 'lifting' (i.e. taking one's proportionate share of oil) govern individual shareholders' initiative in some of these joint operations. This does not wholly preclude effectively competitive behaviour, within these joint operating companies. Each partner within them has some room for manœuvre, even where strict rules obtain. There are provisions giving it some freedom to take or not to take the share of output to which its financial shareholding entitles it; and a group with interests in more of these countries than one can choose the most advantageous places to lift the supplies it wants.

The actual operating companies in most of these areas—IPC and Qatar Petroleum Company, Kuwait Oil Company and the consortium in Iran—are non-profit-making companies. They carry out the physical operations but transfer the oil at cost or a fraction more, at the tanker terminal or the border point on a pipeline, to their shareholder companies or local 'trading company' affiliates of these groups. These companies therefore get their basic share of the profits of the operations in the form of 'cost oil'; and it is these local trading companies, transferring this oil at posted price to other affiliates of the group, that show the profit and pay most of the tax by the host government. In Aramco the pattern is different. This is organized as a profit-making company paying the tax on the oil produced; it sells oil to its shareholder companies at prices corresponding to those they charge (when they resell to affiliates at posted price, they pay Aramco posted prices, but when they resell to a third party at a discount, they pay Aramco the actual sale price realized).

As well as differences in formal structure, there are differences in rules between these joint companies. In Iraq, within the three-company structure that so far has survived the partial expropriation of the concession areas, the constitution calls for programmes of 'offtake' to be settled five to ten years ahead. Each corporate shareholder 'tables' its requirements over a five-year period five years before that period begins—e.g. for 1967–72 in 1962. These forward estimates are totalled, and adjusted to give each 'offtaker' a share of the annual programmes in proportion to its shareholding in the group. Any company that proposes to take less than its proportionate share of the volumes programmed can arrange in advance with another shareholder to take the remainder of its entitlement as 'half-way cost oil'—i.e. at a price halfway between the cost including tax and the posted price. But if it has not made such prior arrangements and when the time comes it has to 'turn back' oil, this oil becomes available to its partners, *pro rata*, at cost, not halfway cost; and it therefore loses all the profit on this oil that it fails to lift.

Details of the Iran consortium rules have never been published, but they appear to operate rather differently. Each partner nominates each year in advance an estimate not of his own requirements, but of the total consortium production for the following year. The figure accepted is the lowest total nominated that will cover the estimates put in by shareholders representing a given percentage majority of the shares in the consortium. This total is then redistributed into entitlements proportionate to the holdings of each shareholder in the consortium. If a shareholder lifts less than his entitlement, there is no penalty, down to 75 per cent of the figure. If he wants to lift more than his entitlement, he will have to buy the excess from any 'underlifters' at full posted price. Over the years, there is often a fairly regular division between those companies that nominate high totals for the next year's production schedule for Iran production—mainly those who are 'short of crude'—and those that nominate low, because they have more crude available elsewhere, either at lower costs or in countries where they are more concerned to increase total offtake.

In Kuwait, rather oddly at first sight, there are no binding rules at all about offtake. This is a concession held directly by the shareholder companies, BP and Gulf, not by the Kuwait Oil Company, which is simply a managing organization (again non-profit-making) handling the physical operations. Each owner can lift as much oil as it likes at cost (plus one shilling) up to the limit of KOC's physical facilities; there are no rules governing offtake, and hence no 'overlifting' or 'underlifting'. Originally this exceptional freedom of operational action—and of potential competition between the partners—was qualified by some undertakings not to compete in marketing written into the joint concession agreement; but in 1951 a revision of the joint agreement excised these clauses. Gulf's large-scale and long-term supply agreements with Shell, on which it receives half of the profits earned by Shell in getting the oil to market, may indirectly restrain its competition with BP, in that Shell and BP market jointly in a number of European, African, and Eastern markets. But in practice, in the last few years, Gulf has been widening

163

its own marketing in European markets; its inhibitions about marketing Kuwait oil in competition with its concession partner seem at any rate to be thinning out. At the production stage, both companies reckon the oil taken out as a 'free good', in that they see no chance of running out of it during the concession period (until 2026) even at rising rates of offtake. For each barrel of oil that either partner takes, it pays a requisite amount in the 'cost per barrel' towards depreciation of the physical facilities that KOC provides. And the companies take this as the proportionate contribution towards developing output of Kuwait oil to the levels that their aggregate demands upon it require.

In Aramco, also, there is no set programme of production for the year ahead, though the partners in it have agreed to a programme of investment that steadily increases its capacity. Each partner company normally undertakes to take up to its proportionate requirement of this rising production; there is no penalty for 'underlifting', but a group that takes more than its proportionate share in any year is entitled to lift as high a percentage again the next, at the expense of the proportions available to any who chose to underlift. The rules of this concession have been modified over the years; details of the present 'incentive dividend plan' are a nightmare to anybody except a devoted accountant. Broadly, however, each partner gets part of its return from Aramco as a proportionate share of half of what the Aramco profit would be if all oil were sold at posted price. This is a dividend on ownership, unrelated to the shareholder's behaviour as an offtaker. The remainder of the actual profits made—which will be somewhat less than the notional 'half' above, since a proportion of the oil will in fact be sold at discounts below the posted price—is distributed between shareholders in proportion to their contribution to Aramco's actual profits, in terms of the oil they lift and the prices at which they take it. This arrangement has much in common with the Iraq 'half-way cost' system, but takes account of the actual prices realized in sales to third parties, which the Iraq system does not.

Under both arrangements, a shareholding group that lifts less than its full entitlement of oil gets some share of profit simply on account of its shareholding (and its proportionate contribution of capital to the development of oil production in the company in question). Against a volume of offtake that is less than its proportionate entitlement, its total profit works out at slightly more than the average number of cents per barrel (though the Aramco system, over a period, may discourage underlifting). Equally, a shareholder that lifts more than its entitlement, by paying half-way cost for the excess or by getting only that proportion of profits on it that is distributed according to offtake, will average across the total volume he lifts rather less than the ordinary profit per barrel. And at times, in such joint arrangements, this may give some companies a chance to manœuvre and gain more than their fellow-partners—if they have chances to get oil cheaper elsewhere.

Under various outside purchase contracts, some of the major companies have the chance to get large amounts of oil at less than 'half-way cost' price—i.e. to buy oil outside and get more than half the profit between cost and posted price. If one can get other shareholders in a joint operating company to take more than their share, one may sell them the extra oil and get a higher average profit on one's own actual offtake. And then it may be possible to make up one's own requirements with oil at better than half the net profit. Across the whole operation it is thus on occasion possible to realize a small margin of advantage in terms of net profit per barrel, at other companies' expense if they are less advantageously placed; and a cent or two per barrel, with the huge volumes involved in this business, can soon run into hundreds of thousands of dollars. Companies that are 'long on crude', in general may thus be able to benefit at the expense of their partners in joint companies who are short of crude and are forced to 'over-lift'. In the Middle East there is even a special word for this commercially logical behaviour—'coat-tail riding'.

When one also takes into account that these partners in the operating companies—which usually dispose of different amounts of voting power in each of them—may be able to influence the total offtake of a country, or indeed the total offtake of one country by their voting on the annual offtake from another, it will be seen that there are quite a number of permutations and combinations of more or less clubbable behaviour in which the members of le club can engage. The ramifications of the internecine behaviour of these companies in the Middle East can be quite tortuous. This is not what Adam Smith meant by competition or what might occur if the Middle East had been developed by companies operating quite separately. But it is hardly what one would expect of some sinister, well disciplined cartel, either. It is a form of 'non-price competition' that nobody could call imaginary.

Even where they were most closely linked in joint operating ventures, therefore, and even before their joint preserve was invaded by outsiders, competition of a sort occurred between these major international groups. Whether it would have grown further in any case, over the years, is a matter of opinion. The same pattern of joint operation has not, in general, been repeated in some of the newer areas when oil for export is being developed, so that some of the majors such as Jersey Standard in Libya will be free to operate entirely on their own. The outsider may feel that relations between the major companies would anyway, during the sixties, have come under increasing strain. In practice, however, it was the advent of the world surplus, and the incursion of substantial newcomers into the business that did complicate the course of this orderly competition. At first, the majors' attitude towards this invasion might have brought their policies more than ever into line, against the disorderly newcomers. In practice, it fairly soon—once it became clear that some of the newcomers, too, were here to stay—began to uncover points at which the majors' interests were more openly divergent. The dispute over Middle East crude prices, with which this book opened, was a fairly clear example. In the original announcement that it was cutting prices, in August, 1960, Jersey Standard spoke of disruptive influences in the world oil market, and did not mention the Russians alone. It singled out also 'discount sales from marketers with unlimited supplies of crude'— which can only have meant some among its fellow majors.

At the same time, even the differently-situated major companies still have more in common with each other than they have with thrusting independents—until these, in their turn, acquire a sufficient size and spread of interests across the world to become concerned with long-term rather than short-term returns. The extent of non-price competition, and how close it comes to merging into price competition, will vary in different periods of the industry's history. But the common pressures return—towards the fullest exploitation of oil resources, while maintaining relative stability of prices and profits to enable the industry to carry on with its job; and towards the 'optimizing' of long-term return via steady and not too cyclical expansion. The extremes of price fluctuation to which short-term competitive interest might drive the industry are not generally to the taste of oil companies that intend to go on being oil companies. Flexibility is transferred from prices to logistic behaviour.

So long as these major companies commanded the main sources of oil for export, and demand for imports was rising as fast as transport, processing and marketing facilities were being expanded (by themselves and others), competition in the international oil business remained weak as well as technically imperfect, and consumers had not nearly enough 'countervailing power' to bring prices down more than suppliers reduced them. But the trade was not entirely closed to newcomers; new capital was gradually moving into the international end of it. Various non-economic and not wholly economic decisions, such as American self-insulation from the growth of the international trade and Russian re-entry into it, rather suddenly restricted the growth of import demand below what had been foreseen, added to the number of newcomers, and made it impracticable for the groups already established, even had they wished, to move over and make room for these. The competition ceased to be orderly. Moreover, it may have become impossible for purely commercial forces to re-stabilize this market, even though some buying up of competitive newcomers by the big groups is entirely likely, and certain of the disorderly independents are becoming big and broadly-based enough themselves to value stability. For now neither the consumer of oil nor the landlord of oil-producing areas would necessarily accept market stabilization via survival of the fittest among the companies, even presuming this commercial evolution would be practicable and sufficient to restore orderly competition.

Interposed between consumer and landlord, the oil business can hardly avoid suspicion from both sides; particularly because the two are in different countries, while the business must always seem to them to exist somewhere, not easily identifiable, in the middle. It is always either 'overseas trading corporation' or 'foreign capitalist'. The economic logic of this industry indeed relies upon the concept of the world as a single market, across which resources can freely be traded to the benefit of all: it is one of the few genuinely international manifestations of private enterprise. Part I of this book has attempted to isolate the strictly economic and commercial aspects of this industry's operations, mainly to the exclusion of other aspects. Even so, it has been impossible to leave out some of the points at which national policies impinge upon and modify the commercial pattern of these operations. It is the impact of such national policies upon the oil industry, and their importance as facts of life for the international oil operator, with which the remainder of the book will be concerned.

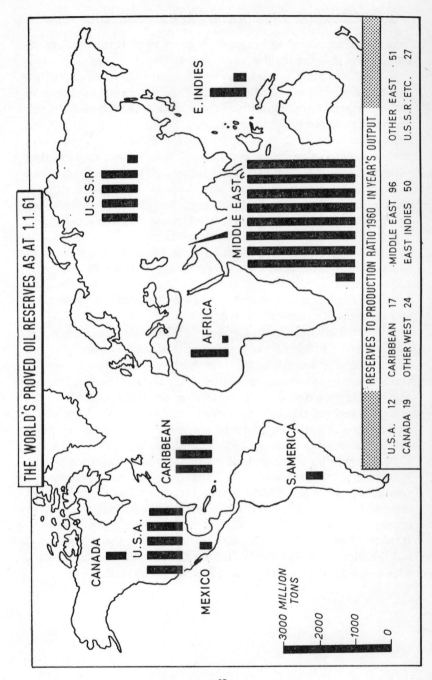

THE WORLD'S PROVED OIL RESERVES AS AT 1.1.61

CANADA

U.S.A.

MEXICO

CARIBBEAN

S.AMERICA

U.S.S.R

AFRICA

MIDDLE EAST

E.INDIES

3000 MILLION TONS

2000

1000

0

RESERVES TO PRODUCTION RATIO 1960 IN YEAR'S OUTPUT

U.S.A. 12	CARIBBEAN 17	MIDDLE EAST 96	OTHER EAST · 51
CANADA 19	OTHER WEST 24	EAST INDIES 50	U.S.S.R: ETC. 27

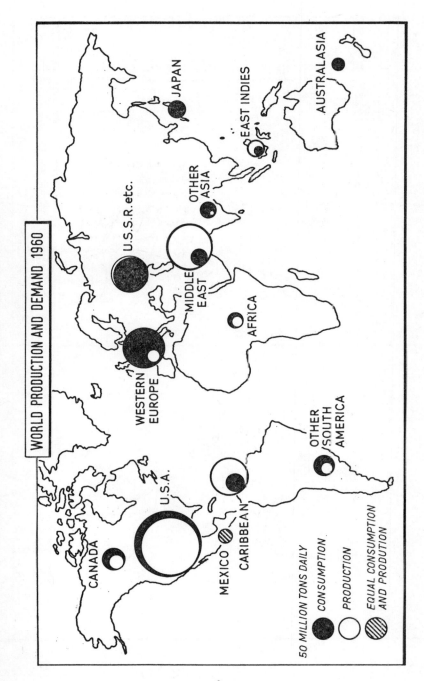

WORLD PRODUCTION AND DEMAND 1960

CANADA

U.S.A.

MEXICO

CARIBBEAN

OTHER
SOUTH
AMERICA

WESTERN
EUROPE

MIDDLE
EAST

AFRICA

U.S.S.R. etc.

OTHER
ASIA

JAPAN

EAST INDIES

AUSTRALASIA

50 MILLION TONS DAILY

CONSUMPTION

PRODUCTION

EQUAL CONSUMPTION
AND PRODUTION

169

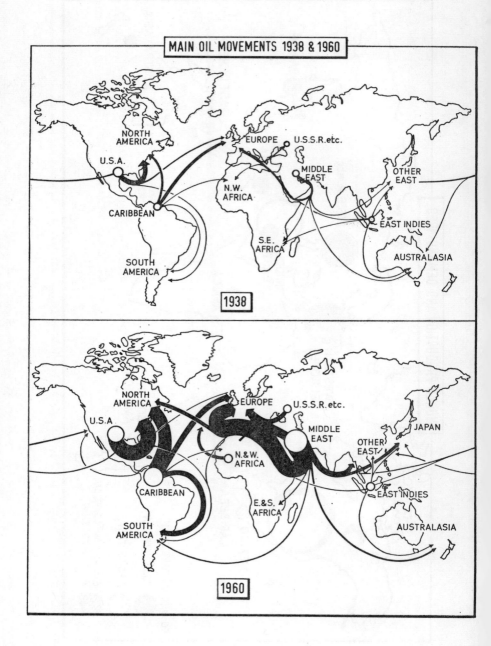

MAIN OIL MOVEMENTS 1938 & 1960

1938

1960

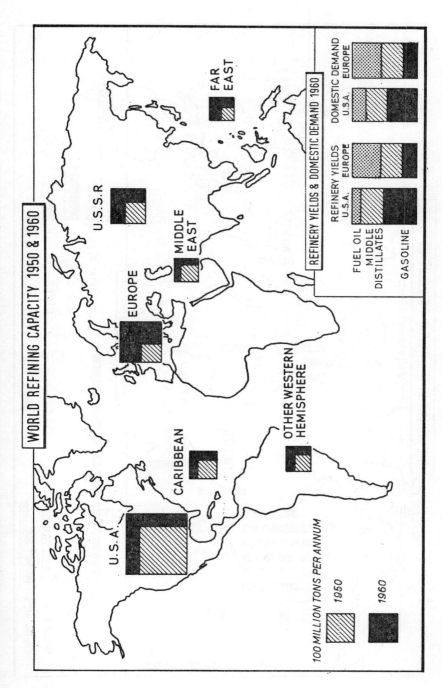

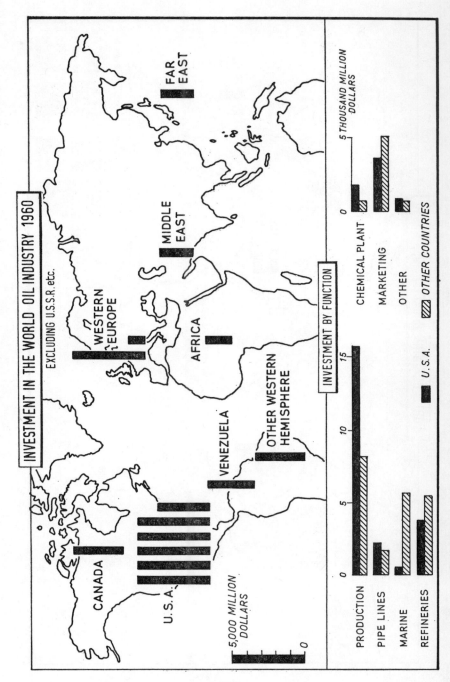

INVESTMENT IN THE WORLD OIL INDUSTRY 1960

EXCLUDING U.S.S.R. etc.

WESTERN EUROPE

FAR EAST

MIDDLE EAST

AFRICA

CANADA

U.S.A.

VENEZUELA

OTHER WESTERN HEMISPHERE

5,000 MILLION DOLLARS

INVESTMENT BY FUNCTION

PRODUCTION

PIPE LINES

MARINE

REFINERIES

CHEMICAL PLANT

MARKETING

OTHER

5 THOUSAND MILLION DOLLARS

U.S.A.   OTHER COUNTRIES

Part Two

Its decisions whether to do
for example, will be affecte
market potential, but by co
ment of 'double taxation' as
country of domicile. In the
companies have begun to u
circumstances in certain kin
matching demand at many p
sources. Taxes have to be fe
purpose will not be simply
integrated net return after
mixture of interests across t
company mix: that is one of
this industry that what suit
manently satisfactory to B.

Its tax system at home, a
abroad, set the basic frame
United States, Britain and
national companies, taxes pai
at home, and royalties paid a
as costs of doing business. T

business in one country as against another,
ed not merely by comparisons of cost or
mparisons of tax, and possibly of the treat-
between each of these countries and its own
last few years a number of the biggest oil
se electronic computers to 'simulate' their
ds of operation, particularly the logistics of
oints with supply from a number of possible
d in as one set of variables: for the ultimate
to minimize cost, but to maximize 'the
tax', that will arise from the company's
he world. And the answer varies with the
the reasons why one can never assume in
ts A, except by chance, will remain per-

nd the treatment it applies to taxes paid
of reference for each oil company. In the
Europe, headquarters of the largest inter-
d abroad can be set off against tax liabilities
lbroad are excluded from tax consideration
heir tax codes differ considerably in detail:

moreover, these countries' treatment of taxation in several of the main oil-producing countries, which have no general double taxation treaties, had to be worked out for individual cases as what is called in the British jargon 'unilateral relief'. The United States allows income taxes paid abroad, so long as these apply generally in the country concerned and are not simply specific taxes for oil operations, as a credit against U.S. income tax liability, and may apply this to dividends from subsidiaries or shareholdings in joint companies, down to a shareholding as low as 10 per cent. The British government allows taxes similar to income taxes to be credited against U.K. income tax where no specific treaty exists: it does not apply this to dividends from profit-earning subsidiaries unless the shareholding is at least 50 per cent; but a British subsidiary operating wholly abroad may be granted the status of an 'overseas trade corporation' and escape liability from U.K. tax except on investment income and on distributed profits. The Netherlands credits tax paid abroad by reducing its own tax in the proportion that the foreign income bears to the total, not by the absolute sum paid in foreign tax. In France company tax is not payable on profits earned abroad through a branch or permanent establishment; but foreign tax paid is treated as a deduction in assessing foreign income, not actually credited against French tax liability.

At the other end of the business, in 'host countries' the liability of oil companies to tax differs rather more than might appear. At any time, some 'general principle' such as 50:50 may be accepted in most countries: but its effects can differ a great deal. When 50:50 was the rule in Venezuela, from 1948 to 1958, it meant that royalties and tax together amounted to half the profit achieved at the price actually realized by selling the oil. This, too, what was it appears to mean in the concessions granted in Libya from 1955 onwards. By 1958, Venezuela had increased its taxes to close on 70 per cent of the profits realized: and Libya in late 1961, maintaining the 50:50 principle, talked for a time about applying it to further concessions as it is applied almost everywhere else in the Middle East, to profits reckoned on the basis of posted prices, whether such prices are realized in all bargains or not. At the beginning of the sixties, we have seen, such prices were being significantly discounted on a growing volume of oil transactions. For 1961, it has been roughly reckoned that this kind of 50:50 tax meant in practice that the governments received 56–57 per cent of the profits actually realized. One deal made in the summer of that year offered a Middle East government a choice between two formulae, 50:50 at posted price or 57:43 at realized prices, which in practice must have meant roughly the same thing. But even under the 50:50 formula with posted prices, so widely used in Middle East countries, the profits actually shown do not necessarily mean quite the same thing. Much depended upon the 'ground rules' originally set down in the different concessions. The income tax had always to be a general tax, even if the oil company was in practice the only substantial taxpayer in a state; otherwise it might not be accepted by the company's home government for the purposes of relief. But what items were accepted as allowable costs before computing profits in the host country, and whether certain items of expenditure were 'expensed' against current earnings in the year concerned, or 'capitalized' and amortized over a longer period, depended on the original terms of each 50:50 agreement, as later worked upon by government and company accountants and lawyers over the years.

The origins of 50:50 in the Middle East offer an example of the way in which the inter-action of tax systems can facilitate—though it may later obstruct—the amendment of financial relationships between oil companies and governments. Following the Venezuelan example, Saudi Arabia in 1949 decreed that an income tax should be imposed: this would have entitled it to 50 per cent of Aramco's income *after* payment of United States tax. Negotiations between the government, the company and its corporate shareholders, and the United States Treasury ensued: eventually the law was drafted to give Saudi Arabia 50 per cent of profits *before* payment of American tax. The Arabian government received considerable help in the drafting of its tax legislation from the American government, which was concerned to ensure that this should be generally applicable and not a special tax, and hence admissible for foreign tax credit against the companies' American tax liability on this income. The result was quite a considerable increase in the Arabian revenue per barrel of oil, over and above the fixed royalty per barrel chargeable before: this royalty stayed at about 21–22 cents per barrel, but was set off against the tax in the final accounting. But the sizeable increase in host government revenue did not bring about a corresponding reduction in the income of Aramco and its parent companies. Indeed, doubts have sometimes been expressed by non-American oilmen operating in the Middle East whether the acceptance of 50:50 cost the American companies operating in Arabia anything at all in net income—on the argument that the whole increase in Arabian tax, eligible for tax credit, was in practice offset by reductions in American tax on the same income.

At the same time, comparison between the companies' situation before and after 50:50 was blurred by the fact that the income on which the Saudi tax was charged originally differed from that on which American tax was. Aramco submitted to Arabian tax in 1950–51 on profits calculated on transfer prices to its parent company 'offtakers', who received a substantial 'cost of sales' discount below the price at which Arabian crude was available to outsiders. This reduced the turnover and hence the profit on which Arabian tax was charged. It may have meant that the Arabian tax and royalty, which worked out at a higher total rate than American tax plus Arabian royalty had done but was applied to a lower profit, amounted in absolute terms to about the same payments to governments, leaving the companies roughly as before. By 1953, however, these special discounts to offtakers had been abolished: the Arabian tax was reckoned on profits on sales at posted prices to parent companies (and at the actual prices realized in sales to third parties). And on the same basic income, the payments to Arab governments under 50:50 became somewhat larger than American tax would have been on the same reckoning of income and profit. A company would be liable for say 58 cents of Saudi income tax, after offsetting 22 cents of royalty, on a barrel of crude oil sold at a posted price of $1·80, if costs were assessed at about 20 cents. On the same barrel, after excluding costs and royalty, and allowing $27\frac{1}{2}$ per cent of the well-head value (i.e. posted price less transport charges from wellhead to port) the companies would at the American rate of $52\frac{1}{2}$ per cent have paid some 48 cents in tax. Offsetting the 58 cents of Arabian tax, therefore, would leave the company concerned with 10 cents of 'excess tax credits'. If it could not make use of such excess credits against other foreign income, 50:50 on the posted price basis could mean payments to governments of about 10 cents a barrel more than payment of U.S. tax and Arabian royalties—on the same income—would have done. When 50:50 arrangements came in in other Middle East countries, cost of sales discounts were applied in some cases; in others, such as Kuwait, the offtake contracts at low prices between the companies producing there and other major companies purchasing and marketing large volumes of the oil complicated matters for a time. Moreover, the companies that produce the oil are generally not the ones that sell it at posted price and submit to tax. But in most, nowadays, broadly the same result holds good: the tax plus royalty in the Middle East more than offsets American (or European) tax on the same income. And it is the business of an integrated group's accountants, dealing with the whole of its widespread international operations, to make sure that on the average, over the years, it is not left with 'excess tax credit' of which it does not get the benefit.

In a sense, therefore, the shift to 50:50 a decade ago represented largely a transfer of tax revenue from the American and the British treasuries to those of the Middle East. The companies became the channel for this transfer—which was admittedly a transfer of tax levied on the proceeds of selling Middle East oil—adding in some cases a little extra out of their own income. When these deals were made, no double taxation treaties existed between these Western countries and the Middle East nations concerned: nor do any now. The initiative of the American Treasury, therefore, was in extending unilateral relief to income taxation levied in those countries. Although it in effect was handing over (or handing back as Arabs would probably prefer to put it) a very large slice of extra income to the whole Middle East, it was not radically altering the provisions of its own tax law for the purpose. Dutch and French tax law, at that time, excluded profits made abroad by their nationals' operations abroad: so in the Middle East the French and partly Dutch companies did not have the same tax liability on foreign income to credit the Arabs' new 50 per cent taxes against. For a time, some people in CFP and Shell will argue, the shift to 50:50 cost these two groups more than any other.

It so happened that the 50:50 formula came eventually, almost incidentally, to tie the revenues of Middle East countries to the prices posted for crude oil there. That, as we have seen, has become inconvenient in the present period of surplus in the oil market. The posted prices have to be kept up, regardless of the discounts increasingly available in actual bargains, and the companies, submitting to a '50 per cent' income tax, pay taxes that are in practice closer to 60 per cent of the profits actually realized. How long the treasuries of the parent countries of the oil companies would continue to accept this excessive tax, effectively at higher than the stated rate, as still being a general income tax fully creditable against home tax on foreign income was a matter for speculation in more companies and countries than one at the time this book was written.

It is worth noting that the unilateral reliefs for double tax available in the United States and Western Europe could be used to facilitate the transfer from a fixed revenue per barrel in the Middle East to a tax and royalty system fluctuating with selling income—or later with posted price and the volume of offtake. They could not, without modification, facilitate any change in the opposite direction—towards, say, a larger element of fixed revenue or a royalty paid in the Middle East over and above the local income tax there, as OPEC suggested in July 1962. For under Western tax systems royalty is 'expensed' before computing taxable income, not credited as a foreign tax can be against home tax liability on the income. A dollar of tax credit—to the extent that it can be used—is thus worth roughly twice as much in terms of net income as a dollar of royalty. The more of a host government's revenue that represents a fixed royalty, and the less that is an income tax, the less becomes the credit available against tax liability in the company's home country. While this distinction between foreign royalty and foreign tax (which has some basis in logic) remains unaltered, along with certain other elements in American tax law, so the tax arrangement that improved Middle East revenues and for a time government-company relations in the early fifties seemed at face value virtually irreversible. At any rate, it could not as obviously be reversed in any way that would minimize the net cost to the companies concerned, as was done with 50:50. The interaction of tax systems, we noted above, can at times obstruct change, as well as facilitate it at others.

'Excess tax credits' may be of use to a company that has other foreign income to take home on which it would be liable to tax in its parent country. These credits cannot be used to offset tax liabilities on income earned in operations at home, which for the American groups are likely to be very sizeable. Nor can they anywhere, in normal cases, be carried forward from year to year. (British Petroleum in recent years has received large repayments of tax from the Inland Revenue. But these appear to have arisen mainly as a result of investment allowances under British tax, during a period of very heavy investment; and they will eventually run out.) Income earned in oil production by American companies anywhere, though not on later operations, also qualifies for the 'depletion allowance' mentioned above of $27\frac{1}{2}$ per cent before computing taxable income. Moreover, it is possible to 'expense'—i.e. to write off against income in the year it is incurred—all 'intangible' costs of drilling as well as other expenses of operation. These 'intangible costs'—i.e. those that do not remain embodied in physical assets on which depreciation can be charged—amount to about 75 per cent of drilling costs. And an American corporation, registered say in Delaware, may be responsible directly for all the international exploration of the group. Not all companies based in Europe can enjoy a depletion allowance on income from production at home or abroad (which derives, perhaps, primarily from the fact that oil production has never represented a significant domestic industry for their parent countries). But they can similarly expense drilling costs, and offset these expenses or 'losses' in countries where production has not yet begun, and may run exploration abroad from companies where depletion allowances are available.

It would seem logical, therefore, for an American oil company operating at home and abroad to use any spare tax credits it has available after paying high taxes in producing countries abroad to offset American tax liability on any not 'fully offset' profits from other overseas activities; and at the same time to carry on through an American company a high rate of exploration abroad, the cost of much of which can be offset against profits at home. Within the United States, again, a judicious degree of drilling and a sizeable proportion of its income at the point of production, on which depletion allowance is available, can minimize its home tax liabilities. Subtract the element of depletion allowance, but add in where necessary 'overseas trade corporations', and one has the European framework for similar avoiding action (though it is worth remembering that European oil companies' income inside European countries is not comparable in proportion to that of the American international majors inside America).

Any such bald summary becomes a caricature in its over-simplification of what is a vast and complex pattern of operations, where tax is only one of the factors motivating decisions, though one seldom wholly ignored in any decision. Tax circumstances in between these end points, the producing and the parent countries, are not without importance in the commercial strategy of an international company. The physical movement of oil from well to terminal, into the tanker, out into a coastal refinery the other end, and from refinery product storage out along the channels of distribution to the final consumer, may be simple and utterly economical. One constant exercise in oil management is to keep it flowing from a number of As to a myriad of Bs with the lowest possible expenditure of time and resources, and as few halts on the way as possible. But on paper, at least, this oil may take a very much less straightforward route to market; the notional itinerary being chosen to get the oil home with the least possible subtraction of tax from its value.

OIL COMPANIES AS TAXPAYERS

From a joint, non-profit-making company in the Middle East, for example, the ownership of the oil, or of the right to take the oil, or of the right to a depletion allowance on the oil taken, may pass to several other local trading companies in the country concerned. These companies—which in practice are sometimes no more than a brass plate in the entrance of a local bank—exist for the purpose of buying oil at cost from the jointly-owned producer, selling it at posted price to an international trading affiliate of the same group and submitting to tax on the profits shown. In certain circumstances, there may be more than one rank of these: A.3. and A.2. companies, as the phrase goes, as well as the A.1. that actually produces and despatches the oil. Moreover, some of these various affiliates of the same major company, under the umbrella of whose eventual ownership the oil may be produced, moved, processed and finally marketed, are liable to be owned at different levels by different intermediate holding companies. The purpose of these transfers of ownership along the oil's route to market may be partly for reasons of foreign currency transfers, but partly also for it to confer profits or losses upon a succession of affiliates along the way. The intermediate holding companies may be able to marry some of these losses with some of the profits that come out on other deals. Sir Henry Deterding is credited with the formulation of the 'straight line', by which the oil moved along the most economical possible route to market. Physically, it still does: but in terms of title and tax liability, the most economical way home may often nowadays be a very roundabout way indeed.

No sensible business firm anywhere arranges its affairs for the benefit of the tax collector. The international oil companies differ from those in most other industries only by having to operate within so many tax systems that their perfectly legal arrangements to avoid leaving most of their shareholders' profits in the hands of tax collectors, by comparison, have to become somewhat three-dimensional. Other liabilities to tax—and other collectors' pressures to maintain the amount paid in taxes—again occur in between producing government and home government. Another complication arising in the late fifties from the political fixity of posted prices for crude oil when discounts were in practice having to be conceded on the sale of products arose from the fact that this tended to squeeze refinery margins down. Refining affiliates that had to buy crude oil at posted prices, but which could not sell their products at prices that would give a reasonable return on their investment after paying for the crude, were operated for a time at a loss.

OIL COMPANIES AS TAXPAYERS

At the end of the fifties, the governments of some countries where such refining was done began to ask awkward questions about these losses and the taxes that these affiliates of apparently rich international companies were therefore not paying. If these were not viable entities, it was acidly inquired, why did not their owners close them down? And if they were vital links in a chain of international movement, manufacture and marketing, ought they not to bear a commensurate share of taxation with other individuals and enterprises in the countries where their owners still seemed glad to go on selling? The question, to a consumer country, seemed a perfectly fair one—particularly a consumer country not getting much in the way of dividends from integrated international oil companies. Faced with this pressure, at the beginning of the sixties, certain of the major companies did quietly take steps to help their affiliates in some of these countries at least to break even, if not to show large profits. This may have meant writing down certain current debts to other affiliates from their books: it could mean 'discounting to affiliates' on crude as well as to independent buyers. Occasionally the international deployment of the oil business, it will be seen, involves it in contriving to pay more tax here and there, not less.

American tax law bulks large in any consideration of the effect of tax on international oil operations, mainly because it was the original home of the modern oil industry, remains the domicile of most of the largest companies, and is one of the only highly developed countries in which some of the tax law has been largely shaped with oil in mind. It has been said above that an American oil company can moderate its home tax liability by engaging in a fairly large degree of production and an intensive programme of drilling, at home and overseas. But it should be added that this hardly amounts even to tax avoidance, if one defines that as ingenious manœuvring within the tax laws. It is simply a matter of doing what the American government wants oil companies to do and rewards them for doing.

These provisions in the tax law were specifically enacted to encourage a high rate of drilling and to maintain a large oil producing industry inside the United States and elsewhere under American management. To the extent that American oil companies take advantage of it (to reduce their tax liability), the object of the provisions is achieved. Not all interests and politicians in the United States approve of the opportunities that this network of general and specific tax legislation offers the oil enterprise to reduce and offset its liability to American income tax. But none of them question that it is entirely proper for the com-

184

panies to take advantage of the opportunities offered. Some of these critics would be prepared to advise complete reconsideration of the purposes for which the United States offers oil these tax incentives: others argue that the purposes might be achieved even if certain of the incentive provisions in the tax laws were pruned back somewhat. All that the outsider needs to note is that significant alterations in these provisions might considerably affect the balance of factors in many decisions for the international companies based in America: and that they could therefore have consequences for oil deals and government revenues far outside the borders of the United States.

Taxation policies designed mainly to bring about oil developments considered desirable inside one country, therefore, can have a very powerful effect upon oil development in the rest of the world, when the country concerned plays so pivotal a role in the industry as the United States does. Consider this chain of consequences and side-effects, sought and unsought. Income from the production of oil, rather than its later transport, processing or marketing, receives special tax treatment in order to maintain a strong producing industry there. 'The profit,' in the phrase that many American oilmen use, 'is made on the crude': and certainly it will bear less tax if it is. The prices of American crude oil on which those profits are made had for many years a logically dominant effect in setting the prices on crude oil produced elsewhere. Tax arrangements facilitated originally by the American Treasury allow all of the tax paid on income from the production of crude overseas to remain in the hands of host governments: and these governments' taxes have become tied to the advertised, not the actual, prices paid for that foreign crude. Other incentives in the American tax system (matched by their foreign competitors) meanwhile promote an extremely high rate of exploration and development drilling everywhere in the world as well as in the United States. This adds to the temptation to pre-empt the chances of possible future bonanzas that are inherent in the high risks but high rewards associated with oil exploration. Where oil is dis- covered in this worldwide effort, governments anxious in their turn to begin to latch on to the tax revenues available from oil-producing income press for its rapid development to the stage of production. And the high rate of oil development—which has hardly slackened as excess productive capacity has grown—has tended inevitably to bring about, exacerbate, and prolong a surplus of oil in the world market. There is no simple pattern of cause and effect here. But the economic and fiscal factors probably do interact. Tax incentives introduced to develop the

American oil industry in a healthy fashion may have contributed to developing and rigidifying some quite unhealthy economic and fiscal distortions in the working of the oil industry outside America.

Taxes are often the chosen instruments of national or nationalist policy towards oil, though not the only ones used: the remaining chapters of this book are devoted to sketching the wide variety of policies affecting oil that are now developing around the world. But it would be unreal again to mention here simply the taxes that affect the production of oil and the businesses concerned with it. A vast sum in taxation of petroleum products, levied occasionally for reasons of deliberate 'oil policy' but more often simply as a very dependable way of raising revenue, is paid every year by petroleum consumers in most countries. Gasoline and other road fuels are expendable goods with a demand that is fairly inelastic to price: just what any finance minister would and does pick for indirect taxation. These taxes, over the long run, have some effects upon the pattern of relative demand for products in different consuming nations: the rates of tax applicable to road fuels, for example, may either enhance or offset the technical advantages of using diesel oil as against gasoline in motor transport. They may also have a considerable effect, over time, on the types and sizes of engine and motor vehicle used in different countries. But these taxes, huge in amount as they are, are often fairly 'neutral' in motive and effect, because the motor fuels are not as easily open to substitution as are say the fuels used for general heating. Excise taxes on petroleum products used as general fuels, which have been imposed in many countries in the last few years, bring us back however to the sphere of policies deliberately applied towards oil, towards imports, or towards all kinds of fuel.

The content of government policies towards oil varies according to their national circumstances. Some have it at home, or are hopeful of finding it. Others have not, but may have command, through national companies, of large supplies of it abroad. Others have not, but have large national fuel industries that cannot produce as cheaply as oil can be imported. Other nations have neither, and want the cheapest oil they can get anywhere. And some nations have virtually nothing but oil.

In addition to these attitudes reflecting national circumstances as regards oil, two other elements are reflected in the attitudes of governments towards the industry. The first is a set of varying social attitudes towards private property, towards foreign enterprise, towards bigness in industry: all, springing from different philosophies and motives, may be applied to bridle the freedom of action of international oil companies. The second is the desire, again common in countries enjoying very different circumstances, for 'conservation' of ultimately exhaustible natural resources.

Emotionally, people and governments in countries that possess oil are for 'conservation' somewhat in the way that everybody is against sin. The trouble only begins when they have to decide what they mean by the term. In principle, everyone can agree in condemning extravagance in the development of any natural resource. Puritans may apply this to the extravagant consumption of oil and other minerals—though even puritan ideas of what rate of consumption is excessive vary over time and between different societies. Geologists apply the term to the use of methods of taking the oil out of the ground that may over time increase the amount that can ultimately be extracted from any reservoir—and to the prevention of methods that do the opposite, such as letting wells run 'flush' that are liable to dissipate the gas or water pressure in the reservoir. There is no doubt at all that in the past much oil has been lost by techniques that worked out the pressure drive in oilfields long before it need have done, and reduced the recovery rate—i.e. the proportion of the oil *in situ* that can be got out—below what could have been achieved even then, let alone today. Improved techniques of secondary recovery can increase that rate, hence 'stretching' the economically recoverable amount of oil from a reserve. But in general 'conservation' is used simply to mean the prevention of wasteful exploitation of reserves in the first place.

Economists are somewhat cautious about the employment of this concept of conservation. 'Waste' to them is production which it would pay to postpone or do without altogether. In order to identify this waste, and hence to decide the point at which one should restrict production, you might theoretically estimate the future value of all the oil liable to be extracted from any given reservoir, on whatever assumption about prices and recovery you thought best: then discount this value according to an interest rate reflecting 'the cost of waiting'; and finally compare this value with the marginal cost of producing and using less oil now. If the discounted future value of oil exceeds the cost of doing without it today, restricting output would be economically logical. But to state such a proposition is not to be able to apply it (nor would the discounted future value to an international oil company be necessarily the same as to, say, an underdeveloped country). Such a calculation would also require prophetic assessment of the future course

187

of technology, both in the extraction of oil and of possible alternative fuels and in their future use. Economists, in short, are well placed to point out the weaknesses in other people's approaches to questions of conservation, but less competent to follow out the ramifications of their own (a posture some may consider characteristic of the profession). Governments have to promote 'conservation' according to less purist criteria.

No country that possesses oil is yet within striking distance of running out of it, though the world's greatest oil producer and consumer, the United States, has already perhaps some grounds for caution, if one extrapolates its recent increases in capacity against the recent increase in consumption. Expert estimates of the time by which domestic production there might pass its peak rate of oil extraction put this no farther off than the seventies.

At the other end of the scale of countries that possess oil come those where vast increases in national wealth have been built purely upon the exploitation of recently-discovered oil reserves. For such countries, these reserves represent a treasure chest, the opening of which has transformed their whole ways of living—but by definition not a bottomless treasure chest. These reserves are 'neutral stuff' of no more than potential value, *in situ*, until the technical resources and capital supplied by 'visiting' oil companies have transformed them into realizable value from marketable oil. Nevertheless, to the governments of these countries, the huge incomes that these visitors have been able to draw up and share with them from these reserves still represent drawings upon a national store of capital.

Different governments have adopted different attitudes towards this extraction of wasting national riches. Some have built conservation policies into the very system of granting the original drilling leases, such as Alberta. Others have ploughed back the oil revenues into education and technical training of their people and the fostering of any other practicable industries inside their borders, against the time when their rich revenues of oil must be expected to decline. A few have invested the huge funds that oil has gathered them in industry abroad, upon the argument that local investment offers too limited a return. Markets in the places where oil has developed outside the United States have been generally too small and too under-developed for oil to attract industries to cluster around it. But the limited opportunities of 'replanting' industrial capital in some of the countries that are now growing rich by taking out their oil must condition those countries' attitude towards the rate of return that they hope to get on the oil taken out. Among such countries, only Venezuela has so far evinced practical interest in the limitation of output for purposes of technical conservation. But some others along with it have considered the limitation of output to 'market demand' at high and stable prices—that is, something on the lines that the state regulatory agencies carry out in the United States. This was already a joint interest of Venezuelan and Saudi Arabian oil ministers even before the creation of the Organization of Petroleum Exporting Countries.

Government intervention in the oil industry of the United States to regulate the volume of output has of late been buttressed with the regulation of imports of oil, as a more open measure of protection for domestic oil—and other domestic fuel industries. This is a kind of government intervention more common in countries that rely entirely or almost entirely upon imports for their oil, and are increasing their dependence upon oil as a general fuel. In this form 'fuel policies' of one kind or another, overt or covert, are to be found in most of the countries of Western Europe. The coal industries of some of these countries, after a decade of inadequate attempts to increase output to meet increasing fuel demand, were during the late fifties suddenly left stranded as consumers who had turned to oil simply as a freely available alternative were followed by those who preferred its convenience, reliability of supply, and of late, its cheapness.

As well as these short-term problems of structural adjustment within their economies, the recent shift to oil and the further possibility of relying somewhat on imports of natural gas pose some longer-term problems for the governments of such consumer countries. Europe has enough memories of postwar balance of payments difficulties not to shrug off too easily questions of the rising import costs of petroleum in future.

There remain uncertainties about oil prices in the medium run; though few people expect them to rise for economic reasons as much as the price of coal, many wonder if foreign governments will not soon be increasing their 'take' and whether companies can avoid passing this on if it happens. There are uncertainties for the longer run about how much a country can afford to run down its capacity for producing coal. The costs of getting coal out of the ground seem certain to grow more than those of oil, but there may ultimately be much more of it there. The world has never been prospected for coal with anything like the intensity that it is now being explored for oil. But even so most oil geologists would agree in guessing that the world's ultimate resources of coal, however big, seem likely so far to be several times bigger than those of oil. This may however in the meantime become irrelevant. Once economic nuclear energy begins to set the ceiling price for all fuels, what will matter for the fossil fuels is not the ultimate total reserves, but the amounts obtainable at that price or less.

The weight that can or should be given to such considerations by countries in different situations *vis-à-vis* oil must be a matter of argument. Nobody is more interested in such arguments than the oil business itself and of late, some of the other fuel industries with which it competes. These are certainly not the private affairs of the oil business; it would be stupid to suggest that the interest of all these governments in all these questions is not entirely legitimate. Oil's private affairs, nowadays, are becoming public affairs.

Attention to what is often called 'the impact of nationalism on the oil industry' tends to be focused simply upon the growing interest of host governments in the oil production of integrated companies—primarily the major international companies—within the borders of countries remote alike from the main markets and from the countries in which these oil companies' headquarters are domiciled. This is a blinkered view. Governments in most countries nowadays are intervening in the affairs of the oil industry, and seeking to bring its activities into line with 'national policies': and perhaps they inevitably must. This is not to say that their policies are sensible, or likely individually or in concatenation to lead to the optimum development of oil and other energy resources. But this industry cannot escape a large degree of political involvement; this is a 'penalty of greatness' for it in the economies that it supports, serves and enriches.

In the remainder of this book an attempt is made to outline some of the ways in which such national policies impinge upon the oil industry, and some of the ways in which the policies of particular countries may soon impinge upon each other. National policies in the wider sense, rather than under any blinkered definition of nationalism, are considered with some attempt at assessing their influence upon the industry in the immediate future. So are the 'supra-national' policies that organizations of governments, both at the producing and the consuming end of the business, may soon be pressing upon this industry.

It may be that such policies are part of the facts of life for any industry of comparable importance in our increasingly organized world. One can argue more convincingly, perhaps, that energy industries are peculiarly subject to such governmental concern. 'Nationalism' as regards energy, at any rate, seems almost universal today. Its nature varies according to the country's situation, from producer to the consumer. In the following chapters, as case studies of different approaches to oil, a selection of countries in differing situations are considered in detail. They range on the one hand from the relatively self-sufficient in oil to those that are large consumers but produce practically none, and on the other hand to the large-scale producers with far more oil than they could ever consume at home. The various categories, chosen for convenience, are inevitably arbitrary, over-simplified and often debatable. Some countries ought strictly to be considered under more than one heading on this scale; and the situation of others is changing quite fast. But these countries have been chosen and classified to show how varied and complex governmental pressures on this industry are becoming; and to emphasize how liable the policies that different governments press upon it are to conflict.

CHAPTER XIII

Self-sufficiency in Oil: I. The United States

Once a month—usually on a Friday morning, in one of the public rooms of the Commodore Perry Hotel in Austin, Texas—three professional public servants of the State of Texas decide roughly how much oil the world's largest single private industry shall produce during the next month. Their decision is not concerned with prices, but it is based partly on estimates of market demand, which means demand at existing prices: as such, indirectly, it does provide a powerful though not absolute support to the level of crude oil prices charged in the American oil industry. The Texas Railroad Commission, again, is concerned only with the 'proration' of crude oil output according to the maximum rate of efficient production and to reasonable market demand inside Texas: there are other regulatory bodies to set output rates in other oil-producing states, and a number of states in which production is not controlled at all. But Texas is the largest producing state, with about 35 per cent of current output in the United States and about 47 per cent of the country's proved reserves. And experience has shown that Texas, as the fully-regulated largest producer, acts as the stabilizing balance-wheel for total American oil production. When demand goes down, Texan output goes down most; when demand rises, Texan output follows upward too, but less sharply. This last point does not please Texas producers, who feel they benefit less on the roundabouts than some less self-disciplined oil-producing states. But with their larger production, they would stand to lose much more heavily on the swings if total production were allowed to rise much above market demand and prices were to collapse.

To the foreign observer, who is frequently lectured by American oil companies operating overseas about their utter and immutable opposition to anything approaching state control or the protection of indigenous fuels against low-cost imports, it is somewhat paradoxical to find that in the United States these companies, and a host of smaller, even more rambunctiously 'free enterprisers' in the domestic oil business there, get on very comfortably thank you with state agencies telling them how much crude oil they can produce, how much they can buy and who from, and of late, federal agencies telling them how much crude and products they can import. Even the last of these, statutory import control, which dates only from 1958, and was originally sharply opposed by some major companies, seems now quite cheerfully accepted by these bitter opponents of 'statism'. Talking inside the American industry during summer 1961, such a foreign visitor could find some companies still prepared to argue about details of the way in which these restrictive import quotas were set and allocated. But none, even those with the largest and cheapest foreign oil reserves, were prepared to argue against protection of the American oil market in principle. Taxed with a degree of doublethink here, some American oilmen confess it disarmingly: 'It all depends on whose ox is being gored.' Others do not. An ability to profess and act upon several mutually contradictory propositions at the same time has its convenience in business as in many other spheres of social activity.

To recognize from the beginning that the privately-owned oil industry, in its own home, is subject to a very large degree of governmental influence, is not to deny that there is some logic in the way that the different elements of government influence there fit together to achieve one end—the maintenance in being of a large domestic oil-producing industry in the United States. Some would define the purpose of government influence here as absolute national self-sufficiency in petroleum, which is probably more than any American government now aims at. Others might say it is the maintenance of an efficient and commercially competitive domestic industry, which is certainly more than these measures achieve. But once given such a purpose—and though it has the obvious danger of making energy costs in the United States higher than they need be, protection from foreign competition is one of the principles behind which American industries grew great— and given the legal pattern of property relationships in the United States, then something approaching the present regulatory and incentive system probably had to emerge too. It can indeed be argued that given the inherent nature of oil production some such system needs to emerge everywhere: the OPEC governments have argued so. But a glance at some of the details of one outstanding example of this system may be useful in illustrating the complexity of the whole system's workings—and some of its side effects.

SELF-SUFFICIENCY IN OIL

A monthly 'hearing' before the Texas Railroad Commission (which was set up in the nineties to regulate railway operations, and proceeding via the supervision of bus and truck transport, gas utilities and pipeline regulations, was in 1919 first set the task of oil and gas conservation in the State) often takes less than half an hour, though once every year there is a regular full-dress hearing at greater length and at any monthly hearing argument or cross-examination may lengthen the proceedings. Held before the three-man commission, it is attended by representatives of the major refining companies that buy crude oil from independent producers in Texas oilfields (to balance out their own requirements and supplies), by representatives of producers, truckers, and other people interested in Texas oil production. The commission is armed with statements showing the 'nominations' put forward by each of these crude buyers to say how much it would like to purchase in the coming month, its actual and desired levels of crude and product stocks, and the rate at which each has been operating its refining capacity during the month before. It is also supplied by the Federal Bureau of Mines in Washington with that agency's estimate of market demand for Texas crude during the next month, and with estimates of stocks and refinery runs throughout the United States. And because its own investigators have estimated and are checking as constantly as they can the 'MER' (maximum rate of efficient flow) of every different oilfield reservoir in Texas, the commission also knows how much oil will be produced from any given number of 'producing days' operation of the 90,000-odd wells in the State that are liable to have their output adjusted up and down according to the number of 'shut-down days' that the commission orders for any given month.

Though the nominations have in fact been put in writing to the commission before the hearing, it is usual for a number of the major crude buyers to repeat these verbally there, saying how much oil they want to purchase and the number of days' 'producing pattern' that they think would be advisable for the coming month. Members of the commission may question them about their estimates: representatives of producers or other interested parties can put in their views. The commission briefly deliberates: then it announces the 'schedule allowable' for the month and the number of 'producing days' that will be allowed for the wells concerned.

This is not as simple a process as it sounds, though most people at these Austin hearings have it down to a fine art. Relying mainly, perhaps, upon their assessment of crude and product stocks through-

I. THE UNITED STATES

out the nation, the commission decides approximately how much crude will be needed from Texas wells in the coming month to accord with the demand they foresee. They have then to deduct from this total certain large elements of Texas oil production that are exempt from variation from month to month in their rates of output—in the jargon, exempt from shut-down day proration. These comprise first the huge East Texas field, which in order to maintain pressure and hence flow from the reservoir is operated at a rate of efficient production much lower than its proportionate share of Texas oil reserves; secondly, fields producing on provisional 'discovery allowables' during their first two years of operation, before their 'MERs' can be properly determined; and thirdly, 'stripper wells' in the later stage of their producing lives, which when producing less than 20 barrels a day are assumed to be produced at efficient rates and are not controlled.

As at mid-June, 1961, to take an actual example, these exempt wells accounted for nearly 1,200,000 barrels a day out of the total 'schedule allowable' in Texas—i.e., the aggregate of maximum rates for efficient production of oil in all the fields there, as reckoned by the Railroad Commission—of just over 6,750,000 barrels a day. This left a possible 5,550,000 barrels a day or so from 'wells subject to shut-down days'. The crude buyers' nominations early in June of their requirements for July, 1961, totalled 2,417,424 barrels a day, or just about 1,220,000 barrels a day over and above the output exempt from control. Allowing for the fact that actual production invariably falls say $7\frac{1}{2}$ per cent of the figure allowed, owing to breakdowns, the commission in fact set an allowable for July, 1961, of 2,629,959 barrels, which represented eight 'producing days' for the wells subject to shut-down days, or eight-thirtieths of the 'MER' that each had been set. This total rate of output for the month from production liable to variable control is in practice allocated between fields according to their share in proven Texas reserves, and within fields between wells according to rules specifically worked out for the regulation of each field. But in practice, as a House of Representatives committee was told by Lt.-Gen. E. O. Thompson, who might be described as the grand old man of oil proration in the United States, in 1957, 'each man knows what his allowable is for each and every well.'

That allowable tells each producer how much he can legally supply from each well each month: and his output is liable to be checked against the throughput of the refinery to which he sells to see that he produces no more. He is forbidden to produce and sell oil in excess

195

of this: a federal law, the Connally 'Hot Oil' Act, which prohibits 'exports' of oil across state lines to escape the scrutiny and jurisdiction of state regulatory agencies, seals one possible escape route. On the other hand, control of the producer is accompanied by regulation of the purchaser. The principle of the 'rateable take' requires every buyer to take oil in equal proportion from all the wells connected to his gathering pipelines, even if for one reason or another he should be forced to reduce his offtake below plan and to practise 'pipeline proration'. This means that a big integrated company will generally be taking much less of its requirements from its own producing capacity (on which it gets full producing profits as well as any profits on later operations) than it might economically choose; and much more from independents to whom it has to pay posted prices for oil on which it hence gets only the later 'downstream' profits. This factor was one, in the immediate postwar years, that made many majors with overseas operations plan growing imports of crude from overseas for their United States refineries. Such crude was not merely cheap oil; it was their own 'cost oil'.

Proration of oil production is not universal in the United States. California, for example, has never operated any state regulatory agency, and being now a net importer of oil among other fuels it is hardly concerned to regulate the volume of production at all. Three of the significant oil-producing states, Mississippi, Wyoming and Pennsylvania, do not authorize proration to market demand, but only to maintain efficient production in their reservoirs. Louisiana sets its 'allowables' for any given field by rather different methods from those of Texas—and it gives its increasing offshore production rather better allowables than comparable onshore wells, since this costs more to develop—and monthly fixes the percentages of these allowables that may be produced, not the number of days in a month that wells may produce. In mid-1961, the percentage set was 30 per cent; but it was estimated that nearly a third of Louisiana production came from wells that could not in practice produce even that proportion of their 'depth bracket allowables', and were hence in reality unaffected by proration. In Oklahoma, which early this century became the first state to engage in the proration of oil according to market demand as well as physical conservation, the production from each lease rather than each well is controlled, which enables the producer to take his permitted output from his most convenient or efficient wells. This state, also, has been ahead of most others in legislating for compulsory unitization—i.e. the

196

I. THE UNITED STATES

management of production from all wells in any given reservoir according to the characteristics and needs of the whole field, provided that a given proportion of lessees and royalty owners approve. But production in this state is declining; only a small proportion of Oklahoma wells can 'make their allowables' anyway. In New Mexico, proration takes place under a new law that has been regarded as a model. In Kansas, a fairly elaborate proration system has been largely nullified by a law setting the minimum 'allowable' for any well at 15 barrels a day for every well, which leaves the state's Corporation Commission little chance to grant the better wells more than that minimum: only a small proportion of Kansas wells, therefore, are effectively prorated.

Though oil is now produced in more than 30 states of the Union, some 95 per cent of it comes from the nine above: and though the ranking of some among these has altered considerably over the years as established fields have been worked out and new reserves discovered, Texas has long been overwhelmingly the biggest producer. Its proration to market demand, therefore, effectively brings production in 'Districts 1-4' of the United States oil market—i.e. the United States East of the Rockies—into line with the demand that it and other experts forecast.

This predominance of Texas, and its consequently greater incentive to stabilize the market, have probably a much greater 'automatic' effect in co-ordinating the effect of state regulation than any direct efforts of the Inter-State Oil Compact to Conserve Oil and Gas ever have. This is an agreement signed in 1935 between six oil-producing states, to which twenty-seven now adhere, and to the meetings of which certain federal departments and agencies, plus the government of Venezuela and the Canadian oil producing provinces of Alberta and Saskatchewan, now send observers. An Inter-State Compact Commission organizes conferences and co-operation between these different state regulatory bodies, which may enhance the like-mindedness anyway to be expected among them. There have been occasions in the past when critics of proration have alleged that action to cut back production had followed upon specific agreement within this commission to keep prices up. Such collusion has always been hotly denied by the members of the Compact—though there can be little doubt of or reasonable objection to the influence which has been exerted at times on all the other regulatory agencies by the eloquence and example of General Thompson. Even so, he and the rest of the Texas Commission have argued that Texas is nearly always left to take alone the brunt of the cuts in output necessary to hold total American production down to market demand.

In addition to the setting of production allowables, the prohibition of sales of 'hot oil' across state lines, and the 'rateable take', conservation in Texas and elsewhere lays down certain rules regarding the technique of production in actual oilfields. There are rules laying down the minimum 'spacing' between wells—which in Texas has been adjusted upwards, probably too slowly, from one well per 10 acres to one per 20 acres and which in some new fields is now one per 40 acres. There are in certain circumstances extra allowables for the introduction of pressure maintenance techniques. In Oklahoma, and in one or two instances elsewhere, state regulatory agencies encourage the unitization of whole fields. Many of the worst and most stupid technical abuses in oilfield development have been outlawed by these commissions, and in certain major fields such as East Texas it seems clear that the ultimate quantity of oil recoverable has been considerably increased by measures of pressure maintenance undertaken as a result of their influence. Yet technically, as well as economically, there remain some questions about the real effects of their regulatory activity.

'We have nothing to do with price,' said General Thompson to that same committee of the House of Representatives in 1957. 'We are forbidden to consider economics; purely physical waste. I know nothing about price.' Behind his disclaimer—and General Thompson spoke as a brilliant administrator, trained as a lawyer, but with a grasp of economics to which many Texas businessmen would testify— lay the experience of years of controversy over the motives of proration and its effects. In Texas that controversy had at times in the past been taken to courts which had reversed the proration decisions of the Railroad Commission. In other states proration agencies are still enjoined—as that of Texas was for many years—from overtly taking market demand into account when setting production allowables.

Texas is no longer so enjoined: and market demand (*pace* the General) surely takes one over the fringe into economics. 'Although no state oil regulatory body gives consideration to price in determining market demand,' said Mr. William Murray, one of the General's colleagues on the Railroad Commission, in an address in 1960, 'it would be naïve not to recognize that market demand proration does affect price. But the effect is to stabilize price and eliminate the rapid and extreme fluctuations from ruinously low prices to the consumer in

I. THE UNITED STATES

times of over-supply to disastrously high prices to the consumer in times of scarcity.' Mr. Murray pointed out that it gave the producer a higher average price over the years, protecting the independent by ensuring the small man a 'rateable take', making his operation 'bankable' by ensuring him a proportionate market outlet, and making wildcatting worth while by promising 'discovery allowable' production for any well brought in. He argued, indeed, that the economies in above-ground storage and pipeline capacity, working capital for stocks of oil, and the denial of exaggerated profit margins to the speculator, tend to reduce the margin between what the producer receives and what the consumer pays. That may be true too: but where the balance of advantage from stabilizing prices works out over the years depends upon which are the longer—periods of over-supply or of scarcity. There seems little doubt that in oil's history so far the times of surplus, in aggregate, have been longer. And to that certain weaknesses of the proration methods used, along with other elements of governmental policy affecting United States oil, may have contributed.

The original need for discipline, both technical and economic, in oilfield development in the United States, arose from the pattern of property rights in land ownership there. The 'rule of capture' which has been mentioned earlier was first adumbrated in American petroleum development in a natural gas case in 1889. Relying on the analogy of water percolating into riparian owners' land and of game lured to a neighbour's land, the Pennsylvania judges told plaintiffs who accused neighbours of 'stealing' the oil beneath their land by drilling wells just across the fence that they could suggest no remedy except, 'Only go and do likewise'. This ruling legally justified the drilling of 'offset wells' as close as possible to wherever a nearby landowner had found oil, and the sub-division of land where oil was discovered into tiny lots, on each of which as many wells were drilled as could physically be put together there. Technically, such overdrilling meant the dissipation of gas-cap and other pressures below ground, rapidly reducing the rate of flow from wells and ultimately the proportion of the oil *in situ* recoverable from any given field. Economically, the pressure upon landowner and oil lessee to get all the oil they could out of the ground as soon as possible led to production without regard to what the market could take. That softened prices; and often instead of reducing the incentive to produce oil, this merely spurred on yet higher output in order to make up the total income of the parties dependent upon production. Even recently, during a period of poor profits in American oil, new techniques of 'directional drilling' have been used not merely to 'offset' other wells, but to drill at an angle under the ground right into a neighbour's 'pay zone'.

Nobody can fault proration where its aim is achieved of limiting oil production to the maximum rates compatible with full efficiency, of preventing the dissipation of gas pressures and the like. Economists, as noted in the last chapter, have somewhat different views from engineers about the proper definition of 'conservation'; and economically proration to market demand, as Mr. Murray says, means a steadying of prices at levels that may well be above the lowest available, at least in the short term. But over and above this, the effect of proration may in itself simultaneously be partly nullified by inadequate regulation of well spacing, and by the guarantee that any new well finding oil will have a 'discovery allowable' and be exempt from cuts in output for two years. These rules may furnish opportunity and incentive for a higher rate of drilling in most American oil-producing areas than would seem justified in terms of new reserves discovered, or of efficiency in reservoir development. Some American oil experts will point with pride to the fact that when effective proration began in Texas in the mid-thirties the state had 60,000 producing wells: today it has about 200,000 and well completions continue in the state at the rate of 17,000 a year. But statistics that are more sobering show a steady decline in the rate of reserves discovered per foot of wells drilled. And it is a matter of argument how much of this drilling represents the genuine search for new oilfields, as against an exaggerated rate of development drilling, aimed at the acquisition of a guaranteed right to produce even a trickle more oil from known fields.

However, the incentives that promote a greater rate of development drilling in American oilfields than undistorted commercial interest would justify arise perhaps more from taxation than proration. The depletion allowance upon producing income, but not upon other kinds of oil income, makes oil production a particularly advantageous kind of investment to engage in, both for established oil operators and for speculators from outside who are in high tax brackets for marginal income. The right to set off, for tax purposes, the 'intangible' costs of drilling and development—i.e., those other than the cost of equipment that can be amortized, amounting to say 75 per cent of total drilling costs—against other income in the year that they are incurred means that the costs of looking for oil are lightened and indeed may, on occasion, become a positive advantage to incur. There are cynical

I. THE UNITED STATES

statisticians inside the American oil business who will point to the surge of drilling activity that seems regularly to take place in the second half of each financial year, and to link this with the point at which entrepreneurs begin to get fairly firm estimates of what their final income, and hence their prospective tax liability, may be. There is even a phrase for it—'drilling up one's tax'. That applies to oil producers as a whole. For the speculator from outside oil, who has of late been supplying quite a large amount of venture capital for oil drilling, this form of gamble with dollars on which he is otherwise liable to very high rates of tax gives the chance of finding property against the revenue from which his unsuccessful exploration costs can be written off and upon which an eventual capital gain may be realized, with a consequently lower rate of tax liability. That is one reason why the odds so often quoted from American experience against finding oil by wildcatting, and the percentage of dry holes even in development drilling, need taking with a pinch of salt in considering risks in exploration and drilling elsewhere. They reflect real problems of geology: they also represent circumstances of tax and proration that promote a somewhat exaggerated rate of drilling.

Output regulation and special taxation treatment together certainly make for a big American oil-producing industry, though not necessarily for economic efficiency in all its operations. Both systems are designed deliberately to encourage a higher rate of drilling than might otherwise occur—and by keeping up exploratory activity, they have encouraged considerable technological improvement in its methods over the years. The actual rate of drilling undertaken is still largely dependent upon the level of prosperity in the crude producing industry and in the American economy generally: after 1956, the number of wells completed tended to fall somewhat and the total footage drilled also to decline (though not as much as the number of wells because the average well completed continues gradually to get deeper). The additions to reserves have not grown in proportion to the footage drilled or the expenditure on exploration: in terms of feet drilled or of dollars spent per extra barrel of proven reserves, the 'cost of replacement' of American crude oil has been rising. It would be unwise, perhaps, to accept these trends as utterly irreversible. New techniques of multiple drilling, on the one hand, and of secondary recovery of much higher proportions of the oil *in situ* in reserves already proven, on the other, offer impressive possibilities of bringing down the cost of making extra oil available for the future. If they can, the governmental backing given to drilling and the improvement of reservoir engineering in the United States will have contributed to both these hopeful lines of development.

But even accepting a big American oil-producing industry with a high rate of exploration to replenish its reserves quite uncritically as a Good Thing, regardless of comparisons with the cost of alternative ways of supplying America with its oil, there would appear to the outside observer some weaknesses in the ways this is at present given governmental support there. Within the proration system these derive largely, perhaps, from tensions between what Professor E. W. Zimmermann has defined as the two basic objectives of the regulatory programme:

(1) the prevention of waste of oil and gas, through which the ultimate recovery of these products from their reservoirs might be greatly increased; and

(2) the protection and adjustments of correlative property rights appertaining to each owner of land in an oil or gas pool.

And this second objective of protecting individual property rights has a good deal to do with basic social attitudes towards small property owners and big in the United States.

The guarantee of a rateable take to every property owner or lessee, combined with inadequate supervision of well spacing, can reduce the technical efficiency of output as well as provide a constant incentive to obtain further entitlements to output, even at the expense of the average rate of offtake for established producers there. Texas, for example, guarantees a minimum rate of gas production even to wells drilled down to tap a gas-cap which may be the (declining) driving force of flow from a whole oilfield. There are limits, throughout American political thinking and legal practice, to the extent to which the pursuit of sheer technical efficiency, particularly via bigness or co-operative organization, is ever trusted to override the rights of the individual. When large integrated companies are denied the right to produce all the oil they want from their own wells, or to produce even their own allowable output all from the wells whence it would be most technically efficient or otherwise suit them best, their potential efficiency is held down. Similarly, when reluctant individual oil producers refuse to co-operate in the unitization of a field where secondary recovery organized on a large scale is becoming vital, technical conservation may be prejudiced as well. But in America the recalcitrant

I. THE UNITED STATES

individualist can always be pretty sure of sympathy: and the integrated company frustrated in its economic logic cannot.

No foreign visitor to the environment of large corporations in the United States in general, and of major oil companies in particular, can avoid realizing the degree to which anti-trust legislation and departmental practice condition their behaviour in a surprisingly wide range of circumstances. Considering the history of the industry, and the extent that the oil industry figured in the circumstances out of which 'trust-busting' sentiments and legislation arose, the Department of Justice's continued interest in it is understandable. But its effect is to make oil executives in major companies lean over backwards in order to maintain postures of exaggerated apparent competition, and to refrain from overt consultation on many issues upon which it would be logical to expect collective views for different sections of the industry to crystallize through open argument. Such companies often spend a good deal of time trying to make management decisions that they believe to be right because of their realistic assessment of circumstances and probabilities appear right according to a quite distinct and largely archaic set of 'perfectly competitive' rules abstracted from market circumstances that no longer exist, if ever they existed anywhere in pure form. This may have its incidental benefits as a form of intellectual discipline for business (rather as the learning of dead languages is alleged to develop all our minds) but it has the danger of being expensive as well as irrelevant. It would perhaps be surprising if the intense collective concentration on private advantage that characterizes management in big American corporations, and not least in oil corporations, were not sometimes to collide with considerations of the public interest. And the realization that circumstances of unfettered atomistic competition are entirely foreign, if not fatal, to this industry, might well justify the Washington vigilantes in keeping a close watch on how it does behave itself in its own peculiar circumstances. But it might be better for all concerned if this industry (and others in America) were not judged, and had not always to explain its practice, in the terms of an early nineteenth-century produce market.

It has already been argued, in an earlier chapter, that the influence of American anti-trust legislation and tax practice upon the behaviour of American oil companies has had repercussions upon the conduct of oil business outside the United States. The same, indirectly, is true of the effects of regulation of oil production there. The repercussions of all three have been complex: and even a pragmatic observer, setting aside any ideals of untrammelled free enterprise and free trade, may conclude that these repercussions have not always been advantageous. But within an American national context any foreign observer has to be careful in passing judgments upon these governmental influences on the oil industry: for they are after all deliberately applied with ends in view that most Americans, including most American oilmen, approve. One may query whether they achieve these ends as well as might be: that is one set of questions. Whether the ends in themselves are desirable is another. Some philosophical liberals (in the European rather than the American sense of the word) dislike nationalism in itself wherever they encounter it. Many liberal economists dislike economic nationalism. But their particular competence as economists is surely confined to assessing what extra costs may follow for a country that adopts such a policy—and also for other countries with which it might otherwise trade more freely. This is perhaps particularly true for an Englishman, coming from a country where a brief but impressive tradition of free trade, long departed, has left us automatically sanctimonious about economic nationalism anywhere else, and trained us not to be really conscious of it when we practise it ourselves. There is something slightly shocking, if curiously stimulating, for an Englishman to hear anyone say bluntly, 'Of course we have to maintain a strong domestic industry', without an apologetic note in his voice.

Economic nationalism in the world's largest oil industry cannot but affect the whole oil business outside it. American oil companies own more of the international oil industry outside their borders than those of any other nation; and while other American industries frequently rank as the largest in the world, few have a comparable grip on foreign production. As we have seen, state regulation arose because the American oil industry, unrestrained, was liable to produce far too much oil; and in spite of their anxiety about maintaining their own level of reserves, American companies are always ready to produce as much more oil as they are allowed. This is still, in the short term, a matter of controlling abundance. Until the late forties, the United States, on balance, was more than self-sufficient in oil, exporting more products than it imported crude. Since then it has been a net importer; and so long as its refiners were free to seek the lowest comparative costs for supplies to their markets, it seemed likely in the early fifties to import a steadily growing proportion of its requirements. Since

I. THE UNITED STATES

then, it has first imposed voluntary and later administrative restrictions to the volume of its imports; but it still imports more oil than any other single country. Only one other industrialized area in the world boasts a comparable degree of self-sufficiency, though at a far lower level of production and consumption: the U.S.S.R., with the bloc of Communist nations, is still a net exporter of oil, and also impinges somewhat upon the world oil market.

Until recently, as outlined in earlier chapters, customary rather than simply competitive patterns of pricing linked the prices of crude oil and products in the rest of the world, directly or indirectly, with prices inside the United States. To the extent that the state regulation of output reduced over-production there and guaranteed remuneration on investment in relatively high-cost home production in the United States, therefore, it offered support not only to the level of prices there, but also in some degree to oil prices everywhere in the world trade. But the lower cost of oil production in other oil-producing regions, particularly the Middle East and Venezuela, gave the companies with concessions abroad a growing incentive to bring this cheaper oil into the United States market. And in the middle and late fifties the growth in imports that could be foreseen in future sent many important American companies without foreign interests abroad to seek concessions, particularly in Venezuela, but to a growing extent in the Middle East. Venezuela, with leases over smaller areas and with a number of new fields being opened up, was easier to enter than the Middle East, where the companies already established had concessions covering huge areas. Newcomers such as Getty and the American Independent Oil Company could gain a foothold only in odd corners such as the Saudi-Kuwait Neutral zone, offshore areas, or some of the tinier shaikhdoms of the Persian Gulf. These were well worth exploring (Kuwait, after all, is tiny enough). They looked the more attractive in view of the expanding markets for oil that such American companies commanded in the United States. It was not simply that this foreign oil was cheap. What was almost more important was that it was free of output regulation. The integrated refiner did not have to buy some of it from all the other producers in the field to which he had a pipeline, pay posted price for it, and keep an equivalent amount of his own oil shut into the ground.

Growing imports of low-cost crude, for a time after the war made it necessary to hold American domestic production level and eventually restrict it further (in Texas). This in its turn brought political opposition from producers whose interests were entirely in domestic oil. For a time these protests were allayed by voluntary import restrictions on the volumes brought in by the major importers, on the principle that imports should 'supplement but not supplant' American supplies. But both these importers and the new ones bringing in production abroad had invested heavily in the prospect of bringing in increasing amounts of foreign crude. And no sensible businessman can be expected voluntarily to deny himself crude supplies which he has invested to bring into being. It takes a government to decide that in the national interest any nation should accept more expensive supplies than it need. The voluntary restrictions were not effective enough to satisfy the vociferous domestic producers of oil; and in 1959 the American government decided to make import restrictions mandatory.

In the framework of existing oil policy in the United States, this action could be regarded as logical enough. It can indeed be argued that it was essential to keep that policy effective—if one takes the purpose of policy as protecting the American oil industry and keeping its productive capacity growing, and not simply as promoting technical conservation. Some American experts are persuaded that continued restrictions on imports will enable the growing needs of the United States to be met for the next twenty years or so from domestic sources, without significantly raising the real costs of oil inside the United States. Such a policy, on that analysis, would not necessarily mean any absolute increases in American energy costs—though it certainly would mean accepting energy at somewhat higher cost than America could in the meantime buy from abroad. There is no doubt that considerable increases in domestic oil production in the United States are technically practicable. It can be argued that developments in drilling and reservoir engineering, allied to more sensible methods of controlling the exploitation of oilfields such as unitization, could offset the increases in cost liable in any extractive industry, even the apparently high cost of 'replacing' the oil one takes out of the ground. (The technical advances in drilling may well occur: whether the more sensible management of oilfields will, under the present régime of controls and taxes, is more doubtful.) But these import restrictions, which virtually completed the control of governmental agencies of one kind and another over supplies of oil to the American consumer, constitute a very substantial intervention indeed in the affairs of what ordinarily seems one of the world's most exuberantly private enterprises.

I. THE UNITED STATES

This choice was the United States' own business. Its effect upon the rest of the world's oil industry, however, was profound. It was possibly more important than any other single factor in precipitating the surplus that was accumulating in the world market from the mid-fifties onwards, though that surplus would soon, in any case, have made itself felt. The first effects upon the world price structure of insulating American supply and demand from the rest of the world market were discussed in the chapters on pricing; the longer-term consequences have still to be seen. No other policy of protective economic nationalism anywhere in the world is directly as important to the oil industry as this one; and it also has significance as an example to other governments, of more kinds than one.

Confident prophecies that Europe could depend on cheap imported oil as its main marginal source of energy in the future without worrying about sustaining its indigenous fuel industries, perhaps depend more than their authors admit upon the assumption that the United States would remain out of the market for marginal supplies of that imported oil. On the other hand, European ideas about putting quotas on oil imports, which are becoming stronger in certain quarters, can point to a Transatlantic example. And the arguments about proration of world oil supplies in accordance with world 'market demand' that have sometimes been put forward by such spokesmen of petroleum-exporting countries as Shaikh Abdullah Tariki and Dr. Perez Alfonzo draw fairly logically upon the experience, and the arguments in justification, of proration in the United States.

It can be argued persuasively, indeed, that the development of state regulation in the home of the oil industry and the stronghold of private enterprise suggests that there is something about this industry that positively invites regulation. This is not a view that would be popular with the private businessmen concerned in this industry. On the other hand, one seldom finds any American oilman who is prepared to condemn all aspects of this powerful and pervasive system of government intervention in private business (the only critics one usually finds prepared to be so thoroughgoing come from outside the industry, such as Professor Eugene V. Rostow of Harvard and some sceptical Senators from states that produce no oil themselves).

According to its own spread of interests, the American oil company with large international ties may be sceptical about the judgment of the regulatory agencies or even about the system itself in that this gives what it considers relatively inefficient companies handsome rates of return. Some began by being positively indignant about import restrictions; but after a year or two, few were inclined to do more than complain about quotas on fuel oil imports, and the ways in which all import quotas were allocated. Import quotas were still valuable assets, which it might be worth buying a company to acquire: but the restriction of imports had made profits a little easier to earn at home than in the chilly international market. A major international company is apt to attach more value to tax allowance for foreign depletion than, say, an independent producer in Texas; but both will argue equally firmly for the absolute economic necessity for the depletion allowance on domestic oil to be 27½ per cent of producing income. Many more oilmen are critical of the actual ways in which output is regulated than of the principle of regulating output: on the other hand, proposals for compulsory unitization, which from the outside looks a more rational system, have generally foundered upon the opposition of the industry itself. Federal regulation of the price of natural gas, again, has brought much justified criticism of the formulae that the government agencies suggest. But not many people inside the industry have been prepared to offer logically convincing alternative formulae for the pricing of this joint but unregulated production by the petroleum industry. And it can certainly be argued that the whole current machinery of regulation, incentives, and protection in American oil, despite the different origins of different elements in it, now hangs together. One might be unable to change one part of it without changing all the rest.

At the beginning of 1961, the advent of a new American Administration raised the possibility of modifications in the whole complicated relationship between the government and the oil industry in the United States. There was little room for the Kennedy administration to be more pressing in anti-trust proceedings than the Republican one that it had succeeded, which had been exceptionally tough and unrelenting towards large-scale business in this respect. The industry however became apprehensive about the attitudes of the new administration and legislature towards depletion allowances, at home and abroad. And it did not put out of its mind the possibility that other significant changes in the whole structure of output regulation and import controls might eventually commend themselves to the bevy of talent that President Kennedy had brought in his train to Washington.

At the end of 1961 the Kennedy administration did order a completely fresh study of oil import restrictions; and it was more generally talking about freer trade policies. Few oilmen outside the United

I. THE UNITED STATES

States, however, were expecting any reversal very soon of the American industry's administrative isolation from the rest of the world oil market. The control over oil imports, in particular, did not preclude further growth of the actual volume of imports into the United States; but it meant that how much more was allowed in would be settled by administrative decision, not according to market prices or net integrated costs in the world oil business. This isolation conditioned the behaviour of major oil companies operating in that world market, and affected the extent to which they could act to reduce the surplus of oil in the rest of it. It had also become a potent factor in oil companies' decisions, all over the world, about the scale of investment in production and transport for the future. It was in a sense ironic that this final twist of protective state regulation of the largest private enterprise industry in the world, by governments believing firmly in private capitalism and acting reasonably in American 'national interest', had probably done as much to soften the world market as the deliberate re-entry into that market, at about the same time, of the state-owned industry of the only other great nation that produces enough oil for itself, Soviet Russia.

CHAPTER XIV

Self-sufficiency in Oil: II. The Soviet Bloc

During 1960, a team of American oilmen visited the Soviet oil industry, and on a return trip a team of Soviet oilmen visited the American oil industry. The reactions of each might be selectively summed up in remarks said to have been made by the two leaders. The leader of the American team asked, 'Why do you employ so many people?' The leader of the Soviet team asked, 'Why do you drill so many wells?' Both questions were telling; they brought out basic differences between the legal and economic circumstances in which managers of the oil industry conduct their business in these dominant countries of world capitalism and communism. To the third party who has to depend on imported oil, however, the oil industries of two rival colossi have at least one thing in common: they can supply broadly enough for their own needs. In this they are, so far, unlike all other industrialized societies.

For three to four years at the turn of the century, Russia was actually producing more oil than the United States. It drew level and passed in 1897–98; but by 1902 its brief spell in the lead was over. Russia did not experience the revolution of mass motor ownership that took place in the United States during the first two to three decades of this century. In fact, it never has. And Mr. Khrushchev, during his eventful visits to America in 1959 and 1960, was ready to say that he thought it never should. The statements of statesmen about technological and social development, over the years, have a way of rebounding upon themselves. Nevertheless, gasoline consumption by the private motorist is certainly not one of the ways in which the Russian government proclaims the ambition of surpassing American standards of living. However, the Soviet production target for oil by 1980, set at 14 million barrels a day, is higher than any forecasts ever made for the United States.

The present level of Russian output—nearing $3\frac{1}{2}$ million barrels of oil a day and about 70,000 million cubic metres of gas a year—is only about 40–45 per cent of that in the United States, and its consumption, for a much larger population, is about only a third as large. And even if one counts in production elsewhere in the Soviet bloc, which can broadly be said to be under a considerable degree of Soviet control (China, it should be interposed, produces practically no petroleum), the total only comes up to about 3½ million barrels of oil a day and just over 85,000 million cubic metres of gas a year—while consumption per head throughout the Communist countries is only about a sixth of that in America. Russia's proven oil reserves, however, are now possibly larger than those of the United States, and its natural gas reserves, though much less developed, are about a third as large. And during the last decade production and consumption of petroleum in Russia and the East European countries has been rising far more rapidly than in America or the rest of the free world. In 1961, Russia was the second largest producer in the world, passing Venezuela: its output was about three-fifths as large as the whole of the Middle East. But both America and the Middle East were producing much less oil than they could readily have done. This may not have been as true of Russia.

Government control of the oil industry in Russia is not a matter of interference with the owners, who no longer exist; it is simply how industry in a Communist country is run. In practice, it does sometimes seem to be regarded as interference by the directly responsible Soviet management: their Russian opposite numbers told the American oil team in 1960 that some of the direction from the centre was too remote from the real facts, though the decentralization of operational control to regional economic councils, during 1959, was said to have improved matters somewhat. But the criteria that affect management decisions in a Communist economy differ considerably from those that concern a Western manager. Both are concerned to improve their technical efficiency and to reduce the cost of specific operations. But the relation between labour cost and capital charges in the two kinds of economy, for example, differs radically.

Russia no longer has any general surplus of labour. But it has a tradition of fairly lavish manning of its plant, partly in order to give green labour 'on-site' training, and nowadays it seems to be applying much the same principles in staffing, to habituate its college-trained engineers to actual industrial operations. By contrast, it is extremely short of capital: at least, its economic planners have to withdraw what they decide it shall invest from a limited national output that still leaves only meagre standards of living to its citizens. But it is not easy for the

Westerner to understand how the concept of capital charges is taken into account in planning Soviet investment. And it still appears that major decisions about large-scale investment, at any rate, are taken somewhere in the administrative hierarchy well above the level of the director of any actual operating unit in the Soviet industry. Price hardly enters into the operating manager's calculations; transfer prices at the various stages are set at cost plus a given level of 'profit', but turn-over taxes, at various levels, are then built into each price to influence the pattern of consumption (and incidentally to provide the Soviet government with its main formal source of revenue). It might perhaps, irreverently, be said that the manager of any given Soviet oil enterprise may still have as much power of independent decision as say the local manager of a non-profit-making operating company owned by several foreign parents in the Middle East. But the ultimate managers who take the really important decisions in the West are at least slightly more identifiable, and accountable in principle to shareholders somewhere.

Some of the key decisions of these unidentifiable Soviet managers, however, are made public from time to time; and there is little doubt about their performance. Over the past ten years Russia appears to have been expanding its crude oil output at no less than 15 per cent a year; there has been corresponding growth in refinery capacity and in pipe-line transport. During the current plan, which runs until 1965, Russia is proposing to increase its use of crude oil and natural gas from 26 per cent and 6 per cent respectively of its total energy consumption to 32·7 and 17·0 per cent. Since the total energy consumption of the Soviet economy is planned to rise by about 60 per cent during the period, this involves almost doubling oil production during a seven-year period, and a four-fold increase in supplies of natural gas. Coal, which in 1960 supplied over 50 per cent of the energy used, is planned to supply no more than 40 per cent by end-1965, though even this represents an increase of more than 20 per cent in its output. During the postwar years in which the great international companies were opening out production in the Middle East, Russia was doing the same in a smaller way for its new oilfields in the Volga-Urals area, which now supply over 70 per cent of Soviet crude production. By 1965, the Russians plan on an out-put of 4·8 million barrels a day of oil and 14,000 million cubic metres of natural gas: by 1970, 7·8 million barrels of oil a day and 30,000 million cubic metres of gas. American oilmen who have visited the Soviet petroleum industry think it can probably achieve this huge effort of development.

II. THE SOVIET BLOC

This geographical shift of Russia's main areas of oil supply has significantly altered not only its pattern but its methods of transport. Baku, in Azerbaijan, formerly the dominant area (upon selling whose oil it will be remembered the original Shell oil business was founded), was fairly well situated for tanker shipment to its markets, across the Caspian Sea, up the Volga, or across the Black Sea to European Russia or to the outside world. The new inland oilfields, however, have had to be served by pipeline—mainly to refineries situated in consuming areas. Russia has had to lay a substantial new network of pipelines throughout its territories and beyond them to feed its satellites and perhaps other customers. An even larger pipeline network has been developed to make use of natural gas from the Volga and the Ukraine—though even by 1965 this is expected to measure only 16,000 miles, a tenth of the present pipeline mileage in the United States. These developments, and particularly the lines designed to carry oil some 2,800 miles into Central Europe, have been somewhat hampered by shortage of capacity for making large-diameter pipe.

The apparent centralization of decisions in the Russian oil industry, and the absence of recognizable criteria for decision, have been mentioned. It would be churlish not to recognize that such centralization can have some possible advantages for an industry that has had to accept state regulation even in America, that stronghold of private enterprise. Under state ownership, there has been no room for argument about how oilfields should be developed and what constitutes wasteful exploitation of resources. 'Mandatory unitization' has been the rule in the older Russian oilfields ever since the Bolsheviks gained control, and the newer fields have been developed under such principles from the start. Russian oilfields, as their team leader observed, have not for years been faced with the problems of 'over-drilling' that still affect American fields even under proration. Oilmen there pay strict attention to what would be considered in the West technical rather than economic conservation principles. One result of this difference in approach is a matter of technique; they begin water injection to maintain reservoir pressure as soon as production from the field begins, bringing in pressure maintenance to reinforce primary production as soon as this is done partly because pressure in the fields is not as high as in some rich fields elsewhere. But it also results in about 70 per cent of all Russian wells continuing to produce by this form of 'primary recovery'. A smaller proportion appear to be 'on the pump' than in the United States, the only other areas where oil production on an industrial scale has been

213

carried on for any comparable length of time (Baku began producing in 1873, only about ten years after the Appalachian fields in Pennsylvania). This use of assisted recovery on so general a scale illustrates another strength of Soviet centralized decision that the West has been recognizing in other technical spheres since the war: the ability to get any new technique applied really rapidly and widely once it is accepted.

For the third time in the history of this industry, Russian oil exports began in the mid-fifties to become a significant factor in the international oil market; and the state ownership of the Russian industry naturally made other traders ask whether these exports ought to be considered in economic terms or in political. Russia had been one of the major exporters in the first twenty years or so of the world oil trade, but its importance had faded before the First World War. It became a very significant oil exporter indeed between the world wars, its sales on the world market reaching a peak of 120,000 barrels a day in 1932. Its attempts to force a way into various markets in Europe and the Near East—after the major Shell and Jersey Standard groups, both of which handled Russian oil for a time after the revolution, had ceased to buy it—contributed to the slump in prices in the late twenties and early thirties which occasioned the various attempts of the major groups to restrain competition through their 'as is' agreements. During those years the Russians were aggressive sellers, but not averse to market-sharing agreements. (Rumania, in practice, was a much more aggressive price-cutter.) They are said to have reached various agreements to restrain competition with the international companies during the period. As their first five-year plans began to take effect, their own internal demand for oil products began to increase. At all events, they reduced their exports of petroleum very sharply within a year of the peak in 1933; and from then until the beginning of the Second World War, they tended to withdraw from the international market, selling the marketing facilities they had built up abroad to Western companies. Mr. E. P. Gurov, chairman of Sojuzneftexport, the Russian oil export organization, claimed at the Beirut oil congress in 1960 that during the decade 1925–35, Russia had supplied 14·3 per cent of all the oil imported by Western countries, and that during the peak years of 1930–33 its share reached 19 per cent. About 14 per cent of Soviet production, he added, was exported during the thirties; its peak export reached 30 per cent of its annual output.

The Russian industry began to export once again after the war,

II. THE SOVIET BLOC

though in the early immediate postwar years it was at the same time importing products from Rumania, and may for a time have been a net importer. But later its production began to develop faster than its internal demand; its exports rose, to its partners among the Communist countries but also to countries outside the Iron Curtain. In 1950, it sent overseas about 22,000 barrels a day, but only 4,000 barrels went beyond its own sphere to the importing countries of the West. By 1960, its total exports had grown to nearly 30 times as much; and of these 60 per cent or more were going to non-Communist countries.

The absolute figures of exports are not as large as that rate of growth might suggest when they are set against the total of world oil exports. The 1961 figures of Russian oil exports, some 33 million tons or 650,000 barrels a day, amounted to about 20 per cent of Soviet oil production and to about 6 per cent of world oil exports in that year. Of these, about 400,000 barrels a day came to countries outside the Soviet sphere, amounting to only about 6 per cent of the imports of all other countries. However, in oil it might be said that it needs only a few more barrels to make the market overflow; and Russian exports were certainly among the influences that helped to soften the world market during the late fifties.

About half of the postwar Soviet oil exports, so far, have been in the form of products, mainly residual fuel oil (some of low-sulphur content), diesel fuel, and low-grade gasoline. (Russia's own biggest demand is for the middle distillates such as diesel oil; with its growing use of natural gas, it may well have surpluses of fuel oil to dispose of, and with its small private car population it has gasoline to spare. It markets only one grade of gasoline from its refineries, with a relatively low octane rating by Western standards; as the American oilmen's report on the Russian industry commented, 'it needs to be no higher than practical', a remark that could have more meanings than one). But the proportion of crude in exports has gradually been growing.

A good deal of this oil, products and crude, has been sold at prices significantly lower than the generally scheduled prices in the markets outside. It would hardly have found purchasers if it had not been available at some sort of discount. But obviously different marketers, in periods of developing surplus, have different ideas about how much discounting is legitimate, how much represents 'distress sales', and how much might be regarded as 'dumping'. During the very sharp period of price-cutting between 1958 and 1961, the Russians do not seem

215

always to have offered the biggest discounts off scheduled prices—the deepest price cutters seem to have been certain independent producers with surplus crude in Venezuela and in the Middle East. But the Russians were sometimes prepared to cut as far as was necessary to gain a particular sale. And in 1960, concluding a four-year contract with the Italian state oil company ENI, the Russians did agree to sell it crude at a very low price indeed—roughly $1·40 delivered in Italy, which meant something of the order of a dollar a barrel f.o.b. Black Sea terminals. This deal, like many others in which the Russians engaged, was not simply a straight sale; there were elements of barter in it, involving Italian steel pipe and petroleum chemicals produced from ENI's plant built to process Sicilian oil.

Lacking any criteria to judge the comparative costs of Russian oil—and remaining doubtful whether cost necessarily played any part in Russian transactions such as the piping of oil thousands of miles from the Urals basin to Central Europe—the international oil companies had mixed views about this Russian competition. There was certainly no doubt that Russian offers were neatly selected to offer the major companies the maximum of embarrassment—though these were quite often markets where the majors were entrenched with practically no other competition, and therefore markets likely to attract any independent seller looking for an opening. Cuba was one such market: India was another; one by one, others have followed. These have generally been underdeveloped countries, short of foreign exchange, strong nationalists and nursing some suspicions of their established suppliers as relics of 'colonialism' or 'dollar diplomacy'. But there is another distinct and very important group of buyers of Soviet oil, led by Italy, Japan and Scandinavia. These are among the most cold-blooded of all oil importers. They have always had a sharp eye for a bargain and a reluctance to tie themselves to any single group of suppliers. Moreover, independent refiners and marketers have always given the major companies more competition there than elsewhere. Businessmen in these countries, moreover, had a natural eye to the possibilities of reciprocal trade with Russia and the East European countries.

Complaints about Soviet 'dumping' of oil began to be made during the late fifties, and indeed formed part of the arguments upon which some governmental organizations in Europe, in particular, considered imposing quotas on imports of Soviet oil. It is always wise for the consumer to regard any such arguments with a certain amount of caution: essentially, they are appeals to his government to help someone charge

II. THE SOVIET BLOC

him more than he need pay. The definition normally offered of dumping, is selling abroad at a lower price than one sells in one's own home market; (it may be added that on a strict application of it, most exporters of most manufactured goods do, and are usually dumping). Quite certainly the Russians were charging other Communist countries much more for their oil than customers in the free world. But as between a capitalist importer and a Communist supplier, it is not clear whether this phrase 'dumping' has much significance at all.

The international oil industry's complaints about Soviet exports, whatever the terminology, do however reflect a genuine difficulty in meeting competition from this entirely different kind of economy—which is also an entirely closed one. The oil companies are used to price cutting by 'distress sellers' without marketing facilities in times of surplus. They are equally prepared to meet competition from more substantial newcomers who are prepared to pay the cost of entry—that is the investment needed in storage, distribution and retailing outlets—in the markets where they are established. But between established international marketers, they can usually expect price competition to be limited by the knowledge that if A undercuts B in one market and gains a larger share, there are always markets where B can gain a similar edge on A.

Sojuzneftexport is among the most substantially established marketers of all in the world oil market; there is nothing 'here today and gone tomorrow' about Russian competition. But in two ways it differs from all other established marketers. Its own market is almost entirely closed to competition from any other group; and during the fifties, in contrast to its efforts in the twenties and thirties, it has managed to sell without paying the normal cost of entry. The kind of deal it has preferred, that is to say, is one between governments, in which an important government can be induced to buy oil from Russia. What the government does with the oil from then on is not Sojuzneftexport's affair. What some of the governments to which it has sold oil have done in fact is to require marketers already established in the area to distribute or even to refine this Russian oil in their own facilities. An alternative is to set up a state oil distribution company to sell the Russian oil at cut prices—possibly giving it power to expropriate the established marketers' facilities. This was the issue over which the established oil companies pulled out of Cuba in 1960, and over which they later came under pressure from the governments of India and Ceylon.

Soviet offers can cause the major companies other embarrassments. One of the events that triggered off the cut in Middle East crude prices in August, 1960, and began a train of events that has not yet ended,was a request from the Indian government to the companies operating there to cut the price of crude oil delivered to their refining affiliates in India. It argued that it could get Russian oil for these refineries for less than the transfer price at which their parents were invoicing Middle East crude to them. Moreover, the Russians might take payment in rupees, whereas the international companies were remitting at least their profits in the foreign currencies of which India was so desperately short. Whether or not the Indian government ever really intended to press Russian crude oil upon these refineries—which had already accepted one price cut—will perhaps never be generally known. But what it achieved by the threat was an undertaking from the major companies to supply the crude as favourably as in any scheduled prices anywhere. The Indians then cited the discounts that were published in Japan in respect of shipments that its importers had been buying in the Persian Gulf; and the major companies did make a further significant cut in the price of crude that they delivered to their refining affiliated in India. This was the first open discounting of posted prices in the Middle East to any refining affiliate by the major companies. And the open discounting of crude prices to affiliate companies was very soon followed by cuts in the posted prices of Middle East crude. It would be wrong to blame Russia for too much of the build-up of forces in the world that eventually led to that price cut. But even in the timing, the availability of Russian oil thus did probably play some part.

Russian oilmen told the American team that visited them in 1960 that over the next few years they expected their exports to rise at about 15–20 per cent a year. This is a much more modest rate than in the previous decade; but it would still imply doubling the 1960 volume of exports by 1965. Some alternative guesses were made within the international companies, after Beirut, by analysts who applied the postwar percentage that Mr. Gurov had quoted to their estimates of future Western imports. One takes one's choice of the guesses. It was notable, during the late fifties, that some European-based oil groups professed to feel much more menaced by the growth of Russian exports than others. Some were ready to argue that Russian exports could still be interpreted largely in terms of commercial competition, and that on the whole the Russians, while never missing a trick, were not out to upset the whole game. Most of the American companies, by contrast, professed much darker suspicions about 'political competition'.

It seems probable that Russian motives in this export drive for oil are mixed; a Russian, indeed, might consider the suggestion that commercial motives can ever wholly be separated from political as quite naïve. There has been ample commercial justification, in the terms of Soviet commerce, for selling this oil abroad for whatever it will fetch. In the rapid development of the Soviet oil industry, local surpluses of crude and products will inevitably be built up from time to time, as they are in any oil industry; sold abroad, they can be worth more than at home. But oil exports would seem to be incidental to the massive development of petroleum in the Soviet economy. And if consumption should from time to time swing ahead of production—as can happen almost equally easily with refining capacity—exports could in turn be cut off without too much regard to Russia's position in the market or the goodwill of its customers. It may be significant that so far the Russians have refrained from setting up any marketing organizations in Western Europe to handle the sale of their products, as they did between the wars—though they have talked, occasionally, about setting some up again. On the other hand, they have pushed their pipelines deep into Central Europe; and despite disclaimers from time to time, they now appear to be launching a number of much larger tankers than they have ever possessed before, partly because a threat of blacklisting from major American companies has dissuaded most independent operators, even in a period of surplus, from hiring out tankers to them.

Guesses about their future policy in the West, depend to a great extent upon how successful one expects them to be in developing and supplying internal consumption. Some arguments have been voiced in recent years that Russia's incursion into the world market may be entirely temporary; that their rapid growth in home demand may soon outstrip their productive potential, turning them into net importers; and that by the end of the century, quite apart from political ambitions, they may need to expand their influence in the Middle East simply to lay their hands on sufficient petroleum. This speculation is so far away in time as to be beyond proof, disproof, or even sensible argument. The only factor within the Soviet sphere—not within Russia—that might offer any support for such an argument is the potential growth that could materialize in Chinese demand for petroleum. This vast area and population is largely unexplored in terms of oil, but its proven reserves are relatively insignificant. It is still mainly dependent upon Russian supplies; and any rise in its tiny consumption of energy per head, however insignificant, could represent a big addition to its total demand. But oil may still be found there in large quantities; Russia might not always remain responsible for supplying it; and China's standards of living may not, in the absence of large-scale oil discoveries, rise as fast as all that.

Russia might consider importing crude from the Middle East, however, for other and more immediately telling reasons. There could be some possible logic, in terms of transport cost, for its buying Middle East oil and using this to supply some of its markets East of Suez, rather than supplying these from the Black Sea. This could have some political logic too; Russia could accept oil from the Middle East countries in return for some of the technical aid that it seems anxious to press upon them; and the deals might present it to these countries in a more favourable light than simply the cut-price competitor that it must appear at present.

The Russian oil industry has appeared nowhere as an explorer seeking concessions; but it has sent prospecting teams to certain countries such as Afghanistan and Pakistan, and is building refineries in Egypt and India. In all cases it is working purely as an agent of the local government, lending money but not investing 'capital'. The activity may cement its relations with such countries and secure further outlets for its crude. And it apparently hopes to avoid the jealousy which the private oil companies' presence in such countries has often aroused. (This approach was not necessarily what the countries concerned might have preferred; Pakistan, it is said, originally proposed a normal concession with Russia putting in the risk capital.) Rumania, the other main producer of the Soviet bloc, is still a substantial exporter, selling abroad nearly half of its output (which was 230,000 barrels a day in 1960) though the proportion is expected to decline. It sells partly in its traditional and fairly nearby markets in Southern Europe, but also sends a large volume of products to Russia, some of which Russia re-exports. In its latest long-term plan (1960–65), the planned expansion of the Rumanian industry was reduced somewhat: its target is no more than 245,000 barrels a day by 1965. Its output of natural gas has been growing much more rapidly—presumably reducing its demand for fuel oil—and by 1965, in fuel equivalent, may exceed oil output. Modernizing its sizeable refining capacity, much of which is probably obsolescent, was one of the tasks set in its current long-term plan. Rumanian oil, in Soviet bloc exports, seemed likely to be sent where it would be complementary to Russian exports: but its exports did not seem to offer or threaten a similar growth potential.

National policy, in this second great area of present self-sufficiency in petroleum, is therefore largely indistinguishable from the business behaviour, be this economic or political, of its oil industry. It seems clear that Soviet oil exports will rise during the sixties, though not necessarily rise to any huge volume, and be deployed so as to maintain and to exacerbate softness in the international oil market. Consumers in some countries, indeed, may look to Russia as the marginal supplier of oil, and logically the supplier that ought to set a ceiling on the price; the rest of the world's suppliers would not like this but might possibly have to lump it. It seems equally clear that Russian political pressure will be deployed in politically unstable oil-producing countries, as well as in politically unstable markets such as Cuba, so as to cause the maximum possible embarrassment to the Western oil companies. It is not clear, however, that Soviet objectives such as its competition in rates of growth with the West will necessitate actual penetration into the Middle East. Commercially, the Russians do not appear anxious to push oil prices down to impossibly low levels; in 1961–62, indeed, they seemed prepared to push their prices up again slightly. There might be some possibility of a deal with the Western oil interests to hold the line such as they have made before; compare their agreement to market diamonds via de Beers. Politically, however, there is as yet little sign that they desire any such accommodation; and the oil business offers a highly convenient range of points at which to pinprick the West.

To the outside observer, it seems surprising that the international oil companies chose to accept the manifestation of 'Soviet economic competition with the West' wholly within their own preserves. By 1960–61, certainly, they were combating it fiercely in certain markets, quoting prices that were sometimes too low for the Russians in order to hold or to recapture customers: the Russians were by no means the only marketers on the offensive. But very severe price cutting to hold one's share of the market, in the areas where they had much to lose and the Russians had nothing, was a somewhat sacrificial business. Was there no ground whatever for more direct counter-attack?

Offers of very cheap crude or products in some Communist markets to which Russia did not find it too easy to deliver might have been a possibility. It was perhaps not quite certain that the state import organizations of these countries would have been ready to turn down cargoes of really cheap crude or products—particularly as Russia was not offering its Communist partners in Comecon anything like the discounts that it offers to penetrate Western markets. Like other oil marketers, it engaged in price discrimination where it could: its satellites constituted effectively a captive market. Even if the Western companies did not get the business, they might have a chance of embarrassing Russia where its prices are high. Some of these companies were inhibited more than others by embargoes on trade with the Soviet Bloc. But Western governments that inhibit them from countering the Russians in a way that commercially might hit them 'where they live' are not necessarily helping the West. It is said that one international group, during the fifties, seriously considered an attempt at large-scale penetration of the Chinese market with cheap oil, but that American opposition to 'trading with the enemy' dissuaded it.

Some American and European companies would prefer a diplomatic or strategic counter to Soviet exports: they spend much time arguing to European governments that quotas on imports—although they oppose these as a general principle—should be tightened up against Russian oil. They are in danger, always, of appearing to seek government intervention on their own commercial behalf—which is an unwise line for an industry so generally opposed to government intervention of any other kind. More commercial forms of counter-attack, attempting to compete with the Russians 'where they live', might be better suited to the competence—and the dignity—of international private enterprise.

CHAPTER XV

Seeking Their Own Petroleum

N ations that are self-sufficient in oil, as we have just seen, generate and may export their own *embarras de richesse*. But self-sufficiency in oil, to nations that do not possess it, appears a most enviable condition—both to the less developed economies that visualize a new dynamo of cheap energy and even perhaps a commodity for export to bring them riches overnight, and to the developed economies whose dependence upon petroleum is inevitably increasing, and which may well yearn to secure command of adequate supplies. The countries that one picks out to illustrate such circumstances must be chosen arbitrarily. There are one or two such as Mexico and Austria, which have produced as much oil as they consume, but have been unable to take full advantage of their virtually complete self-sufficiency: others such as Canada and Brazil, which in practice fall well short of doing so, whatever their potentialities; and Argentina, which has recently succeeded in its autarchic quest.

Exploration for oil or gas is going on, today, in most countries in the world; and most countries can boast at least a trickle or a puff of their own. The continuing demand for new concessions or even for areas that other explorers choose to relinquish demonstrates to governments everywhere how worthwhile a gamble exploration seems to experts, even when oil isn't scarce. There are few other economic sectors where international capital can be attracted so easily. Most countries afford to any production that they can develop some degree of protection against competition from imported fuels—and equally insert into concessions or exploration licences specific obligations to develop without delay any oil that is found. Most of the industrialized countries other than the United States and Russia have had to resign themselves to overwhelming reliance on imports. Some countries where oil has been found in impressive quantities, for lack of local markets, have quickly graduated into the ranks of the exporting countries. But in between there remains a handful of countries where supply is in balance, or is expected soon to be with demand—though the two seldom develop at the same rate.

Few countries in recent years have had a more dramatic discovery and development of oil than Canada; but few, equally, have had their hopes of oil prosperity cut down more sharply to size. When the Leduc field in Alberta was discovered during 1946, it seemed to open up the possibilities not only of self-sufficiency in oil for Canada, but of the country's becoming a significant exporter.

The oilfields, admittedly, were in the far West, while Canada's largest centres of consumption were in the East, using imported crude oil and products. But with support from the Canadian and the United States governments, pipelines were laid from Edmonton to Ontario and onward to the American Middle West (the Interprovincial pipeline system) and to Vancouver and the U.S. West Coast (the Trans-Mountain pipeline) which gave this landlocked oil access to coastal and mid-continental refineries. And prominent among the foreign oil companies that poured capital into Canadian oil—some $2,140 million between 1947 and 1956—were large American companies and certain of the international majors. These were also the most important owners of refineries in Montreal, serving the markets of Eastern Canada with products from imported crude. Whether or not Canadian crude could be expected to replace foreign crude in Montreal, these companies were counted upon to export a corresponding volume of Canadian crude to United States refineries.

Canada's oil boom in the early fifties lived up to all these expectations; production rose to nearly half a million barrels a day by 1957, and exports to the United States to 156,000 barrels a day. During the Suez emergency of the winter of 1956–57, the Trans-Mountain pipeline was running at its full capacity of 200,000 barrels a day. But within eighteen months the flow through the line was down to 11,000 barrels a day. The total volume of exports had fallen away to about 80,000 barrels a day (though there were prospects of growth in exports of natural gas and natural gas liquids). Production continued, after a check in 1958, to rise slowly, but it had reached no more than 524,000 barrels a day by 1960.

As to self-sufficiency, the volume of imports had been held at about 300,000 barrels a day up to 1955, with the Canadian crude supplying the growth in consumption. From 1955 onwards it had begun to grow again, but this had been more than offset for a few years, by the dramatic rise in Canadian crude exports. But from 1957 to 1960, domestic production rose by only about half as much as Canadian consumption. In 1960, Canada's productive capacity amounted to well over a million barrels a day, against a national consumption of some 850,000 barrels a day; yet more than half of its productive capacity was idle, and imports of crude and products amounted to about 425,000 barrels a day. The industry was still putting more cash annually into exploration, development and production that it earned as income, and did not expect to eliminate this annual 'current deficit' until say 1963. It would take many years beyond that to recoup the deficit accumulated before that break-even point.

This flattening out of fortune was largely due to developments in the world market, but elements of governmental policy were involved alike in the disappointments of the Canadian oilfields and in the nation's reactions to them. Exploration and development in Canada were not cheap, and the respectable amount of reserves that was discovered (4,750 million barrels by end-1961, after fifteen years in which 2,250 million barrels had been extracted) was not of the massive order of the Middle East.

The provincial government of Alberta, moreover, from the beginning of its oil development, imposed a system of relinquishment of parts of leased areas in the interests of conservation; and in 1950 it imposed a form of prorationing. Both policies made sense in terms of the efficient exploitation of the oilfields. Unfortunately, when it came to exports, the large integrated producers who could have found this oil markets in the United States were faced with the fact that all producers had the right to share in whatever extra output was produced. This reduced the profits they could gain from prorated Canadian oil in comparison with using their own crude from Venezuela or the Middle East. It did, in fact, reduce the growth of output in Alberta relative to that of Saskatchewan, where no prorationing system was in force (much in the same way as Texas generally has to take the main cuts in the regulation of output in the United States).

Canadian oil is accorded privileged treatment (along with Mexican) under American import restrictions, as oil able to enter the United States by pipeline, motor carrier, or rail. But this still did not persuade American importers to take up less of their import quotas for the cheaper foreign crudes from Venezuela and the Middle East. And the slump in tanker freight rates made those imports from distant areas, in comparison with Canadian oil overland, yet cheaper.

In 1961, the Canadian government laid down production targets for Canadian crude for the next few years which postulated the reservation of the whole Ontario market for Canadian crude, plus a virtual doubling of crude oil exports to the United States. It left in abeyance, for the moment, the hotly-disputed argument about moving Canadian crude to the Montreal refineries serving Eastern Canada. This would have involved building a pipeline nearly 2,000 miles long, at a cost of say $400 million; but it would also have involved commitments by the Montreal refiners to accept the large volume of crude required to make its operations economic. The Canadian federal government has not been persuaded yet by domestic producers and the government of Alberta to take that decision—which would mean compelling major companies to supply Eastern Canada from more expensive crude than they can bring in from abroad. But it has set production targets that require a roughly corresponding rise in domestic production. At one end or the other, it is putting pressure on the oil industry, and particularly on certain of the international majors, to make use of more high-cost Canadian crude in one place or another than they might choose to on economic considerations alone. And in 1961 it increased crude production much more than its consumption rose. Its production, at 647,000 barrels a day, rose to 72·5 per cent of its consumption. National policy was forcing an increase in Canadian self-sufficiency.

Not many of the other countries in which governments are putting their influence behind the search for self-sufficiency in oil began with the initial, heady success that Canada enjoyed. And others adopted 'national policies for oil' at earlier stages in the development of their oil industry. In Brazil, for example, exploration was begun by the state just before the last war: a little oil was found in the early years, and after 1953, when Petroleos Brasileros (Petrobras) was formed, there were more substantial additions to reserves. By the end of 1960, the total proved reserves amounted to some 700 million barrels, against 50 million barrels in 1954, and output has now reached about 100,000 barrels a day. In 1954, when Petrobras began operating, that volume of output might have been a national achievement, for domestic demand was only about 150,000 barrels a day: but by 1960, demand had doubled. Local crude production, from Petrobras wells and others, was equivalent to about a third of local consumption; but the actual amount of oil that still had to be imported, nearly 200,000 barrels a day, had grown too.

Moreover, the output achieved was almost all from one field, the Reconcavo basin in Bahia; and in 1960, Mr. Walter Link, the company's chief geological consultant, submitted a very pessimistic report on the possibilities of finding commercial oil anywhere else. Brazil has 1·3 million square miles of sedimentary areas, and between 1954 and 1960, spent some $300 million on exploring various among apparently promising areas: but this latest expert suggested the abandonment of exploration of many such areas, and a reduction of effort in others.

Petrobras is owned mainly by the state, with some municipal and private capital in it; as a 'national' entity it has a monopoly of petroleum production and the sole right to build additional refinery capacity (since 1953). It has only a limited direct share in marketing, but the international companies marketing in Brazil are obliged to distribute the oil that it refines (in what may now amount to about five-sixths per cent of Brazil's refinery capacity); and locally-refined oil products are protected by a preferential rate of excise duty. Its bargaining strength against local affiliates of the majors rests upon these various aspects of its legal privilege. The obvious main weakness of Petrobras, at the beginning of the sixties, lay in not having found enough oil. One might put this down simply to the fact that Brazilian terrain, in spite of superficially favourable characteristics, simply did not contain payable oil. Certainly one could not complain that too little effort had been put into exploration. The oil business, across the world, has had to write off some sustained and very expensive exploration ventures. In Papua and New Guinea, it put in about $200 million over about twenty-five years, and all the oil it had from a few new declining fields was worth no more than about $45 million. In Australia, nearly $150 million has been spent without finding much oil (by private companies and drillers working for the government); though from time to time, as in 1961–62, there have been promising enough discoveries to attract fresh explorers. But no single fruitless venture in any other country has quite equalled the $300 million that Petrobras put into exploration between 1954 and 1960. And a state company, spending the resources of a fairly poor state, has not the spread of operations elsewhere, some of which offer far easier rewards, to offset its bad luck in the one chosen territory.

It was hardly surprising that at the end of 1960, Brazil had set up a government commission to reconsider its oil policies. Some other countries that had begun by seeking self-sufficiency on their own account have gradually, over the years, conceded a somewhat large place to the major oil companies—though they have generally retained very considerable privileges for their nationalized or nationally owned 'chosen instrument'. The Turkish government looked for its own oil from 1933 to 1954, and found some; but after twenty years, short of capital for refining and for further exploration, with its imports increasing much faster than its production, it decided to grant exploration concessions to private oil companies. Bolivia, which in 1937 expropriated the Jersey Standard subsidiary that first developed oil there (paying in compensation about a quarter of Jersey's valuation) and handed the properties over to Yaciementos Petroliferos Fiscales Bolivianos, kept all oil operations in the hands of this state-owned corporation for fifteen years. The state corporation discovered fresh reserves, and built refineries and pipelines: it did eventually achieve self-sufficiency in oil for Bolivia. But this partly reflected the slow development of the economy and of internal oil consumption; oil did not stimulate economic growth in the company as much as had been hoped. Moreover, YPFB was short of capital, and this hampered its development of crude production for export, to earn foreign exchange. From 1952 onwards, the government began to offer concessions to certain foreign oil developers; and in 1955 it adopted a new petroleum law that opened most of the country's territories to development by private foreign capital. About a dozen foreign groups took up concessions, among them Gulf, Shell and Standard of California, three of the international majors; they also included, interestingly, four private Brazilian companies.

The state corporation continued to develop in its own areas in Bolivia—hampered by government policies of economic stabilization that involved cutting oil product prices down to an artificially low level, and obliging YPFB to supply other government departments without payment. By the beginning of 1961 YPFB was supplying the country's limited internal oil requirements and exporting a few thousand barrels of oil a day. It retained a monopoly of refining and marketing; but if the large-scale private oil effort now going into development there is fruitful (and Gulf has already found significant discoveries), the foreign groups would presumably be interested primarily in exporting crude.

Argentina, again, is another example of a Latin American country that has shifted emphasis in oil development from a State corporation to the invitation of private capital from abroad—on somewhat special terms. Its state oil corporation, Yaciementos Petroliferos Argentinos, was founded in 1922, but was not given any formal monopoly of oil in the country, and oil has continued to be produced by private companies there through YPF's history. From the mid-thirties, however, the government began to restrict the expansion of private development, and private oil output began to decline. After the war, oil consumption in the economy began to rise rapidly, while domestic production, which in 1946 had supplied about half of this consumption, did not at first keep pace. But by 1960 crude output totalled 172,000 barrels a day, of which YPF produced 125,000 barrels a day. Through a fairly large-scale drilling programme, which was mainly however development as against exploratory drilling, the country had trebled its estimate of proven reserves to 1,550 million barrels and was on the verge of achieving its goal of self-sufficiency.

It had run, however, into the same financial difficulties that other state corporations in Latin America had encountered basically through shortage of local capital; and in mid-1958 the country had altered its oil policy. It confirmed YPF's monopoly of oil development in Argentina, but provided for YPF to make arrangements with private oil companies to explore, develop and produce oil under contract to it. The forms of contract differed as between different foreign companies. Some provided for these companies to sell any oil eventually produced to YPF at a given price, while others provided for recovery of the foreign venture capital through a percentage of the value of any crude produced, plus 'benefits' of a given percentage on all oil produced over a given period. This form of contract, in which title to the oil was retained by YPF but the foreign contractors would effectively 'self-finance' their exploration from any oil discovered, was a fairly new one to the international oil industry.

It is not easy to classify Mexico in any book about the oil business. It presents object lessons in the history of relations between the host governments of oil exporting countries and the companies operating there, which will be considered in Chapter XVIII: it has, in the twenty years since it nationalized its oil, been an exporter, a self-sufficient supplier, and a net importer. Petroleos Mexicanos, or Pemex, the state company to which the expropriated company installations were handed over in 1938, took over an oil industry that was perhaps past maturity: it had been the world's second producer at the beginning of the twenties, but production had fallen away, and limited exploration in the thirties had added little to the country's proved reserves.

When Pemex took over Mexico was producing about 128,000 barrels a day, and refining about 118,000 barrels a day: since local consumption was less than half the total output, it had been a large exporter (at the time as big as Venezuela). It lost export markets for products from coastal refineries; it was short of equipment and trained men and could not get either easily from a naturally hostile oil industry. After the war, with Mexican internal demand for petroleum growing, Pemex initiated a substantial exploration programme, with some success: it was able to keep its output rising, for a while, slightly ahead of internal consumption and to modernize its refining capacity (and to find large gas fields). From 1957 to 1959, however, it was a net importer, with imports of products exceeding its own exports of crude and products. Pemex was less successful financially than operationally, mainly because, until 1959, the Mexican government held product prices artificially low. In that year the group was reorganized financially; and by 1961 it was supplying 97 per cent of the country's demand. The government had sought aid from the World Bank and Pemex had employed a number of American drilling contractors: but Mexican oil was still a public monopoly barring private enterprise.

One further example of the country seeking self-sufficiency in oil might be taken from within Europe—which is not even today wholly the importing market that it is sometimes taken to be, and might in future develop considerably more indigenous oil and gas production. In Austria oil came under government ownership essentially as a result of anschluss and war, rather than of nationalist or ideological pressures.

In 1938, the RAG group, a joint subsidiary of Mobil and Shell, had its exploration rights in lower Austria, from which most Austrian production of oil came, expropriated under German law. After the war these fields fell into the Russian occupation zone of Austria; and when the occupation ended in 1955, the Russians handed them over to a state-owned corporation, the Austrian Oil Administration, OeMV, but retained the right to reparations deliveries of a million tons of oil a year until 1965. From 1958, onwards, however, the Russians effectively reduced the burden of these deliveries, first by sending Austria half a million tons of Kuibyshev oil a year cost-free, and later by cutting the rate of reparations deliveries to half a million tons, and agreeing that reparations deliveries should end in 1964. These reparations had turned Austria from a self-sufficient country into a net importer; at the end of the fifties it was producing about 45,000 barrels a day and consuming a roughly similar volume of products, plus about 1,128 million cubic metres a year of natural gas. By 1960, agreement had been reached on compensation to Shell and Mobil, part of which was lent to OeMV by RAG as an advance against fees for processing RAG crude at its new refinery at Schwachat near Vienna. State and private development of Austrian oil and gas seems likely to continue fairly amicably side by side. But local production is levelling off while Austrian consumption grows: the country cannot avoid greater dependence on imports. To a land-locked market, oil imports must come by pipeline: with one terminal of the Comecon line from Russia at the Czech border, and a line planned from Trieste, Austria should soon be able to buy either Western or Soviet oil.

The search for self-sufficiency in oil in the countries which we have examined, does not necessarily involve the participation of state companies; and these when set up have not necessarily been able to maintain monopolies conferred on them at least in the field of production and exploration. But it often does mean 'nationalized' oil development; and in countries where it does not it often means other forms of governmental pressure upon private companies engaged in oil development there to conform with 'national policies' in oil. Mr. Walter Levy, the American oil consultant, in a study that he prepared for the World Bank in 1961, argued very powerfully that exploration and development, at any rate, are usually too expensive and risky an operation for the governments of underdeveloped countries to engage in on their own. With the limited capital resources they usually possess, he thought they might well concentrate on investments offering a more guaranteed return, since the international oil industry was prepared to put in the risk capital. This was wise counsel; and recent experience, as seen above, suggests that some nations, independently, are being forced to the same conclusion.

Nations seeking self-sufficiency for their growing oil markets, again, have the chance to benefit from a tendency in the exploration effort of the world oil industry that has become obvious in the last few years. This is the readiness of international companies, established majors or newcomers, to explore for oil in countries where there is a developing market—which offers a likely, and even perhaps protected, outlet for the oil if they do find it. Oil—and gas—is worth a great deal more on the spot where it can be sold than in areas remote from markets, where its development may be much harder to command.

CHAPTER XVI

Consumers Commanding Oil

'If we cannot secure the access to this island of oil ships, we cannot secure the access to this island of the whole of the great volume of our trade on which we shall depend in war as in peace, if we are to maintain ourselves effectively,' said Mr. Winston Churchill in the House of Commons on 7th June, 1914. 'The proposition that the Navy should be able to keep our ports open and to keep our trade routes safe in time of war for all the vast merchant fleets which traffic with this island, and yet should lack the power to bring in the comparatively few but, from our point of view, specially interesting oil cargoes, is a proposition which is naturally, inherently and, if need be, demonstrably absurd.'

These are perhaps not the obvious terms for a First Lord of the Admiralty to use in justifying the purchase, originally for £2,200,000, of a controlling interest in the Anglo-Persian Oil Company. But Mr. Churchill was emphasizing the commercial, as against the strategic, significance of the government's purchase of a stake in oil. 'Nobody cares in war time,' he went on to say, 'how much they pay for a vital commodity, but in peace—that is the period to which I wish to direct the attention of the Committee—price is rather an important matter, and as we hope that there will be many years of peace to every week of war, I cannot feel that we are not fully justified in taking up the time of the Committee in considering how, in years of peace and in a long period of peace, we may acquire proper bargaining power and facilities with regard to the purchase of oil. The price of oil does not depend wholly or even mainly on the ordinary workings of supply and demand.' Mr. Churchill was concerned with the question of supplies for the Royal Navy, which was becoming, in the interests of efficiency, more dependent on oil; a long-term contract for naval supplies was, indeed, one of the corollaries of the share purchase. But he was setting out in this debate nearly fifty years ago exactly the mixture of motives, not entirely strategic but not entirely commercial, with which the governments of many countries who have to rely on imports for their oil regard their increasing dependence upon it, and with which some are seeking command, or assurance, of supplies. Sir Edward Grey put it more bluntly in the same debate, 'What you want is an independent source of supply which is, as far as possible, uncontrolled by any agency which can exact undue prices or what the customer considers undue prices.'

In the long run, the consequences of this decision were momentous and complex. It certainly assured oil supplies for the Navy; it also assured governmental backing for the development of Anglo-Persian (which became first Anglo-Iranian and later British Petroleum) throughout the Middle East, notably in securing a half-share in the concession in Kuwait. It incidentally must have proved perhaps the most profitable investment of British public money in any industrial operation in our time. Less happily for Britain, there is little doubt that this identification of government and company had more than a little to do, over the years, in forming political attitudes towards the company in the Middle East, which eventually culminated in the nationalization of Iranian oil and may also have had something to do, ten years later, with the drastic and unilateral abrogation of the Iraq concession.

What is germane in this context is that the decision to buy control of this company represented the first open manifestation of the vital interest to the government of a country lacking indigenous oil supplies of securing a source of supply that it recognized as strategically vital. But it was the prototype. Britain sought and gained command of securely 'tied' supplies of oil from a promising source that later turned out to be part of the richest oil-bearing region yet discovered. Over the years it extended that command in the region, though its chosen instrument was not able to obtain exclusive rights anywhere except in Iran, and later lost them there. Nor was BP its only lien upon international oil: the 40 per cent British in Royal Dutch/Shell, in spite of hard words about that 'combine' when Anglo-Persian was being bought, has linked this group's interests with Britain's almost as firmly as those of BP.

The Netherlands, alike, had its own oil needs guaranteed through ownership of the other 60 per cent of Royal Dutch/Shell. Victory in the First World War gave the Allies the chance to cut Germany out of the stake in Middle East oil that it had invested in Iraq; but this, in its turn, cut France in. France had already begun seeking some control over its supplies of oil products, at least, by developing a refinery industry behind tariff protection. Access to Iraq oil, for which it created CFP, gave it command over growing supplies of crude, though not enough to cover all its needs.

These three major industrialized consuming countries, which until recently lacked petroleum resources within their own frontiers, have thus large enough strategic and financial interests in petroleum else-where for their governments, very often, to behave more like producers than consumers. Through CFP, France has somewhat enlarged its Middle East interests over the years, though not nearly as much as Britain has through BP. The Royal Dutch/Shell group widened its interests with the Iraq Petroleum group, was allotted quite a sizeable share in the Iran Consortium, and most recently gained the Kuwait offshore concession; but up to now this group, and hence the Nether-lands, have had much larger interests in the Western hemisphere and the Far East than in the Middle East. France, since the war, has invested heavily in developing oil production in one of its own spheres of interest, Algeria, and other parts of the 'franc zone'; though all these are now attaining independence, they and their oil seem liable for a time at least to remain economically associated with France.

This command of oil, eroded somewhat though it continues to be by the emergence from tutelage of the oil-producing states, significantly modifies the commercial stance of the British, Dutch and French governments in dealing with the oil business. Their oil policies are not identical: Britain and Holland, whose 'invisible' income from inter-national oil profits is generally held to outweigh their 'visible' disburse-ments on buying supplies of it, favour liberal import policies (though not so liberal as to make oil too cheap). France has a smaller financial interest in international oil; only recently has it had the prospect of its tied or associated oil production exceeding its internal demand; its approach is *dirigiste* rather than liberal. But all three countries share this mixture of interests in general energy policy. They are somewhat less concerned than other industrialized consumer countries in protecting their domestic coal industries; they are also less concerned that their home consumers should get oil cheap, and comparatively disinclined to encourage new competition to the established oil marketers, which might bring prices down.

The BP group seldom behaves like the semi-nationalized or 'national' companies of the kind that other countries have created recently. Com-mercially, it behaves like one of the international majors (which it is) controlled by private ownership (which it is not). But the decision that Churchill took affirmed a policy that was acted upon consistently throughout the interwar period: that British diplomatic interests in the Middle East were inextricably tied up with oil. Nearly half a century later, this was the principle upon which Britain risked its whole influence in the Middle East, in the Suez affair. From Sir Anthony Eden's memoirs of that time, one gains the impression that Britain's impending shortage of fuel, and its utter dependence upon getting Middle East oil through the Suez Canal, were perhaps the two economic 'facts' that ever became firmly implanted in Sir Anthony's mind. That they did not happen to be facts did not alter their importance in that odd and damaging aberration of British foreign policy.

Britain did not develop a significant home refining industry until after the Second World War. Although the government gave some support to the experimental development of oil from coal, by hydrogenation at Billingham, its view, summarized by a committee in 1939, was that home refining made little difference to the strategic security of oil supplies, and was uneconomic. Dollar shortage, doubts about political stability in the Middle East, growth of the British market to a size where it could absorb large enough quantities of a wide range of products to fit refining yields without burdensome surpluses, and the development of petro-chemicals—all these reversed its view after the war. It has now the largest refining capacity in Europe (though capacity in several other countries is being expanded faster); a sizeable export trade to Europe in products; also higher product prices than most, and more comfortable refining margins. In 1960, nearly 40 million tons of oil were consumed in the United Kingdom, and only a trickle, about 1,700 barrels a day, was produced. The only fuel Britain really has at home is coal, produced by one of the world's largest mining industries; and this coal has been suffering severe competition from imports of oil. Yet the British government never displays quite the same attitudes towards these imports that the governments of certain other coal-producing countries in Western Europe do—being conscious that though the country commands no oil, it commands considerable oil profits.

The liberalism that British governments generally profess in energy policies, claiming to rely on 'consumer's freedom of choice', has a basis of financial advantage. In Whitehall, it was calculated that the high net import cost of visible trade in oil is still somewhat more than offset by invisible earnings of the oil industry—the balance of earnings on tankers, and the net result of many forms of payment back and forth in the oil combines. It seems fairly clear that the margin of financial advantage to the country must have been thinned down drastically in recent years.

CONSUMERS COMMANDING OIL

But the details of its 'oil balance of payments' remain a closely guarded secret.

Despite professions of liberalism, the government has made considerable interventions in the fuel market in Britain. The prospect up to about 1955 of a widening gap between demand for energy and the possibilities of increasing coal supplies led ministers first to direct the nationalized electricity industry to start burning oil in a number of its power stations, and later to commit Britain to a sizeable investment programme for the nuclear generation of electricity. The Suez affair heightened the fears of an energy gap (though in fact supplies of fuel were already becoming larger than could be sold). The government, during this short period of 'oil shortage', trebled its nuclear programme and committed itself to heavier investment in nationalized coal. When oil became abundant again, and estimates of the cost of nuclear electricity began to mount, the government eventually cut back its nuclear investment. It also planned to reduce the amount of oil that would be used in power stations. This did not prove easy in practice: the electricity authorities were finding that oil at coastal stations in the South of England could be at least as cheap as coal at pithead power stations in the Midlands.

Nor had the professed liberalism meant entirely free imports of fuel. Until 1961 Britain gave no formal protection to coal through taxes on fuel oil, as many other consuming countries did. But it also did not allow private consumers to import coal, which could have been had very cheaply from America or Poland during periods of low ocean freights. Equally, it has granted almost no licences to import Russian oil. The major companies' command of the best terminal and storage facilities and their exclusive dealing contracts with most filling stations precluded all but a small fringe of price-cutting independent competition in the dealer gasoline market until about 1959–60, though competition for commercial consumers' business, by the end of 1960, had become almost as severe as on the Continent. The electricity authorities had been refused permission to make contracts for American coal in 1955, as the steel industry was in 1961.

There had always been, therefore, significant hidden elements of protection for established interests—both in oil and coal—in British energy policy. But in the Budget of 1961, the protection became admitted. Until then, only petroleum products used as transport fuels had been taxed: but in the 1961 budget, the government re-imposed an excise duty of 2d. a gallon on other products. This meant nearly £2 a ton on fuel oil of which consumption had been rising at a dramatic rate. The effect, in the short run, was quite marked: consumption of fuel oil, which from 1959 to 1960 had been rising by 26 per cent, was up by less than 10 per cent in the twelve months immediately following the imposition of the duty.

It could be argued from this that Britain's energy policy was changing. There were, indeed, occasional comments from within the Treasury and the Bank of England that suggested some disenchantment with the net benefits to Britain's balance of payments of behaving like a producer, and favouring expensive oil—particularly when Britain's competitors could buy their oil products cheaper. There were, certainly, important interests in British consuming industries such as steel who were anxious to buy not only cheap American coal but cheap Russian oil, both of which they argued were necessary to get lower prices out of their main suppliers inside Britain. Yet the British energy policy remained as mixed as ever. The Treasury said it had put on the fuel oil duty, an effective protection for coal, simply as a 'revenue duty'. Its decision was taken, reputedly, against the advice of the Ministry of Power. Yet within six months, the Ministry of Power was promoting petroleum imports to compete with coal: it authorized imports of a technically unproven and temporarily more expensive form of petroleum, liquefied natural gas. And in this technologically adventurous exercise, the nationalized gas industry, formerly largely dependent on coal, was associated with an importing group in the ownership of which figured one of the oil companies that Britain considered utterly dependable, the Royal Dutch/Shell group.

Holland is the home of Royal Dutch, the senior (60 per cent) partner in the Royal Dutch/Shell group; and though until recently the Dutch government had no shareholding in any petroleum operations, it has a natural concern with an industry that bulks so large in the economics of the home country and its associated territories. Holland lost much of its sovereignty over Far Eastern oil with the accession of Indonesia to independence after the Second World War, but the output of the Royal Dutch/Shell group was already widely spread elsewhere. In the Netherlands Antilles the refineries of Shell at Curaçao and Esso at Aruba, processing Venezuelan oil, make these Dutch islands one of the most important export refining centres in the world. In Holland itself the great refining and petrochemical complex round Rotterdam is a very substantial exporter of products to the rest of Europe, though the pipelines now running from Rotterdam to inland refineries around Karlsruhe and Stuttgart may tend to limit the marketing area for products refined coastally there.

The Dutch government, to the oil industry, acts as a very friendly neutral. Holland has a smallish coal industry, which has encountered the same difficulties in competition with oil of recent years as have others in Europe. Beyond ceasing to issue licences for imports of American coal since the fifties, and putting on regulations about keeping minimum stocks by oil marketers, the government has taken no measures to protect coal or limit the switch to oil. Its coal mines supply only about a third of its energy requirements, and it has no hydro-power: so reliance on imported energy for the majority of its consumption is neither new nor frightening to it. There is some small oil production in Holland, and exploration for natural gas has recently located deposits that may well be the largest yet found in Europe. Here the government, through its state mining organization, has taken a 40 per cent shareholding in the company that will develop the gas, and has formulated a policy that will moderate the rate of expansion of sales of this gas at home, though it hopes to promote exports. In a sense, Holland is here protecting imported oil, as well as home-produced coal, against this new source of indigenous energy. Could liberalism go farther?

Within the European Common Market, the Dutch government has been one of the strongest advocates of a liberal policy towards importing energy. At the end of 1960, it did concede the principle of a limit to duty-free imports of petroleum products from the Netherlands Antilles into Europe as part of the price for association of these Caribbean Islands with EEC: at least, it agreed that if these imports passed a certain total member countries or the Common Market Commission could decide to put duties or quantitative restrictions upon further imports. Without this, its partners in the Six would not have agreed to association. This minor concession to restrictive policies towards energy imports demonstrated that Holland has to temper its liberalism for the sake of its special interests; and the principle of restriction on products refined within an associated territory, though from foreign crude, may become an important one in European energy policy. Nevertheless, there are few governments in the world whose liberalism in energy policy is as unadulterated.

Self-sufficiency in oil production is a new postwar aim of French governments; but it was not the first interest they had shown in self-sufficiency. After the First World War, France had imposed various forms of protection to encourage refining within the country. The measure that finally did bring about a significant development of French refining, the oil law of 1928, laid the foundations of a considerably greater degree of State supervision for oil companies operating there than exists in most of Western Europe. Refining and marketing has remained largely in the hands of local affiliates of the major international companies; but these are subject to strict licensing. Refiners and marketers are licensed, and new permits are not freely granted; licensees have obligations to maintain reserve stocks of a given size, are allotted quotas of imports of crude, and are subject inside the market to price controls on their products.

The creation of CFP, with its share in the Middle East, resulted from a diplomatic rather than a commercial French initiative. The Treaty of San Remo, after the First World War, transferred to France German rights in the Turkish Petroleum Company, which in 1929 became the Iraq Petroleum Company, and CFP was founded in 1924, to exercise these rights. Today it is also a participant in the Iranian consortium, and with BP in certain offshore concessions in the Persian Gulf; and it has played a part, though hardly a dominant one, in the development of the Sahara. Its Middle East production is larger than it can sell through its 'Total' distributing subsidiary, which operates in a number of European countries and at the end of the fifties was extending its interests into others, such as Britain; but it sells considerable amounts of crude to other major companies and to independent buyers. It is the largest refiner in France; at the end of the fifties it was beginning to refine a growing proportion of Saharan oil— as other refineries in France were also obliged to—and this was putting it to fresh efforts to sell refined products in fresh markets in Europe.

Few potential oil-producing areas in the whole history of the oil industry have ever been explored and developed with the single-minded intensity that France put into the Sahara after the war. By the end of 1960, expenditure on exploration and development there had reached about NF1,000 million, or the equivalent of some £600 million since exploration began in earnest during 1947; and France was investing heavily in exploration and development in other parts of the 'franc zone', such as Gabon and the Middle Congo. At the end of 1960 there were about 40 drilling rigs in operation in the Sahara alone, and another 90–100 were active in France itself and the rest of the franc zone. By 1961, output of Saharan oil had reached some 320,000 barrels a day. For the franc zone as a whole, the 1961 total was of the order of 400,000 barrels a day. By 1965, the French hope, the Sahara might be able to produce 600,000 to 1,000,000 barrels a day. Oil began to be discovered from 1954 onwards, and very important finds of oil were made in 1956 at Hassi Messaoud; all the significant discoveries were hundreds of miles from the coast, and involved vast investment in pipelines to bring this oil, and the gas from the Hassi R'Mel field located in 1957, to the coast of the Mediterranean. It was not until the end of 1959 that oil began to be exported. By spring 1962 Algeria was on its way to independence—even if the French retained considerable economic links with it.

These Saharan finds represented perhaps the most important single addition to major oil-producing areas made during the fifties—along with the adjacent finds, in rather more favourable circumstances, that followed in Libya. But they were still small in comparison with the 180 billion barrels of proved reserves in the Middle East. Even Iraq, which has the lowest total of proved reserves of the four major Middle East producers, had nearly five times as high a figure as the Sahara at the end of 1961. In this industry one tends to think of proved reserves as to some degree proportional to the scale of effort in exploration. It may be worth noting that the huge reserves of the Middle East have been located by the drilling, over many years, of perhaps 1,100 wells; the far more concentrated effort in the Sahara, in the space of a dozen years, has not compared in its rewards. And the money spent has been even more, in proportion, than the physical effort of drilling; for drilling in the Sahara, owing to the even worse physical and climatic conditions there, is more costly than in most parts of the Middle East.

But the most significant difference between the exploration and development of the French Sahara and that of most other oil-producing areas outside the United States was that it was carried out mainly by nationals, backed by the government ruling the area. Shell was associated with CREPS, one of the companies in the Sahara, from the start; other major companies later accepted the French government's invitation to take leases in the area. But all operate in partnership with French nationalized or semi-nationalized companies; and the biggest successes so far have been gained by these nationalized companies. This Saharan success was the crown of a community-wide exploration effort organized by the French government after the liberation, as one of its dogged national efforts to restore *la gloire*; it has been a more constructive and fruitful effort than some.

No sooner was this particular contribution to glory brought to fruition than France agreed to hand it over to a new, nationalist Algeria. The new Algeria succeeds to the 50 per cent governmental share of profits on Algerian oil, to a sizeable share in the ownership of S.N.Repal, the main French operating company in the Sahara, and to smaller shares in other companies developing Algerian oil and gas. But it needs French co-operation—and capital—to get the full benefit of this costlessly inherited national oil industry.

Both French business circles and the Algerian rebel government have professed great confidence in maintaining the *modus vivendi* on oil reached in a protocol to the Evian agreement of early 1962. France needs the oil; and independent Algeria will need its oil resources developed. Several other countries attaining some degree of independence had been left with oil companies that had entered the country under the previous régime. No other one has ever had to deal with companies that were so tightly linked by ownership with the colonial government that seemed at last to be relinquishing sovereignty. The French government has a substantial holding in CFP, as has the British government in BP, but these companies' relationships with Middle East host governments are hardly comparable; for the Saharan development had essentially been part of a governmental initiative to gain 'self-sufficiency' for the franc zone.

Its location alone would have secured Saharan oil a significant place in the French market and probably elsewhere in Southern Europe; its only immediate competition from nearby is in Libya. But the state backing of Saharan oil made it certain that this would receive privileged entry into the French market at least; and the degree of control the state possessed over refining and marketing companies in France enabled it to require all refineries to handle a quota of oil from the new source. Indeed, it would like to seek the same preference for the Saharan oil elsewhere in Western Europe. This is one of the main tangible benefits, in economic terms, that France has to offer the new Algerian state.

Introduction of the Saharan crude posed some technical and commercial questions, regardless of its political backing. There is some dispute about the actual composition of this very light crude. But it does appear clear that it gives a much higher yield of gasoline and a much lower yield of fuel oil than is suited to the French market, where like most of Western Europe, it is the demand for fuel oil and the middle distillates that is growing fastest. Processing this oil in refineries in France, therefore, meant surpluses of the lighter products, which had to be exported (if markets could be found). Apart from pressing Saharan oil upon the major companies that refine and distribute there, the French government, in 1959, bought its way into the refining and marketing business. A new company, Union Générale des Pétroles, was set up and purchased a 60 per cent interest in the Caltex refinery and marketing system in France. In setting up this marketing company the government offered some reassurances to the existing marketers that it would not receive preferential treatment. But these, in the background of a state where preference for the national enterprise is virtually automatic, were none too reassuring.

Another fresh supply of 'franc petroleum' may be only a few years behind Saharan oil in crossing the seas to Western Europe—Saharan natural gas. The projects to supply this liquefied in ocean tankers to Britain have already been discussed in Chapter VI; as was also mentioned there, it may alternatively cross the sea by undersea pipeline, or in 'trains' of refrigerated barges. Large supplies of natural gas, incidentally, may make up for the low yield of fuel oil from Saharan crudes. State companies in France are already distributing natural gas from the Lacq deposits to industrial firms and utilities in France; the problem there was to develop a new market for the large supplies available.

While France controlled Algeria, the international companies that obtained concessions there had the unusual experience of dealing with a 'host government' whose economic experience was as industrialized and as sophisticated as their own. They also had to deal with something they generally distrust elsewhere: a government with substantial shareholdings in most of the oil operations in the area, and in any case requiring more than 50 per cent of ownership to be French. The Sahara was economically a special case, in that this government had invested most of the riskiest capital, before oil was found. After Algerian self-determination, moreover, they now have to deal also with a new and at least, radical Arab 'host government' which can draw on Middle East experience, has a powerful ally in marketing its oil in the still-financially-interested French government—and which has also, by political succession, inherited without monetary investment certain direct shareholdings in the oil business of a kind that most companies were reluctant to concede to longer-established 'hosts'.

The chance of 'tied' oil supplies through national ownership of countries operating abroad attracts other industrialized countries in Europe and Asia. Portugal is now seeking what it thinks of as 'self-sufficiency' through exploration for oil in Angola. It may get oil from there sufficient to cover its needs. But how long Angola will remain 'part of' Portugal is perhaps questionable. Italy and Japan, however, are both anxious to command supplies of oil through their own companies— though for the moment, in circumstances of oil surplus, the main role of both is as 'arm's-length buyers' of oil using all their bargaining power to get it as cheaply as they can from anywhere. Italy's chosen instrument, a thorn in the side of the international companies, is a fully-nationalized concern, not one with partial government ownership such as BP or CFP. The Japanese company now producing part of the Middle East oil that Japan imports is privately owned. But links between the government and this group of banks, utilities and other Japanese businesses are close: the company may be given some preference for its crude, and it now appears that Japan is taking strict powers of control over all imports, which would facilitate this. These countries, like France, would seem likely to offer special privileges to their own companies in competing with other supplying companies. But for the moment, their ambition to gain a stake in production in no way inhibits Italy and Japan from thinking, and behaving, as single-minded consumers.

CHAPTER XVII

Consumers in the Market Place

The less a Japanese oil importer pays for his oil, the more foreign exchange he gets to buy it next time. Japan has a tight control on foreign currency for imports, as a result of continuing balance of payments difficulties during recent years. It also has the fastest rate of growth in oil consumption of any comparably developed industrial country. Up to 1962 its Ministry of Trade and Industry (MITI) allocated foreign exchange for the purchase of oil, mainly from the Middle East, partly in relation to how much each importer had spent in the previous three months, and partly in relation to how much oil he managed to buy with this money. Moreover, freight charges do not affect this: foreign exchange to finance transport seemed to be granted automatically. As a result, every Japanese importer was under extra pressure to get the lowest f.o.b. prices he could—which means the biggest possible discounts off posted prices.

This, in recent years, Japanese importers have made notably successful efforts to do. Few other 'arm's-length buyers' have as regularly secured sizeable discounts—varying in 1960–62 from about 15 to 30 cents a barrel, or 10–15 per cent below posted prices—for Middle East crude oil. Moreover, the redoubtable Ministry of Trade and Industry makes public, regularly, details of the bargain prices actually achieved, *pour encourager les autres*. This has been fairly embarrassing for the oil companies posting these prices, who have to justify them as realistic to the governments of countries where their own associated refineries usually pay at posted prices for the oil that they import.

Publicity did not necessarily push these discounts down farther. The heaviest price-cutting usually takes place when it can be kept secret from all but the favoured few customers. Indeed, publication of these 'MITI reports' may possibly have helped to stabilize the level of discounts in the Persian Gulf for a time. Companies supplying Japan with crude have taken to offering special 'non-price' inducements such as loans to importing firms, rather than concede bigger, better-publicized discounts. But the system has advertised the result that can be gained by hard bargaining to other customers around the world. Many Japanese importers are associated with Western companies: most of the international majors, in particular, have a stake in Japanese refining, which has now a capacity of 47 million tons a year, or 970,000 barrels a day. But, until 1962, the law precluded foreigners from owning more than 50 per cent of any Japanese concern, so established companies were hardly in any commercial position to counsel moderation in bargaining to these associates. Moreover, the cheaper one could invoice the oil, the more chance one had of expanding one's share of an extraordinarily buoyant market. So the tempting Japanese market has retained its softening influence on world oil prices. The discounts that the Japanese managed to secure, at the beginning of the sixties, were having repercussions elsewhere: more repercussions, probably, than the bargaining of any other powerful, and uninhibited customer.

Japan, which has an oil partnership with Indonesian national companies in Sumatra, has also appeared in the Middle East, with a company holding concessions from Kuwait and Saudi Arabia for offshore oil exploration in the two countries' Neutral Zone. This company, offering a degree of Arab government participation not only in the producing company but in later operations such as transport, refining and marketing, conceded to the governments 56 per cent of profits to Saudi Arabia and 57 per cent to Kuwait. They were exceptionally fortunate in their development, striking oil with their first well; and by 1961, they began to ship oil back to Japan. It had been expected that the Japanese company would receive somewhat special treatment, but at the time that it began to ship crude, at any rate, it did not. And as its prospective customers, some of them shareholders in the oil venture, were able to get other Middle East oil at substantial discounts and were not anxious to take even Japanese-produced oil at full posted prices, this company too had to discount the prices it had agreed with its host government.

Commitments to the International Monetary Fund to remove Japanese foreign exchange restrictions, in 1962, resulted in some changes in this governmental encouragement to bargaining. But 'liberalization' does not, in Japan, seem to guarantee liberalism. Under the nation's 1962 Oil Law, MITI gained more power of its oil industry, not less. Though this power was no longer operated through the foreign exchange control, the ministry was required to lay down a five-year oil plan, to be revised annually, which would govern local production and imports of both crude and oil products. The construction or expansion of Japan's refining capacity, which has been growing at a tremendous rate, becomes subject to ministry licensing. Moreover, MITI has the power to fix 'standard selling prices' for oil products. This legislation is permissive; it will not necessarily be administered to the limits of MITI's new powers at any one time. But the Japanese government, understandably remaining careful about its balance of payments, has reserved very considerable powers to 'assure the stable and cheap supply of petroleum'. Japanese importers, moreover, are encouraged to use these quite impartially; in 1962, when Russian suppliers proposed to increase the prices of certain oil exports to Japan, they were very quickly told that if they did the buyers would go elsewhere for their imports.

Japan, however, was only the best-publicized—save perhaps Italy—among a growing selection of consuming countries, in East and West, industrialized and underdeveloped, that were bargaining really hard for cheap oil. Some were among the industrial nations of Western Europe that needed large-scale imports but commanded no significant share in ownership of the world oil business, such as Germany, Sweden and Italy. Others were developing nations that so far had been unsuccessful in finding sizeable oil production at home: short of oil, short of national income per head, and very short of foreign exchange, such as India and Ceylon. Others, barely significant consumers at all, were new nations seeking to bargain for national refineries and foreign investment as the price of access of entry to their nascent markets. Some of the newly independent African nations seeking a government shareholding in refining and marketing, were setting foot on a road earlier taken by such European nations as Spain and Portugal. Certain of these consuming countries, incidentally, are inhibited in their bargaining for the cheapest energy possible by compunction for ailing domestic coal industries that cannot really compete: but not all of them.

Competition is rumbustiously free in certain of the highly industrialized markets that depend most heavily on imports. Sweden and Switzerland, for example, have hydropower but no other significant home production of energy. They rely on imports of oil and coal for 50–60 per cent of their fuel supplies—which are high in relation to their population, as both countries enjoy high standards of living. Hydroelectric capacity, once installed, offers power at almost nil running cost, so it needs no tariff protection against imported fuels. In neither of these countries, therefore, does the government exert much influence upon the free choice of fuels—except to encourage customers to bargain hard. In recent years, both have been receptive markets for price-cutters. Consumers' co-operative movements play a considerable part in petroleum marketing in both countries. The Swiss organization, Migros, founded by a remarkable businessman who disliked profit, the late Herr Duttweiler, has indeed extended its activities into Germany. In Sweden every petroleum consumer, down to the individual motorist, expects a discount. Motorists collect receipts for every tankful, send these vouchers to their suppliers, and are nowadays paid cash discounts not only by the co-operative movement and individual suppliers but by the major marketers too.

Sweden, it may be added, is quite a significant buyer of Russian oil, under two-way trade agreements with the Soviet Union. It has not become deeply dependent on Soviet oil, nor is ever likely to put all its eggs in this or any other basket. But it is not moved by arguments about Western strategy to deprive itself of this source of cheap energy, which also serves to lever down the prices Western oil suppliers charge. This nation has price-cutting independent traders who regularly get large discounts on crude oil and products. Switzerland, also, has shown little patience with marketing affiliates of internationally integrated companies that invoice their oil in at artificially high prices related to world postings and hence show a paper loss: it has imposed on them a special tax régime.

Another group of Western consumer countries displays more mixed attitudes towards cheap energy imports, because of solicitude towards uncompetitive domestic fuel industries. Belgium, for example, has a market for petroleum products where discounts and price-cutting are now very pronounced. Its best known oil company, Petrofina, is an international refining and marketing group with only limited integration back into production, and is credited with the aphorism: 'Only fools and affiliates pay posted prices.' Yet the Belgian government has intervened in oil-coal competition with a sizeable tax on fuel oil. It has the weakest coal industry in Europe, which at the time of writing has had to be granted a temporary insulation from the competition even of other European coal suppliers, with restrictive quotas on all coal imports and subsidy of the weakest mines. This need to protect weak domestic fuel tempers its appetite for really cheap oil.

Western Germany has a large coal industry, and also a sizeable domestic production of oil: both need and receive protection from imports. Its Ruhr mines could not, in the late fifties, stand up to competition from imports of American and Polish coal, let alone from really cheap fuel oil. Nor could its oilfields, which cover some 20 per cent of its petroleum consumption, match the low landed costs of imports from the Middle East, to say nothing of Russia. Germany has at present, as well as heavy taxation on the black oils, an import duty on crude oil, which protects its home-produced supplies. Though it is committed to bring this duty down to nil by the beginning of 1964, under certain obligations of the European Common Market, Germany seems unlikely completely to abandon protection of its own oil—or its own coal.

Germany, moreover, has no significant financial interest in the world oil business to consider (its interest in Middle East oil, early in the century, had been taken from it after the First World War and handed over to France). It wants cheap energy; but not at too heavy a cost, imposed too rapidly on its declining coal industry or its growing oil production. It began by requiring the oil companies operating in Germany to join with coal producers in a form of selling cartel, by which markets would have been shared. This did not work, because outside suppliers still came in with cut-price oil, so the government imposed a tax on fuel oil, and later increased this.

Oil marketers were soon absorbing this tax, and selling fuel oil at discounts that made it as much cheaper than coal as before. Moreover, a certain amount of Russian oil flowed in to sharpen price competition for general fuel in the German market. There was much more independent competition, moreover, among the filling stations selling gasoline to the German motorist than those selling to his British counterpart; independent stations account for 15–20 per cent of gasoline sales. And when profits on dearer gasoline are squeezed, it has a severe effect on the refining margins and total profits of any marketing company, as the accounts published by some of the companies operating in Germany (as in Switzerland and Italy) began to show. Some of the major companies' refining and marketing affiliates in Germany, in 1959 and 1960, showed losses. And the West German tax authorities began to become none too co-operative about accepting these accounts for tax purposes. The German parliament, moreover, sponsored a full-scale inquiry into the world oil industry by the country's main economic institutes—which in 1962 produced a set of cost comparisons that emphasized how much its indigenous coal and oil producers needed protection from imports for survival.

In considering the policies of governments in these countries that rely on imports for their petroleum, such as Germany, Belgium, and to some extent also Britain, in spite of its financial connexions with the world oil industry, one has to recognize the importance of their indigenous fuel industries, and the considerations involved in letting their coal industries, in particular, run down. These industries, in the ECSC countries and Britain, employ some two million men and produce about 450 million tons of coal a year. They were the original foundation of the prosperity and industrial advantages of these countries. Politically, neither coal miners nor coal owners are without some weight. Moreover, the coal-producing countries of Western Europe, since the end of the last war, have ploughed very large amounts of capital into the modernization of their mining industries. And though these industries nowadays earn comparatively little in exports, they supply fuel without making any claim on a country's balance of payments.

Such considerations regarding their own indigenous fuel industries were reinforced with continuing uncertainties about petroleum. Politically there were memories of the crises over Abadan and the Suez Canal. In both crises, supplies of oil to Europe had in fact been fairly well maintained and quickly restored, largely through the managerial flexibility of the major companies. But both were reminders of a certain vulnerability in the main supplies of cheap energy for Europe. Commercially, as well, these governments had other doubts about running down indigenous supplies of energy in the confidence that imports would remain cheap. When oil began to be offered at big discounts, the governments were told by the major companies that the extremes of price-cutting in 1958–60, were simply 'distress sales'. Not until 1961, when the chairman of the German subsidiary of Jersey Standard predicted low oil prices for 10–15 years, did any of these major companies commit itself to a guess about how long the surplus and these soft prices would last; and this, it was later made clear, was an individual and not a company view.

Insurance against what still seemed a rather uncertain fuel, and one largely outside their own control, was one of the motives behind protective policies in these countries. There were others. The social consequences of throwing miners out of work and breaking up their traditional mining communities were considered, reasonably enough. Some arguments put forward in the coal industries that coal capacity once abandoned could never be brought back into production, may have had some weight. These are rather similar to certain arguments often advanced for the conservation of petroleum resources, and like them, open to argument on economic grounds.

But it would be unfair to exaggerate the degree of protection that the consumer governments of Western Europe did, during this period, accord their coal industries: all the mining industries concerned had to accept fairly drastic cuts in capacity as well as in production. The cuts were certainly still not adequate to the full rationalization of European coal mining that will eventually have to be faced. But they still represented a fairly sharp reduction in size in a short time. Nor did the governments that afforded their different degrees of protection to coal always maintain this regardless of cost (as they did tend to maintain nuclear energy programmes). In most cases the special protection was described as temporary and designed to be reduced automatically over a period.

Occasionally, in countries that have a growing demand for oil and large reserves of increasingly unwanted coal, enthusiastic engineers discuss the possibility of making the one out of the other. Germany did develop processes for making oil from coal between the wars, and operated a number of plants during the war when it was cut off from peacetime sources of oil; but the economics of these plants made sense only in a siege economy.

There are places in the world, with far cheaper coal, where these techniques make more sense, though whether they could anywhere at present be fully competitive is very doubtful. A South African state corporation, Sasol, built and is operating the largest synthetic oil plant in the world near Johannesburg. This is now an impressive piece of chemical engineering (though its early history was marred by the failure of some new items of plant that were 'scaled up from the drawing board' without any pilot plant stage). But the synthetic motor spirit, diesel oil, and other products that it produces are protected both by a preferential excise duty and by extremely high rail and road costs of moving oil products from the coastal refineries at Durban to the Rand; proposals for a pipeline have been turned down officially time and time again. So even Sasol, getting coal at roughly five shillings a ton from its own highly mechanized 'captive mine', can hardly be considered a genuinely competitive proposition. In such areas, where vast reserves of coal, or perhaps of lignite, can be had really cheaply, synthetic production of oil may eventually become a commercial proposition; but the costs of producing oil have to rise considerably before it will.

In Italy, by contrast, imports of cheap energy are welcome, except at one point. The government had no compunction about allowing purchases of oil at the cheapest prices that could be found, since it has neither oil nor coal production at home. But when fuel oil prices began to be cut heavily they affected sales of natural gas, and reduced the earnings of ENI, the state hydro-carbon combine. Italy already had a high tax on fuel oil; ENI began to attack the oil companies at the other end, by cutting the prices of the gasoline sold through filling stations. The government supported ENI's price cuts by cuts in taxes on gasoline, and the resultant large reductions in price, as mentioned before, were followed by a much greater increase in sales than anyone (including ENI) had expected. Such cuts must certainly have reduced total refining margins in Italy: ENI's reasoning appears to have been that it might stop its competitors cutting the price of fuel oil as savagely as before. This 'secondary effect', indeed, did seem to be working though by the autumn of 1961, when fuel oil prices hardened somewhat; however, many other influences were at work on the market for fuel oil.

This kind of co-ordinated operation in the market between the government and the nationalized energy combine is just the kind of thing that the privately-owned oil industry fears must happen with state enterprise in the oil business. It is, however, only one of the mixture of reasons why they dislike and fear ENI. And though he does a good deal of business with some of them—and at any time one can safely guess that one or two international companies are toying uneasily with the idea of making fresh deals with him, over or under the counter— Signor Enrico Mattei, chairman of ENI, does not trouble to conceal that the dislike is mutual. He constantly argues that the major international groups act like a cartel. He suggests that their operating margins, in between oil product prices that he considers too high and payments to host governments that he calls too small, can easily be squeezed further. And he adds that dealings direct between governments of consuming countries—through organizations such as ENI— and those of producing countries could give both a better bargain than complete reliance upon the international companies as intermediaries.

Signor Mattei is a personality of considerable dynamism; meeting him, the outsider is inclined to feel, rightly or wrongly, that he may have more in common with the ruthless private oilmen who built up this business than some of the men at the top of its smooth and mature bureaucracies today. He was appointed, after the war, to wind up a small and ailing state-owned company that possessed the natural gas monopoly in the Po Valley in Northern Italy. Instead of winding up, he saw its possibilities, developed the gas on a very large scale and sold it with some rather imaginative marketing techniques, and then built up the ENI group into a powerful oil refining, distributing and marketing company serving the Italian market. Here again his marketing was imaginative—and lavish. He led the way in competition to woo the Italian motorist with elaborately equipped petrol stations—relying for finance, it would appear, upon the surplus from his gas sales. The price of his gas is fixed in accordance with fuel oil prices, though slightly lower; as fuel oil nowadays bears a substantial tax in the Italian market and ENI pays no tax on its gas, this gives the group privileges in competition plus financial backing for its other ventures.

ENI's power in petroleum marketing in Italy, and its political connexions, have so far fairly well insulated it from the effects of criticism in Italy, of which there is plenty from other people as well as the oil companies. Its main vulnerability has been its failure—after years of fairly intensive search in promising areas—to find any significant oil in Italy. It has brought in some production in Sicily, where Gulf Oil also has producing wells; but the majors stopped exploration of the Italian mainland after the passing of a new petroleum law in Italy in 1958, which gave ENI peculiar privileges in any area where any oil was found, regardless of who found it.

Criticism of ENI for not finding oil in Italy has become less cogent since the world oil surplus gave independent consumers without oil so much bargaining power to get it cheap. Basically, Italy is an importer of energy interested in keeping world market prices as low as is consistent with the continuance of supplies. The policies of ENI display rather more mixed motives. In the late fifties, ENI obtained concessions in various countries of North Africa and the Middle East in order to seek the crude supplies it could not locate at home and had to buy from the major companies with which it was on bad terms. By the late fifties, Signor Mattei had switched to bothering the international industry, much more practically, as a cold-blooded independent refiner and marketer buying the cheapest oil he could. He made sizeable long-term contracts with the Russians for oil at prices which could have been matched in the Middle East only by savage cuts in the companies' profit margins on production. He was not the only substantial buyer of Soviet oil, but as an established opponent it was towards him that the international companies directed most of their criticism of such purchases.

In 1961–62 Russian supplies (to other Italian refiners as well as

CONSUMERS IN THE MARKET PLACE

ENI) made up some 15–20 per cent of the country's purchases of crude, a proportion that some of its European neighbours were prepared to argue was dangerously high. From its exploration overseas, ENI was beginning to get growing supplies of its own cost crude from Egypt and Iran. This appeared to be setting it some commercial conundrums. After paying an income tax and royalty amounting to 50 per cent of profits at whatever price it posted for such oil, plus a half share in the commercial profit—which was the apparent effect of its concession terms off shore in the Persian Gulf—would ENI's 'cost crude' in the Middle East be a better bargain than the Russian crude it was buying for about a dollar a barrel at Black Sea ports?

It was perhaps not surprising that ENI appeared to be developing the oilfields that it had located without any great haste. And most of the group's new foreign investment, in the late fifties, was understandably shifted towards marketing and refining—in Western Europe, in newly independent Africa, here and there in Latin America and Southern Asia. This was logical for ENI: it was not necessarily logical for Italy. The country had other claims upon its available capital that were at least as pressing as foreign investment in oil marketing. Even among its critics in Italy a foreigner occasionally encounters a certain nationalist pride in Signor Mattei's exploits, and a grudging admission of the contribution the ENI group has made to Italy's current economic *resorgimento*. But even among his friends, one often hears doubts whether one nationalized group should be committing the country to so much foreign investment.

A fully nationalized company seeking concessions in the territory of another national state is a relatively new thing in the world oil business: the ROP sales network set up by the Russians in the thirties was simply a matter of marketing, where state enterprise is less unusual. There is a certain amount of oddity in one governmental entity seeking a concession from another government though the point has never deterred BP, with its strong state holding. Some of the largely nationalized French companies have been awarded concessions in the Spanish Sahara; and even Kuwait's National Oil Company is thinking of seeking concessions elsewhere in the Persian Gulf. Some of the underdeveloped countries, cautious about possible diplomatic consequences, have inserted clauses debarring any nationalized companies from exploring within their frontiers. The ENI group has, however, been one of the competitors ready to offer what appear on the surface at least better terms than the major companies do. But whether the form of concession it has offered is much more favourable to the host government than say the Shell deal with Kuwait in late 1960, remains to be seen.

Companies such as the ENI group, and possibly the French UGP, threaten the oil companies with competition from another kind of oilman. Signor Mattei has no need, and would be unwise, to follow the same lines of competition as the great private businessmen who built up the international companies. Within Italy, his strength is partly political; the state monopoly that he has built up, and his strength with at least some of the elements in any conceivable Italian government make him very formidable indeed. He does not challenge the international majors on their chosen ground; his sphere of operations overlaps theirs, but is not wholly the same. The example of ENI may make the major companies more apprehensive about the possible importance of France's various nationalized and semi-nationalized companies than they would otherwise have been. UGP, for example, is an ENI that has oil to start with. It has a more powerful government in European diplomacy to back it, and a government with a tradition of *dirigisme* in oil affairs. And it may have fewer political opponents than Signor Mattei has.

The international majors recognize these new forms of competition, from enterprises backed wholly or partly by the state, or guaranteed a privileged position in particular national markets, as a threat not only to their immediate commercial position but to the whole flexible management with which they run their international operations. This development of 'tied' national companies is one of the less palatable elements to the companies in the large scale switch to oil that is occurring in Western Europe and other major markets. And the influence of companies seeking to secure 'national' oil is likely to spread beyond their own national markets or spheres of oil development.

Many of the same elements—the reluctance of governments short of foreign exchange to accept posted prices that independent customers do not pay, the purchase of cheap oil from anywhere that might break prices that are considered artificial, and the setting up of state companies to squeeze the established international majors—are appearing among the emergent underdeveloped countries. Mixed with this, in most cases, there are elements of anti-capitalism, red or pink, and of anti-Westernism: but the ideological mixtures vary.

When the Indian government in 1960 and 1961 threatened to buy Russian oil unless the international companies would sell it their products cheaper, history was repeating itself. In the early years of the century, Shell had sold Russian oil in this market to compete with Standard Oil. In the early twenties the roles were reversed: for a time the Americans sold Russian oil in India against Shell, which had lost investments in Russia and was boycotting Bolshevik oil. Since the Second World War, oil supplies in India have come almost entirely from the major European and American companies. Price competition between them has been as orderly in India as elsewhere. But the Indian government has never been slow to learn such Western techniques, technical or commercial, as it considers of advantage to it.

It is also brutally short of foreign currency to finance the imports it needs for development. And it has never enjoyed the currency dispensations in paying for oil imports that more favoured European customers did in the years just after the war. The same difficulties brought collisions between the companies and governments in Cuba and Ceylon.

Cuba's reaction, in 1960, had been to 'intervene in', or in plain language seize, the oil refineries of international companies that could not supply oil except for payment in convertible currencies, and naturally refused to process the Russian crude President Castro thought he could get for blocked currency. This expropriation was so largely political, in the process from 'anti-gringoism' towards a Caribbean version of Communism, that it is probably a case apart. And the marketing company set up by the Ceylon government in 1961 to sell Russian petroleum products cheaper than those of the international companies' marketing affiliates—which was given almost unlimited power to requisition these companies' facilities in the process of undercutting them, and in spring 1962, seized about a third of their facilities, which handled about half the island's sales of oil products—was again the instrument of a party rather close to Communism, though the companies were not deprived of the whole of their business.

India is far from Communist, though its own Congress party has strong elements of socialism. Its pressure upon the refining and marketing affiliates of the international companies operating there has been more moderate in form, but not much less tenacious in purpose. In mid-1960, its pressure upon these companies to obtain discounts below posted prices plus freights for the crude their parent groups supplied played a part in breaking the Middle East crude price structure. In 1961, a governmental committee, after examining the profits that these refining and marketing affiliates earned, suggested that petroleum products could have been had much more cheaply—in scarce foreign exchange—in India. The companies denied this, arguing that products, in the Indian Ocean markets, were in fact not moving at significantly discounted prices, even if crude oil was. The Indian government, already committed to building its own refineries (for its limited indigenous crude production), talked of extending these plans to add refineries that could bargain for crude supplies in the world market. More practically, it held down its allocations of foreign exchange allocations for oil purchased by the major companies' refining affiliates, and set up its own importing marketing company to bring in and distribute petroleum products from Russia.

Various other mixtures of state ownership with private enterprise in oil refining and marketing, arrived at more peaceably, were coming into being in the early sixties in the newly independent states around Africa, in South-East Asia, and in the Philippines. There was quite sharp competition between international major companies—and ENI—for marketing rights in these countries. To get them, and the consequent outlet for his crude oil, the successful bidder had often to agree to build a refinery—and usually to accept some state or national participation in the ownership of it. Where major companies succeeded, they had to swallow their dislike of state enterprise. Some of these refineries gained monopoly or preferential supply rights for the country concerned; processing rights were usually granted to other marketers, though this sometimes involved a certain amount of horse-trading with others who had been successful in the bidding elsewhere.

Many of these underdeveloped markets for oil—generally small in volume, though with possibilities of rapid growth—are therefore taking advantage of a buyer's market for oil to exact a share of ownership, to save expenditure of foreign exchange on oil, and to secure cut-price oil. Few have gone as far as one or two European countries did in a similar buyer's market between the wars. Spain, for example, where a government importing agency has virtually a monopoly of petroleum refining inside the country, is one of the only markets outside the Russian sphere wholly closed to marketing competition by the international companies with which it has to bargain for oil supplies; Portugal has a powerful state-dominated refining monopoly. Neither is ideologically opposed to private enterprise. But they represent prototypes of an attitude, recently spreading, with which the international oil industry has to reckon—that the government may find it profitable, ideologies aside, to take a hand in bargaining for oil.

CHAPTER XVIII

Consumers: Common Interests

After the Organization of Petroleum Exporting Countries was formed at Baghdad in Autumn, 1960, the question was often asked whether it would be matched by an Organization of Petroleum Importing Countries. The possibility does in fact appear soon to have been discussed, seriously or not, in some of the deliberations of consumer governments in Western Europe. For the time, no rival firm was in fact set up; it might have appeared deliberately obstructive. Many people in the West believed that OPEC could have a useful role to play, and should be given every chance to establish itself. But even without an OPIC, it might perhaps be said that there were sufficient organizations of oil consumer governments already—as the board of OPEC perhaps realized in locating its headquarters in Geneva. The international or supra-national organization is no stranger to the problems of energy—including oils—in Western Europe at least, though oil until recently remained more detached from the central interest and influence of such organizations than any other fuel.

From the end of the war onwards, and particularly during the rebuilding of the West European economy with large scale aid from the United States, the governments of the region engaged in fairly continuous consultation upon their common economic interests, at a variety of levels. At the beginning of the period they were engaged fairly seriously in the 'rationing' of energy. Actual rationing was never carried out on any international scale—except, as it happens, for the semi-formal rationing of oil supplies during two periods of emergency when first oil supplies from Iran and later supplies through the Suez Canal were cut off. But during the early years there was consultation over, for example, the amounts of coal exports that producers could make available to meet the total demands that the coal-importing countries set out. And a good deal of discussion went on over 'the dollar element' in imported oil and in the operations of American oil

S

companies in Europe, during the years in which dollars were so scarce a currency in Europe. These consultations took place mainly within two bodies—the Organization for European Economic Co-Operation, which was originally an organization of governments receiving Marshall Aid, but which lasted after aid ceased, and the Economic Commission for Europe, a section of the United Nations secretariat concerned with the whole of Europe, including nations from the Soviet bloc.

Oil companies operating in Europe were often concerned with the deliberations of these bodies (as indeed from time to time they were with logistic arrangements under the North Atlantic Treaty Organization). They were mainly concerned with OEEC, as observers, in oil and energy discussions, though on occasion they had to deal with ECE, and encountered its rather different, characteristically independent, approach to economic matters. It was ECE, in a study of the development of the demand for the black oils in Europe, that first singled out for comment the problems that this rapid rise in demand might pose in European refining. In 1954, it had a brush with the companies when it published a fairly critical report, purely from the point of view of the consumer, on the price of Middle East oil. After that report, ECE seems to have been more or less 'warned off' oil. This became for a time the preserve of the somewhat 'safer' OEEC, which had a specialized oil committee publishing periodical, less controversial, but expert and useful reports. Its general reports on energy, moreover, were significant documents in setting the background against which other European groupings began later to formulate more ambitious and 'positive' energy policies. At the end of 1961, OEEC became OECD, the Organization for European Co-operation and Development. (One of the top officials of the new body, ironically, was the main author of the controversial oil report that had earned ECE so much reproof a few years before.)

Perhaps partly because its own reports, which needed approval line by line from nineteen governments, were of necessity more cautious in approach, OEEC twice in succession in the mid-fifties appointed commissions of independent experts to study future demand for energy in Western Europe and the way in which this demand might be supplied —matters of great concern to the oil business among other fuel suppliers in the OEEC area.

The first commission, led by Sir Harold Hartley, a distinguished fuel scientist and industrialist, was appointed in 1954—and reported in May, 1956. Following its suggestion in this report, OEEC decided to repeat the exercise. A second commission of experts (with some members in common) was set up in 1957, and reported at the beginning of 1960. The statistical projections about European demand for energy, looking, four years apart, forward to 1975, produced practically identical results. The two groups' conclusions from the statistics could hardly have been more diametrically opposed. Both marshalled intrinsically impressive arguments; but it is possible that in retrospect they will be considered primarily as indicative of the sharp change in the European fuel market between the dates when they came to report, and the change in the intellectual fashions of thinking about fuel. As the second commission sensibly remarked, 'the probable errors in our forecasts stem from the sort of mistakes of general optimism or pessimism that are likely to affect at a given moment all who attempt such forecasts, rather than from errors that may be involved in particular approaches to the problem'. The comment applied to statistical projections: but it was eminently true of the general conclusions of both the Hartley and Robinson reports.

The Hartley report was published just before the Suez crisis, but well suited the mood that soon resulted from that crisis. Sir Harold frequently described it, frankly, as 'a coal report', which hardly did it justice. It made projections of total energy demand, and reckoned the amount of imports of fuel that might be necessary to satisfy this demand if the total output of indigenous fuels, mainly coal, could not be raised faster than it had been of late; and recommended very heavy investment to step up the rate of expansion in these domestic fuel industries, in order to moderate the growth of oil imports. The commission was apprehensive about the cost in foreign exchange that large scale imports of oil and American coal would impose on Western Europe. It was deliberating, one may note, during a period when Europe was having to import American coal very expensively indeed.

Three and a half years later, reaching virtually identical conclusions about the amount of energy that Western Europe would need in future years, the report of a similar commission headed by Professor E. A. G. Robinson showed not the least concern in accepting that a large and growing proportion of this expanding demand should be met from imports. In the three years since the Hartley report, even though these included the Suez crisis and a short-lived oil shortage, it had become hard to sell all the coal that could be produced in Europe. This second report, accordingly, was concerned more with what consumers wanted than what it would be possible to let them have. Consumers were switching to oil on a very large scale indeed: unsold stocks of coal were mounting; and imported fuels were able to undercut indigenous supplies in price. So far as the Robinson commission could see, imported fuel seemed likely to remain cheap; and it could see no justification for any measures likely to bring about the production of fuel that would probably not be able to compete.

The commission was not worried about the effect of growing imports of fuel on the balance of payments, since it held that a prosperous European economy could export enough to pay for whatever range of convenient imports it chose. It scouted arguments about the security of oil dependence on the Middle East, on the grounds that potential oil sources were since being greatly diversified. (This was true to some extent: but the report may not have taken account of the effects on oil costs if the industry ever should have to 'do without the Middle East' again or the extent to which its confidence about cheapness depended upon the continued insulation of the United States from the world oil market.) It was coolly sour about the economic prospects of nuclear energy; and it postulated a considerable reduction in the output of the European coal industries, to whatever point was necessary for them to compete with imported fuels such as oil and natural gas.

Oil, up to that time, had never been one of the fuels that came under more positively co-ordinating international organizations than OEEC. Coal, from 1953 onwards, had come under the European Coal-Steel Community set up under the six-country Schuman Plan, and producers in each of its member countries were subjected to a growing degree of supervision, plus the obligation to publish and abide by price schedules (at least inside the community), and to follow other rules of competition. Oil, as an imported commodity, did not; and this became a source of growing irritation to coal industries in the Six as its competition began to bite deep into their markets. By the time that the Robinson Report was published, the European Common Market had come into being. While ECSC had worked on fairly cordial terms with OEEC, the new community in which its members were now joined by the Treaty of Rome was by no means as enamoured of the nineteen-country organization in Paris. Moreover, the common market was founded upon a customs union that involved some degree of protection against imports; and it had no limits to its purview of economic affairs. Crude oil, as a raw material, appeared to be included in the duty-free list of imported commodities agreed under the Treaty of Rome (though in 1961 the French seemed inclined to dispute this). Refined products were not, and settling duties on them under the common external tariff seemed likely to be a lengthy process. The Common Market, moreover, happened to have come into being during a period of drastic change in the pattern of energy consumption in Europe, with some of the older coal industries in a state of what the High Authority of the European Coal and Steel Community in Luxembourg was inclined to call 'manifest crisis', and a number of new sources of primary energy being developed within the community or in territories associated with certain of its members. This immediately raised the question of unified energy policies for the European Six, which will turn out to affect the oil industry very significantly.

Some of the national energy policies inside these six European countries, which have already been discussed, are sharply discriminatory against imported energy. Others that are less directly discriminatory, such as the French, involve a large degree of *dirigisme* that is liable to be directed increasingly to serving 'national petroleum' of one kind and another. Many cross-currents, economic and political, affected both the policies that are being discussed and the three communities—ECSC, the Common Market Commission, and Euratom—which since 1959 have had the task of formulating a co-ordinated energy policy. For a time it seemed possible that what emerged would be a lowest common denominator of agreement—in which case one would not expect any joint energy policy to be very positive in its impact on the different fuel industries. But this was not what happened. Brussels and Luxembourg are full of enthusiasts for the European idea who were naturally anxious that it should engage in positive rather than passive policies. There is indeed some rivalry between the older Luxembourg community that has been concerned purely with coal and steel and the new Common Market commission, which is in principle concerned with all kinds of trade. And rivalry between bodies of planners does not make for unambitious planning.

A common energy policy for the Common Market need not necessarily mean protecting indigenous or 'associated' sources of fuel, but the oil industry has been understandably worried that in practice it might. Indeed, the first idea that was put forward for discussion by the inter-executive group set up by the three community secretariats, early in 1960, could easily have been interpreted as implying protection for coal. This was the idea of a *prix d'orientation* for fuels in Europe. Essentially, this was to be a price, or range of prices, suggested by the energy planners after consultation with all concerned, as a reasonable level to aim at for a few years ahead: a competitive price at which indigenous fuel industries would be able to aim in planning their forward investment. In a market open to imports, this would obviously mean some form of import parity price. Indigenous fuel industries could not expect to invest in output at a higher cost than the long-term marginal price at which energy could be brought in from abroad, be this oil, gas, or American coal.

At the time that this proposal began to be discussed, some of the interests consulted, including the major oil companies, were inclined to suspect that it might soon be converted from a guidance price into a minimum price, to which fuel importers might be expected to adhere. The first range of prices suggested was based on estimates of the landed price at which American coal could be imported into Europe on a long-term basis, and not merely at times of very low freights: it would have given coal industries in Europe a range of say $16–17 a ton to match. This might have been possible for some mines in Europe, though not many. Unfortunately, this price was also roughly twice the figure at which fuel oil, allowing for the difference in calorific value, could have been imported into Western Europe at the time. A price oriented to compete with American coal might have left a smallish amount of coal to be produced within the community. A price based upon the figures in 1960–62 at which fuel oil was actually being sold inside Europe—in fairly large quantities and by fairly large marketers, hardly in the category of 'distress sellers'—would have been one that practically no mine in Western Europe would be able to match. In such circumstances, it was difficult to see what a guidance price could have achieved—unless it were turned upside down into some sort of minimum price below which imports might not have been allowed to be sold.

By the time that the executives of the European communities concerned with energy did come up with definite proposals for a common energy policy, in July, 1962, the open proposal for a *prix d'orientation*—though not necessarily the idea underlying it—had disappeared. So, on the face of it, had the basic principle of protection for indigenous energy. This was a policy that accepted as a certainty the growing dependence of these six European countries—which Britain might be joining as a seventh—upon imported energy. The executives reckoned that total demand for all kinds of energy among the Six might rise from say 470 million tons of 'coal equivalent' in 1960 to 700 million tons by 1970 and 800 million tons by 1975. At the outside, assuming no further switching to oil, they assumed that coal, which in 1960 provided 52 per cent of the total demand, could not by 1970 provide more than 35 per cent. Allowing for local crude oil and natural gas production, and for a rapid development of nuclear power, the bulk of the increase would have to come from imports—primarily from imported oil.

Accepting this, the common energy policy these executives proposed was based on two principles: cheap energy, and security of supplies. The ruling price of energy in Europe, they held, should be the price at which energy could be imported from outside; it would be locally-produced energy that would have to adapt itself to this price level, not imported energy that should in some way be brought up towards the price levels of home production. Crude oil should remain free of duty; there should be a low level of customs or excise duties on oil products competing in the general fuel market and on imported coal; and there should be no general system of quotas upon imports of energy. The only quotas on imported fuel they proposed were upon oil and coal from the Soviet bloc, which they considered an insecure source on which Europe should not become too dependent; here they proposed that a community quota should be imposed to keep these imports down to a given percentage of total energy consumption.

This new policy did not outlaw any support of local fuel production at a level higher than the need to meet the price of cheap imported energy would have left competitive. The executives had indeed calculated that bereft of all support, coal production in Europe might well have fallen under this policy from about 230 million tons in 1960 to perhaps 90 million tons by the seventies. They allowed for the support of some production of coal—and of crude oil—over and above such a core of competitive output. But they proposed that anything over and above this that could not compete, but which the governments wished to keep in production, should be kept going by subsidies, not by protective import or excise taxes on competing imported fuels, or by quotas on the imports brought in. The subsidies, they calculated, would need to be substantial: two dollars a ton would keep in being 50 million tons of coal a year over and above the 'competitive' 90 million tons a year, but to keep total coal production up to anything like present levels—say 200 million tons a year—a subsidy of $5 a ton might have to be paid. If paid only to mines that were uneconomic, a $5 subsidy might cost in total $350 million a year; paid to all coal producers, as it might need to be on the principle that one should not merely pension the inefficient producers, it would cost a billion dollars a year. The national governments concerned would pay part of this subsidy, under the executives' plan, financing it from general taxation; but part might come from a special community fund, which might be financed from levies on all fuel—or perhaps all imported fuel—sold in the region.

Technically, the weakness of this calculation was still the one that had bedevilled ideas about a *prix d'orientation*—that the price of 'imported fuel' is not uniform. The calculations about the tonnage of European coal that could compete with this 'ruling price of imported energy' were in practice based upon estimates of the long-term landed price of imported coal. In the meantime, fuel oil, in terms of calorific equivalent, was much cheaper than this. So a given subsidy, designed to keep in being a given tonnage of coal against the competition of imported coal, would be unlikely to be enough to protect that much home production against imported fuel oil. True, these proposals about subsidies were based upon forward estimates about import prices, and home production costs, in the seventies. By then, some of the economists in Luxembourg and Brussels are prepared to argue, fuel oil will have reached parity in price with imported coal. This may be true; it is one of the possible developments in the European fuel market that in some ways might suit almost everyone concerned, from local coalowners to Middle East oil-producing governments, except perhaps the consumer. But if it should not happen this elaborate subsidy system would probably not achieve what its designers intended.

In many ways, this was a more liberal energy policy for Europe than the oil companies that supply Europe might have feared would emerge. Some of its liberalism, however, went farther than they would have liked: in particular, its emphasis upon the principle of non-discrimination, which is central to Common Market thinking about commercial policy. This was reflected in the proposals for energy policy by a suggestion that certain of the rules of competition that the coal industries in ECSC have to follow—in particular the publication of the actual prices they charge, and the obligation not to give any customers special discounts that they do not offer to all customers—should be applied, in one way or another, to oil. It was suggested that oil marketers should be obliged to publish, *a posteriori*, details of the prices at which they sold all their products to all their customers. Even without specific rules against discrimination, this would invite all customers to press to get the same prices and discounts that the customers with most bargaining power had been able to exact privately.

Though the European secretariats listened with interest to the oil companies' arguments that this was impracticable, it was a proposal unlikely to be withdrawn. These are conditions of competition under which coal is obliged to operate; moreover, the coal industries concerned are enjoined by national law and the rules of ECSC from price discrimination, or giving some customers special treatment. In the oil industry, as we have seen, price discrimination tends to be the rule in most markets except in the sale of gasoline at filling stations. Such discrimination, it can be argued, is essential when so large a proportion of the costs of refining represents joint costs for all products. Anyone who has seen some of the different rebates that are in fact granted in the oil industry at any one time, between customers of apparently similar size and bargaining power, can incidentally realize how difficult it would be to compile schedules of realized prices to give anything approaching a realistic picture of the 'average' rebates granted on scheduled zonal prices. It is entirely natural that the coal producers should object to a form of competition in which they are generally not allowed to indulge; but equally natural that the oil industry should object to abandoning the method of price competition that is most natural to its economics. And the publication of realized prices, if they were fully disclosed, would tend to make this form of competition much more difficult, whether or not marketers were enjoined by law from engaging in it.

This was one major element in the proposed energy policy for Europe —which at the time that this book went to press the governments were still considering—that worried the international oil industry. Another was the plan for a special community group to consider oil developments—and prices—within Europe as steadily and in as much detail as the High Authority in Luxembourg watches the coal market, though without the detailed powers of control. Such a supra-national committee might engage in no interference at all; or alternatively in quite a lot. The oil industry was uneasily aware that planners, once assembled, usually seek something positive to do; and also a little worried that the European executives, in spite of their kind words about the international oil companies, might soon become deep in informal contacts with their inter-governmental opposite numbers in the Organization of Petroleum Exporting Countries in Geneva, or with particular governments among the oil-producing countries.

At times during this period, the very range of different and partly conflicting interests of the six members of these European communities seemed liable to preclude any form of agreement on a positive energy policy. Germany, France, and Belgium are major coal producers. France has interests in Middle East oil and other interests, growing steadily more important, in Saharan oil and gas. Holland is one of the parent countries of the Royal Dutch/Shell group, and could become important as a large exporter of natural gas close to North-West Europe. Italy relies for its fuel mainly on imports from the cheapest bidder, and the organization that exploits its only significant indigenous fuel, natural gas, is a thrusting competitor in the world oil market. Britain, which at the time that this book was completed was approaching membership of the Common Market, would introduce another party to these arguments that professes generally liberal policies towards importing energy, even if it does not always follow these policies.

One among these diverse national interests, however, seemed liable to provide the oil companies marketing in Europe with more embarrassments than the others. The French government did not seem particularly inclined, during the sixties, to offer its state coal mines much special protection—beyond the fact that its imports of coal were entirely in the hands of a state agency, and the rather tight control that it already possessed over the marketers of oil inside France. What it did seem interested in was to press Saharan petroleum not only into the French market but into the whole of the Common Market. A proposal that it aired from time to time during the discussions on fuel policy in Brussels—and also during discussions on the external tariff of the Common Market—was the possibility of giving some preference by quotas, import duties, or excise duties to oil products refined from 'Community oil'. This oil could be variously defined. It would certainly include Saharan crude; it was liable to be widened to include CFP's crude from the Middle East; and it might even be stretched to include products refined from other oil produced by companies with headquarters in the Common Market—under which Shell might qualify. This proposal might obviously be developed to extend to the rest of the Common Market countries the same kind of *dirigiste* régime under which the oil companies have to do business in France. Moreover, it would obviously make a considerable amount of difference to the prospects for Middle East crude if Saharan petroleum should be guaranteed more than its natural degree of access to the markets of Europe. These French proposals were not pressed; but nor were they discarded. And when the French government reached an accord with the Algerian nationalists early in 1962, its interest in a Saharan preference was reiterated. The energy policy proposals set out in mid-1962, indeed, did specifically leave room for giving some preference to oil from 'secure sources' on which Europe could rely. Whether this could be said of Algeria was a matter for argument, after the country became independent; but the French were prepared to aver that it could.

Governmental attitudes towards energy policy in these supranational communities of Europe, as late as autumn 1962, remained shifting and uncertain. So perhaps, did the attitudes of the major oil companies towards the communities' proposals about energy. The American companies, in particular, were as loath as ever to become involved in any formal conferences or 'Groupements' that could later be interpreted by their anti-trust authorities as some form of conspiracy not to compete. On the other hand, it was possible to argue that if the oil industry was to gain as effective a hearing for its point of view as the other fuel industries, it would have to have some continuing form of representation in the discussions of these organizations, rather than the occasional individual informal discussions that did in fact take place. It was easy to argue that the oil industry ought to make more positive contributions; less easy to see, however, what it would have to contribute except concessions that it would find most distasteful.

The question of how dependent the European Economic Community ought to become upon imported fuels, and how far it could safely run down its own indigenous fuel industries while doing so, was one thing. An equally important question for the main suppliers of those imports of fuel was whether the decision was to become a matter of supra-national policy, rather than a myriad of individual decisions representing market choice. Circumstances in which the world's main commercial imports of oil might become largely controlled by governments or associations of governments would tend further to whittle down the flexibility in operations that is perhaps the main talent of the international oil industry. It would, moreover, tend to increase pressure upon them from the other end of the business—their host governments in the exporting countries. Some of these, already, are toying with the idea of more direct contact with the governments of their consumers—trying to bypass the industry that works in the middle.

CHAPTER XIX

Producers for Export:
The Western Hemisphere

A ll kinds of governments, this book has argued, are nowadays
intervening in the oil business; but when you say 'the governments' to any oilman, he thinks of one kind first—the 'host
governments' of the countries from which his industry exports oil. The
oil industry is more important to these governments than to any others,
and its relations with them are centrally important to it. These relations
are always formally governed by legal contract: but even the most binding contract cannot guarantee goodwill, and more than once in the
history of this industry the contracts themselves have not turned out in
the long run to be binding either.

In its effect, the oil concession can be almost a revolutionary instrument, quite transforming the economy of any country where really rich
deposits are found and developed. And the social pressures that this
economic development can generate in turn may bear upon the whole
structure of established relationships in such a country—including,
ultimately, the concession agreement itself. An oil concession, until
recently, at least, has generally been designed to hold one economic and
social relationship in such a country stable for usually very long periods
—yet success in its fulfilment necessarily implies accelerated change.
This paradox is not always amusing to either party to the agreement.

Some of the nations into which this international industry took the
idea of developing oil commercially already possessed established legal
systems governing the exploitation of their mineral resources. The first
mining law covering Venezuela, for example, was a decree of 1784,
making over to the Spanish crown 'whatever fossils, juices or bituminous substances from earth' were found, regardless of who owned
the surface, and the same principle was retained after Venezuela attained
its independence in 1811. One or two countries where foreign capital

268

ventured to develop oil, such as Mexico, began with individual land-owners' rights to oil tapped from their land as in the United States.

Politically, however, most of these bargains with the government have put the oil company into an anomalous position inside the country where it is developing oil. Of necessity, its closest relationship must be with the established government and ruling groups. The relationship can be and indeed has to be shifted when these alter, but not until then. Yet its own impact on such a society must generally be to widen the ambitions of people below the ruling groups, by bringing greater riches, education, and professional training to some. This need not mean social unrest; it depends on the wisdom of the government concerned. But it often does, particularly when oil wealth merely seems to widen the difference in standards between rich and poor. And if it does, the big foreign oil company, as perhaps the country's largest employer and tax-payer, may well become the butt of criticism from both above and below.

As an 'overmighty subject' that has arrived to tap the country's wealth and carry it away, it is anyway an object of suspicion. Any government, royalist or revolutionary, will be tempted to canalize popular discontent on to so convenient a scapegoat. Moreover, many of the original con-cessions were made years before anyone in the countries concerned quite realized what oil wealth could mean: some of them must have been among the first commercial contracts that the governments concerned had ever entered into. There were, often enough, items in the small print that they regretted later. Moreover, once the company found the oil it was difficult for the government concerned to remember—if it had ever appreciated—the amount of risk originally involved in what had turned out to be a successful venture. Squeezing the oil company a bit more, then, is likely to be a convenient course with any government facing popular unrest. But neither giving up more to 'the old régime' nor refusing it will necessarily earn the company any popularity with the radical groups pushing from below. To the radical nationalist—who need not have the least leaning to Communism, though local and foreign Communists may well try to lean on him—the foreign capitalist, par-ticularly in an extractive industry, begins as an object of distrust. It happens, moreover, that from Mexico to the Sahara, a large proportion of the places where oil exploration has struck it rich happen to have had either memories or the present reality of colonial tutelage preying on their minds. And the colonial rulers, even those of yesterday, were often of the same nationality as some of the oil developers of today.

These countries where oil has been produced primarily for export, however, are far from identical in their circumstances—or their attitudes. Apart from Rumania, on one side of the world, and Indonesia on the other (with the oil industry in the first now nationalized, and in the other hanging on, but under considerable government pressure), all the significant oil exporters have come from Latin America or the Middle East. Development of both started at much the same time, but Latin America moved into the lead, in terms of volume, in the early years of this century and held it for nearly half a century. The oil industry had encountered most of the governmental attitudes that it is ever likely to—from any single host government at least—before the Second World War, and before certain of the present largest oil exporters from the Middle East had ever loaded a barrel of oil into an ocean-going tanker. And it is in Latin America, also, that we have already begun to see problems of 'maturity' in oil development in countries that have never managed to build up much other large-scale industry on the spot, but have remained essentially dependent on a wasting natural resource.

By the time that commercial production of oil in Venezuela began on any significant scale, in 1917, from the Mene Grande fields close to Lake Maracaibo, Mexico was already the world's second-largest producer and exporter of oil: it had, moreover, begun upon the revision of its legal attitudes towards oil development that were to lead, twenty-one years later, to the expropriation of the oil companies operating there.

Drilling for oil in Mexico had begun about the turn of the century: British interests founded Compania Mexicana de Petrole, 'El Aguila' SA, better remembered as Mexican Eagle, and many American companies came south of the border to explore for oil. Production began in 1901; in 1910 came the fabulous 'Golden Lane' near Tampico, a line of fields 300 yards wide over a length of about fifty miles, one of the most prolific oil areas ever discovered. Mexican oil was developed by a large number of foreign producers who either bought the land or worked it on the basis of fragmented oil leases roughly similar to that of the United States. Some of its fields do seem to have been wastefully exploited, in those years when techniques were relatively primitive, without regard to technical conservation.

After years of revolution, two provisions in the country's new constitution of 1917, one bringing all land and subsoil rights under state ownership and the other establishing labour's 'rights' to what were then revolutionary hours and conditions, there began a long period of legal dispute with the oil companies. These rumbled on for about a decade at the diplomatic level between the United States and Mexican governments, with the British government occasionally taking a not necessarily helpful interest. (Most of the private oil interests concerned were American, but the Shell-controlled Mexican Eagle company was among the largest operators, and the early twenties were a period of most bitter British-American rivalry in the international oil industry.) In the meantime, Mexican production reached a peak of some 500,000 barrels a day in 1921, and thereafter began to decline. Physically wasteful exploitation of the fields had had something to do with this; but the political turmoil of the time, and the companies' continuing dispute with successive governments about their title to the areas from which they were producing oil, cannot have encouraged very adventurous further investment. After an agreement was reached at the diplomatic level in 1928, by which oil rights acquired after 1918 were exempted from the constitutional 'nationalization', production rose somewhat. But by this time the world was in depression and oil was in surplus: the rate of drilling, everywhere, went down. And there were richer oil prospects elsewhere in Latin America.

Venezuela, by contrast, had an oil boom in the twenties: it took no more than a dozen years from the beginning of production to become the world's second largest producer of oil. And though output dropped for a few years after 1930, it picked up again by 1934: by the end of the thirties, producing 520,000 barrels a day, it was almost equal to Soviet Russia, the world's second producer. The Venezuelan government, dominated during all the years since oil production had begun there by one dictator, Juan Vicente Gomez, obtained a flat-rate royalty on all concessions granted prior to 1918, and a percentage royalty on those granted later. The valuation of the oil for this purpose, until the early forties, was based, by a netback formula, on the prices for products, first in New York and later on sales from the island refineries of Aruba and Curaçao, off Venezuela, where a large proportion of crude from the Maracaibo area was refined. From a modest 163,000 bolivars (about $54,000) in 1917, government revenues from oil rose to 20,866,000 bolivars in 1925, and to 112,756,000 bolivars, ($44 million) by 1938. At the time, this revenue represented about 13 per cent of the total declared value of the oil: it incidentally accounted for 35 per cent of Venezuela's total tax revenue.

During the same year, private oil development in Mexico came to an abrupt end. A government under President Lazaro Cardenas had been pressing for a change in the legal status of the operating companies' oil

271

rights there, and for sweeping improvements in the pay and conditions of their 25,000 Mexican workers, who were already the highest-paid in the country. The companies offered alternatively an excess-profits tax, or very large increases in pay. But in November, 1936, the trade unions presented demands that would effectively have taken away the companies' power to run their own business (quite apart from an extra $80–85 million a year in labour cost). The dispute dragged on for a year or so, with strikes halting production: in November, 1938, the Mexican government passed an act expropriating the companies. (Eventually, it agreed to pay compensation amounting to $180 million by instalments, and has kept its word: payment of this compensation, which the companies argue covered only about 60 per cent of the value of their properties, was completed in 1950 to the American companies concerned and will be finished to the British, Dutch and Canadian interests by 1963.)

All that remains of Mexican Eagle today is the 'Mex' in the name of the Shell-Mex distributing organization. The fortunes of Mexican oil under state control, which have not come up to nationalist hopes, but have not been disastrous, were reviewed briefly in Chapter XV. But it is a salutary reflection for all concerned that at the time of nationalization, the Mexican government was getting a royalty of 14 per cent of the value of oil produced, plus a small tax payment. Within ten years, the international oil companies were paying host governments 50 per cent of their profits, and professing at least to like it.

It was the Venezuelan government that pressed them to do so—and has since pressed on regardless. At the outbreak of the Second World War, the danger of submarines reduced tanker shipments of products from the Caribbean refineries. This not only reduced the volume of Venezuelan exports and output, on which the government drew its oil revenues: because throughput at these refineries was reduced, their overhead costs rose, and the Venezuelan revenue per barrel fell too. In 1942, the companies operating in Venezuela, Creole (Jersey Standard), Mene Grande (Gulf), Shell of Venezuela, Mobil and Texas, agreed to value Venezuelan offtake according to the prices of similar crudes in the Gulf of Mexico, not according to the products yielded. In the next year, for the first time, Venezuela began to charge the companies a small income tax and gradually this element in its oil revenues began to grow in relation to the percentage royalty. For all companies as a whole—but not each one individually—the tax was claimed to make the government revenue from oil equal to the net profits of the companies. In 1948, the law was amended to provide for a 'surtax' of 50 per cent on any sum by which any company's net income in any year exceeded the government's total revenue derived from the company's oil operations. This formula set the 50–50 pattern for particular companies by which the major international companies, ever since, have set so much store.

Politically, this was a period in which the Gomez dictatorship ended with the death of the President. Some years of democratic government ensued, and then the army, under General Pedro Jiminez, seized power in 1952. From about 1944 onwards, moreover, the country's oil industry was in a boom again. Output doubled between 1943 and 1946; by 1955 it had doubled again, and in 1957, the annual output topped a billion barrels. Venezuelan output was not rising as fast as in the Middle East in the postwar years, but up to it was still, by far, the world's largest oil exporter. Moreover, its future prospects looked excellent. Venezuela was the area favoured by most of the American 'big independents' that in the fifties began to search overseas to gain command of sources of imports into the United States. These groups paid large bonuses for concessions in the Lake Maracaibo area, frequently well offshore into the middle of this great lake, and in the Gulf of Paria area in Eastern Venezuela, close to Trinidad. Apart from Jersey, Shell and Gulf, there were about a dozen groups of American companies established in the country, with promising concession areas—and with obligations to get oil into production as soon as they located it—by 1956–57.

The oil revenues of the Venezuelan government in 1957, reached nearly $1,240 million—about 85 cents a barrel on regular production, plus about $370 million in 'occasional taxes'—mainly bonuses for the grant of the new concessions that were actioned off in 1956–57. This amounted to about 71 per cent of the country's total tax revenues. The next year, the Jiminez régime was overthrown, and after an interim during which a military junta ruled the country, a democratic government under President Romulo Betancourt took power. One of its first significant financial measures, under an expert and ambitious petroleum minister, Dr. Juan Perez Alfonzo, was to seek a bigger share. Dr. Perez Alfonzo had once estimated, in 1943, that in the first twenty-five years of their operations in Venezuela the split in profits had been 77 per cent for the companies and 23 per cent for the nation's revenues. He was determined to tip the balance, from its nominal 50–50, the other way.

In 1958, the military junta increased the progressive-rated part of its corporate income tax from 20 to 47½ per cent for companies in the top bracket of income and the later Betancourt régime put this new tax régime into practice. Along with royalties and other taxes, this brought the government's total take in taxes from 52 per cent of profits in 1957 to 65 per cent in 1958, and 69 per cent in 1959. Surplus, however, was again appearing in the world oil trade; America was restricting oil imports; and since their profits in every oil-exporting area of the world were coming under pressure, the oil companies were naturally disinclined to increase output in an area where the government was increasing its share of whatever profit they did make. In 1958, Venezuelan offtake dropped by about 5 per cent, and though it recovered in 1959, growth since has remained slow. The government's oil revenues, from regular taxes per barrel, however, rose significantly, in spite of a reduction in crude oil prices in 1959, reaching about $1·03 a barrel in 1959, and yielding the government about a billion dollars, as against $866 million in 1957, the peak under the earlier tax formula. In 1959, also, the local trade unions secured very substantial increases in wages, with governmental backing for the oil workers who already had by far the highest wages in the country: this increased the actual costs of Venezuelan oil. In 1960, output rose only 2·7 per cent, as against an increase of 15·6 per cent in the Middle East: in 1961, by 2 per cent as against 7 per cent in the Middle East, though Dr. Perez Alfonzo has claimed that its revenues compared as well with 1960 as did those of the Middle East.

There was no cut in the prices of Venezuelan crude oil in August 1960, at the time of the Middle East cuts. This might have affected the prestige of the régime more than its actual oil revenues. These appear generally to be set according to profits on the actual prices at which companies sell their oil or transfer it to an affiliate, not according to posted prices. A number of American companies, at any rate, have said they report their taxable income, and have it accepted, on the basis of the actual prices realized, not of the prices posted; and during 1960, we have it on the testimony of Creole, the majority of Venezuelan oil was being 'lifted' at discount prices.

Venezuelan oil imports into the United States were not allowed to rise; and there was a slump in world tanker rates that cut down the limited chance it had of selling to Western Europe. By reducing the advantage of being closer, this made competition, particularly between its 'newcomer' groups, very bitter in markets still within reach, such as the rest of Latin America, Canada, and the Pacific archipelago. Dr. Perez Alfonzo warned companies that he would not be prepared for tax purposes to recognize more than a 'normal' rate of discount (undefined) on sales of crude and products. There were still some companies, presumably for purposes connected with their 'total' tax situation, that found it 'net profitable' to invoice crude to their refineries at full posted price, and take any loss that had to be accepted on the later refining and marketing. These would have declared an income for tax based on posted prices; so they may have been particularly in favour of a crude cut in Venezuela to match the Middle East price cuts in August and September, 1960.

The cut did not take place: so for some companies that were paying tax on an income related to posted prices but having to accept discounts at later stages, the Venezuelan government's share may in effect have been even more than the 69 per cent of total oil profits that it said it collected in 1960. At all events, net profits per barrel of crude remaining to producers in Venezuela in that year are said to have averaged 25–30 cents a barrel: this might be compared with 60–80 cents a barrel in the Middle East and some 1·15 a barrel in the protected American oil-producing business. The producers' reaction was predictable—to hold down output inside Venezuela, so far as they could, and to reduce drilling activity drastically. By 1961, there were no more than 31 drilling rigs working in the country, against about 90 at the end of 1958; this was the lowest figure since the war years. Only one seismic party, representing the earliest stage of exploration, was still at work; and certain of the 'newcomer' groups of the fifties were slowing down or suspending operations in acreage for which they had paid hundreds of millions of dollars in bonuses.

A slowdown in the rate of growth of Venezuelan output is perfectly acceptable to the Venezuelan government, but the slowdown of 1957–61 has been more than it would have chosen. Dr. Perez Alfonzo, in October, 1959, said he was perfectly prepared to see the rate of increase slip to about four to six per cent a year, enough to cover the budgetary deficit, and to let oil remain in the ground for future generations. During the Second World War, he had opposed the passing of the country's Law of Hydrocarbons of 1943, which in return for somewhat more favourable oil revenues had extended existing concessions for forty years. In the short period of democratic government between 1945 and 1948, before Jiminez seized power, the policy of 'no more concessions' was originated. This did not stop the Jiminez régime granting a large number of new concessions during 1956 and 1957; but when the Betancourt government returned in 1959, this was part of its oil policy. Dr. Perez Alfonzo blames the Jiminez régime for letting in the smaller newcomers, which he rightly identified as 'soft sellers' following the imposition of import restrictions on the American market. He would prefer to deal with a few big companies; and to develop the rest of Venezuela's oil through the state petroleum corporation that was set up in 1960.

The Betancourt government has expressed a good deal of interest in oil conservation, and has talked of imposing proration schemes upon the producers in the country: it has indeed sought the advice of the Texas Railroad Commission on the matter. It has criticized the Jiminez dictatorship for a tendency to profligate exploitation of the country's reserves: though this dictatorship had ploughed vast amounts of money back into developing the country. Some of the bills are still being paid: and the Betancourt régime has done little itself to reduce budget deficits. So far as physical conservation is concerned, the country has certainly of late been producing about 15 per cent of the world's output while it has officially only 6 per cent of the world's reserves: and the virtual halt in new exploration by the private companies will certainly leave the new petroleum corporation, which bravely says it can act as 'the balancing factor . . . in these activities', plenty to do.

This government policy towards the oil industry, like others in Latin America, is liable to change abruptly, as is the government. But it is an elaborately-considered one, and it expresses a good deal of nationalist resentment in the country—which may increase if Venezuela's oil revenues decline further. Some opposition to Dr. Perez Alfonzo's policy has at times been voiced publicly; but this can be shrugged off as simply accepting the foreign companies' viewpoint.

Any analysis of the degree of pressure now being exerted on the oil business by governments all round the world makes it obvious that some of these governments must inevitably collide—or co-operate—with each other. The Venezuelan oil policy had always taken account of this: Dr. Perez Alfonzo was a leading spirit in the formation of the Organization of Petroleum Exporting Countries, and has been equally anxious to deal with American import restrictions, one of the strongest government interventions of recent years, on a diplomatic basis. He had consistently argued that Venezuela ought to be given a favoured and irreducible quota of American oil imports, on grounds of 'hemisphere security'. Given a guaranteed quota, he said in 1959, Venezuela would prorate the total among all producers: and with the advent of the Kennedy administration, and a newly hopeful attitude towards Latin America, he had renewed the claim. But it is among producers that he is most interested in promoting government co-operation.

Several of the other countries that produce oil in Latin America are following different 'national policies' in search of self-sufficiency: one or two of them export oil. Commercial production and continuing exploration has gone on in Colombia for nearly forty years, without its ever emerging as a large-scale producer. So far, about 1,400 million barrels of reserves have been discovered; just over half of these have been tapped already, leaving reserves of some 650 million barrels. Four of the world's major companies operate there, Texaco on its own and in partnership with Mobil, Shell, and Jersey (on a small scale, one of its concessions having reverted to the state in 1951); these produce about four-fifths of the country's output, which in 1960 was less than 160,000 barrels a day, only about a twentieth of Venezuela's. There are ten other independents looking for oil, but so far producing practically none; and the state concern *Empresa Colombiana des Petroles* (Ecopetrol), which has production from some relinquished and declining fields, and has engaged in a number of partnership contracts for secondary recovery and further exploration with private groups. The country's two refineries, one owned by Ecopetrol but both operated by the Jersey Standard subsidiary, have enough capacity to supply Colombia's internal market, which only takes about 50,000 barrels a day, leaving two-thirds of the country's crude production for export.

Colombian taxes at present take 40-50 per cent of oil profits. But in 1961, it passed a new petroleum law enabling it if it chose to increase this share beyond 50 per cent, increasing surface rents and royalties and limiting depletion, cutting concession areas by half and requiring relinquishment of half of the original concession area each year. Both the country and the oil companies have waited patiently for bigger developments in oil (the companies, together, were said to have invested about $1,000 million to the end of 1960, and to have recouped only about $150 million). Exploration has proceeded for a long time in Peru without developing more than miniscule production. Trinidad possesses one of the earliest-recorded deposits, or seepages, of petroleum, in its famous pitch lake; oil drilling began there as early as in the United States, and at present there is an output of some 150,000 barrels a day. But the island is of greater importance as one of the refining centres of the Caribbean.

PRODUCERS FOR EXPORT

Latin America was the first great oil-producing area developed by foreign enterprise: it has also been over the whole period, an area of political instability, with social revolution following upon the establishment of nationalist independence. The oil industry has been one of the few lasting economic institutions in some of the countries where it was developed: but it has received a good deal of nationalist dislike for the foreigner, mingled with envy from the landless poor. It has also tended to be identified, through its own fault or not, with reactionary governments. It is unfortunately perfectly logical for foreign enterprise to prefer the 'strong hand' in government of such a troubled area: dictators often mean stability. Over the years, the oil companies have managed to reduce this identification with particular régimes, and in general to establish their independence of local politics. That, in its turn, may merely cause them to be identified with their own parent governments, and to acquire a new vulnerability as symbols if these parent governments, in turn, become objects of envy and dislike or are pilloried by leftist régimes as supporters of reaction. To have learned the object lesson of Mexico did not make it possible to live with Cuba.

CHAPTER XX

Producers for Export:
The Eastern Hemisphere

'We have no legal department in the Kuwait Oil Company,' said Mr. William Fraser, managing director of that company, in a discussion of the nature of oil concession agreements at the Second Arab Oil Congress in Beirut in November 1960, 'and we practically never need to refer to the text of the concession.' Mr. Fraser, himself a Scottish lawyer, was commenting upon the argument of Mr. Frank Hendryx, an American lawyer then working for the Saudi Arabian government, that sovereign governments had the right and even the duty to alter these contracts with private companies if and when circumstances changed and the concessions no longer served the needs of their citizens but operated against them. This is a thesis that tends to incense the concessionaire companies; there had been some elaborate legal attacks upon it, tinged with rancour, from some of their spokesmen. Mr. Fraser, characteristically, spoke in human rather than legal terms: and his hearers were aware that in Kuwait the working relationship is possibly the best in the Middle East. He ended by saying, 'If we have a point to raise, we go to the government. If the government has a point to raise, it comes to us. We talk it over as friends, and settle it as friends. It is only then that we call in the lawyers and bring out the agreement.'

About two months later, it is said, an American visitor was talking with Shaikh Jabir, whose responsibility for financial affairs in the government of Kuwait covered the affairs of petroleum. She was asking about the functions of the new Kuwait National Petroleum Company, which had been financed with government and private Kuwaiti money to take over, as a beginning, the distribution of oil products inside this small and fantastically rich little country. Shaikh Jabir mentioned that the new KNPC might possibly take up the 20 per

279

cent interest to which the government would be entitled in offshore oil production from Kuwait, as and when this began under the new Shell Concession agreement. He added that it might later take over exploration and development inland in Kuwait, in the areas to be relinquished by the Kuwait Oil Company. 'But Your Excellency,' asked his visitor, whose knowledge of oil concessions in the Middle East is considerable, 'I was under the impression that the Kuwait Oil Company's concession did not make any provision for the relinquishment of unexplored territories, as for example those in Iran and Saudi Arabia do.' Shaikh Jabir smiled. 'You are right,' he answered. 'It does not, but I believe you attended the oil congress in Beirut. Did you not hear Mr. Fraser say that when we have something to discuss as friends, we are not concerned with what is or is not in the agreement?'

Within twelve months, this retort was a fact. The government of Kuwait—which in the meantime had achieved complete formal independence, had been threatened with annexation, and had withstood this threat partly by the support of British arms—was in fact by early 1962 asking for the relinquishment of part of KOC's concession area, regardless of the terms of the concession. And though the company seemed successfully to have resisted some rather exuberant versions of this request, in May, 1962 it did agree to relinquish 50 per cent of its concession acreage straight away, and 5 per cent more in five years' time.

Whatever is or is not in it, the oil concession agreement is at the core of the unique relationship between host governments and paying guest companies in the Middle East. Partly because these have often been nation-wide agreements, or at any rate have reserved huge territories to single operating companies, in contrast with the grant of many smaller 'mining leases' in Latin America, the terms of each concession have been of far greater importance in the Middle East than in that other great area of oil development by foreign companies. In the Middle East, again, these concessions have from their beginnings been the concern not only of the countries concerned but of the parent governments of the foreign companies concerned, to a greater degree than those in Latin America ever were. Most of the joint operating companies now operating major concessions in the Middle East evolved as the result of considerable diplomatic negotiations between these parent governments as well as with the governments of the actual countries. To the Middle East government, 'the companies' appear as homogeneous an entity, politically as well as economically, as 'the governments' do to any oilman.

The concessions, too, tend in effect though not in form to operate all of a piece. In spite of many differences of detail between even the main agreements covering oil development in the Middle East nations, the layman may perhaps reasonably consider them as one body of contractual doctrine for the governments and companies concerned. Not all explicitly include a 'most favoured nation' clause requiring any further advantages conceded under later agreements elsewhere in the region to become operative under this one too. But in practice any further point granted by the major companies to any government will pretty soon be granted to all. Not the least important activity of the departments of oil in these governments, already, is the comparative scrutiny of each other's agreements, to make sure they are not missing something other governments get; it is, moreover, one of the declared intentions of OPEC to facilitate such comparisons.

If one can consider these main concessions in the Middle East together, then, it should also be noted that the body of contractual doctrine that they form is in practice a constantly evolving one. The thesis frequently argued by their lawyers—that in this unusual form of contract between a government and a business enterprise operating within its borders the government has an implicit right to change the deal to suit changed circumstances—is obviously not one that companies that are parties to such contracts could ever admit. Whether international lawyers would admit it is doubtful, though there are obscurities in the law covering legal agreements between governments and private 'individuals'. In practice, however, the concessions and the working relationships they govern do change over time. None of the major concessions in the Middle East today lays down the same terms as it did when it was originally made.

Considering the huge changes in relations between industrialized and underdeveloped countries that have taken place since certain of these contracts were negotiated—and the very long periods, often 60–70 years, and in one case 90, over which they run—the layman will not find this surprising. The law, we are told, cannot recognize the argument that when these contracts were made the rulers of the countries concerned were unused to any such binding commercial documents, with their appendices in fine print—or that the agreements, many years ago, could not suit the present interests of these developing nations. But the layman may find some force in them. These are the arguments most engagingly and saltily presented by Shaikh Abdullah Tariki when he says, 'We are the sons of the Indians who sold Manhattan Island. We want to change the deal.' The companies might fairly retort that, as purchased, Manhattan Island was worth virtually nothing. But repartee aside, the fact is that in the real world, whatever the fine print says, the deal is—constantly—changing.

A history of the oil concession in the Middle East, as a legal instrument, seems never to have been written. It appears, even to the layman's cursory inquiries, to differ in kind from the mining codes under which oil has been developed in some other countries and under which, for example, the great British and American metal groups operate overseas. It was in 1872 that the Shah of Persia granted to one Baron Julius de Reuter, a British subject, a seventy-year concession to construct railroads and street-car lines and exploit all mineral resources save gold, silver and precious stones—a concession that Lord Curzon later called 'the most complete and extraordinary surrender of the entire industrial resources of a kingdom into foreign hands that has probably ever been dreamt of . . .' But that concession was cancelled after Russian objections; nor was any oil found by a search in the nineties under a later concession to de Reuter.

The d'Arcy concession signed on 21st May, 1901, did not cover railroads or tramcars (though it did include more relevant transport facilities, pipelines). But it gave William Knox d'Arcy, a Devon man who had become a gold millionaire in Australia,

'a special and exclusive privilege to search for, obtain, exploit, render suitable for trade, carry away and sell natural gas, petroleum asphalt and ozerite throughout the whole extent of the Persian Empire for a term of sixty years.'

This agreement was to become economically and politically one of the most momentous ever concluded in the history of the oil·industry and of the whole Middle East. It was revised, denounced, revised again and the area reduced but prolonged, broken by nationalization, replaced by a different kind of agreement and different signatories. But the development that it set in train has produced oil ever since 1908; and as present agreements go, it is likely to go on producing oil until 1993.

That original d'Arcy concession, it may be intriguing to note, provided both for profit-sharing and for a government shareholding in the operating company to be set up, features we tend to think of as postwar innovations in the Middle East oil business. It was altered, in 1919, to provide among other things for government participation in all net profits arising from the 'mining, refining and marketing of Persian oil' through subsidiaries 'inside or outside Persia', which no major company offers in any present concession. In 1933, after a lengthy diplomatic dispute and hearings before the League of Nations over a Persian proposal to cancel it, the concession was re-negotiated to substitute for profit-sharing a fixed royalty on oil produced plus a share in dividends over and above a given amount, with an annual minimum. In 1949, it was to have been revised to provide for a larger royalty per ton of oil, a larger minimum payment in respect of dividends (which had been held down through the Labour government's limitation of dividends policy in Britain), and a payment in lieu of tax, from which the company (by that time Anglo-Iranian) had until then been excused. Later, while the new draft agreement was being considered by an oil committee of the Iranian Majlis (under the chairmanship of one Dr. Mohammed Mossadegh) a proposal came from the company offering a 50:50 sharing of profits. It could indeed be said that most of the variants that have ever been proposed for the major agreements between oil companies and governments in the Middle East that we have ever seen were put into or proposed for that Iranian concession at one time or another. The Persians in 1950–51, as it turned out, did not like any of them. There followed nationalization, three years of effective boycott of Iranian oil throughout world markets, and eventually the consortium agreement of 1954, under which Iran accepted back various of the things that it had rejected by nationalization—including Anglo-Iranian, now renamed British Petroleum, as the largest consortium partner—but retained title to the ownership of all oil produced inside its frontiers.

The consortium agreement provides, as today do the concessions covering the main oil production of Kuwait, Iraq, and Saudi Arabia, taxes amounting to 50 per cent of profits made on the production and export of oil. It provides for the management of oil operations in a defined area of southern Iran by two operating companies, the first covering exploration and production, the second responsible for operating the Abadan company. These are non-profit-making companies, somewhat on the lines of the Iraq Petroleum Company, carrying out their activities for a fee. They transfer part of the oil in kind or in value, to the National Iranian Oil Company, which incidentally has operating rights throughout large parts of the rest of Iranian territory. The rest goes, for a fee of a shilling a cubic metre, to trading companies in Iran representing the members of the consortium, in amounts corresponding to their shareholdings in the consortium.

The other major operating companies, like the original Anglo-Persian Oil Company and eventually the Consortium, came into being as a result of commercial initiative more or less liberally admixed with diplomatic influence. Control of Anglo-Persian, as originally formed to take over the d'Arcy concession, was taken over early in its history by the British government. One result was that its oil concession inside Persia itself, until after nationalization, never had to be shared by any other commercial or national competitor; Anglo-Persian, however, gained extensive interests elsewhere in the Middle East over the years. What eventually became the Iraq Petroleum Company in 1928 has been the subject of commercial enterprise since 1904, with concessions being sought, gained and challenged by German, British, Dutch and American interests. After the First World War the German interests were dropped out (being eventually handed over to France in consideration of other claims on the Near East). British and American manœuvring continued, with use on the one side of much play being made about Britain's responsibility as mandatory power for Iraq, and on the other of the 'open door' doctrine for all foreign (but particularly American) capital. In 1928, a group of British, Dutch, American and French companies (with the assistance of M. Calouste Gulbenkian) signed an agreement that allowed for the creation not only of IPC but also of joint companies to exploit oil in a large area of the former Turkish empire. Not all of Iraq was covered by the 'Red Line' agreement, or originally, by IPC; other concessions were granted later to other companies for the Mosul and Basra areas, but in the late thirties these were abandoned and taken over by IPC.

Conclusion of these agreements did not end competition from Americans in the Middle East; it meant only that the American shareholders in IPC, Jersey Standard, Socony, and originally Gulf, refrained from competing for concessions within the 'Red Line'. Gulf, for example, abandoned a concession in Bahrein that had been offered to it by a British syndicate formed to seek concessions, allowing it to be taken up by Standard of California, at that time a newcomer to the Middle East. When Gulf did later withdraw from the agreement, selling out of IPC in order to negotiate for a concession with the Ruler of Kuwait, it found that the British government invoked a prior agreement by the ruler not to grant a concession to any but a British company. The upshot, in 1933, was for Gulf to join with

Anglo-Persian in setting up the jointly-owned Kuwait Oil Company to sign a seventy-five-year concession from 1934 (it was later amended to run until the year 2023). In 1933, also, Aramco was formed, on the grant of a concession by Saudi Arabia to Standard of California; Anglo-Persian competed for this concession, but was apparently unwilling to match the £50,000 in gold that Socal's negotiators deposited within forty-eight hours of the offer of a concession. In 1936, the Texas Company bought half interests in Socal's concessions in Saudi Arabia and in Bahrein, allowing the California company a half interest in its own Far East marketing network, under the name Caltex.

These negotiations between the wars effectively drew the map of the major Middle East concessions that exist today; but there remained some changes to come in the ownership. During the war, with development in Saudi Arabia necessarily reduced and delayed, Saudi Arabia was in difficulties, seeking subventions from the British government; eventually, at the instance of Aramco, the United States brought Saudi Arabia within the sphere of Lendlease. The American government appreciated the companies' insistence that British influence was growing over Saudi Arabia to an extent that they did not like at all; at one time it proposed to buy all or part of Aramco's concession itself. This fell through. Nor was an offer by Aramco to sell the government large quantities of oil very cheap ever taken up. But the refinery at Ras Tanura was built in 1943–45, as an American military project; and it was with considerable backing from the American government, particularly in respect of export licences for scarce steel pipe, that the TAPline to carry part of Saudi Arabian production overland to the Mediterranean was eventually built just after the war.

In 1946, however, Standard of California and Texaco, which up to then had been outside the 'Red Line' group of companies, obtained extra financial support—and access to far wider marketing facilities—from two of the companies inside. Jersey Standard and Socony purchased a 30 per cent and a 10 per cent interest, respectively, in Aramco and TAPline.

These American partners in Aramco, in 1950, brought the 50:50 profit-sharing principle to the Middle East. It had originated in Venezuela, as described during the last chapter, at a time when a series of governments there were pressing the oil companies for a larger national interest in the oil industry. It was brought to the Middle East at a time when governments were beginning to show an interest in gaining their oil revenues through taxation rather than through various kinds of royalty income. The first Saudi Arabian income tax law, enacted in 1950, and covered by an agreement in December of that year between the government and Aramco, provided for a tax that would bring the government share, including the existing royalty, up to 50 per cent of the operating profits of the company. These were originally operating profits net of American income tax; the next year, with the assistance of experts from the U.S. Treasury, this was revised so that the Arabian tax was charged before U.S. tax.

At this point the implicit 'most favoured nation clause' that we have mentioned in these major concessions in the Middle East came into play. It was not necessarily convenient for Anglo-Iranian and the European partners in IPC, operating under different tax laws, to match this 50:50 pattern of sharing; but matched it had to be. Anglo-Iranian, whose proposals for a revised agreement were at this very time before the Iranian Majlis, promptly offered to reconsider them, in the light of the new Saudi agreement; this offer did not come in time. Although IPC in December, 1950, had already agreed to a higher royalty on oil production for the Iraq government, it agreed to the new basis; an agreement was finally signed early in 1952. The Kuwait concession was revised along the same lines in 1951; those in Bahrein and Qatar were converted to 50:50 in the following year.

The move to 50:50 transformed the basis of the relationship between the oil companies and their host governments, in more ways than one. Immediately, it gave the governments a vast increase in revenue; this was at the expense more of American and later of European tax revenues than of the companies' own income, but that made it no less of a benefit to the oil-producing states. It also, however, gave them an interest in the maintenance of the posted prices for crude oil, and it also meant that any reduction in posted price bore directly upon the governments' revenues per barrel. It is said that during discussion of the American companies' initiative over 50:50 in New York, at a time when the European companies were not wholly enamoured of the new proposals, a representative of one of the British groups said to his opposite number in an American group, 'Calculate how far the crude price has got to drop before you're paying them less than they were getting on the old formula.' That has never come to pass; but world surplus has, and a time when crude oil prices would logically be dropping.

Nor did the cornucopia of 50:50 sate the oil countries' appetite for wealth from their treasure chest that these ingenious foreigners had opened. Within a few years, attracted by the riches accruing to all concerned, there were other foreigners arriving, offering even bigger shares—at least on paper—to be allowed to find and tap new treasures. In 1957 and 1958, Iran granted offshore concessions to three foreign enterprises—including Agip Mineraria, an offshoot of the nationalized Italian group ENI, and Pan-American Petroleum, two groups of American independents—on an entirely new basis. These provided for operating companies to be owned by half the foreign groups and half by Iran's own NIOC, while operating companies would share profits 50:50 with the Iranian government. The concessionaire companies were to bear all exploration expenses until the discovery of oil in commercial quantities; in effect, therefore, these concessions on the face of it offered Iran, through its shareholding and its taxes, 75 per cent of the profits on any oil that might be found. Concessions were to run for twenty-five years with options of renewal; they contained specific most-favoured nation clauses; they provided for the relinquishment of unexplored areas within time limits; and they guaranteed 'Iranization' of given percentages of staff, and in two cases promised preferential treatment for Iranian flag tankers. In 1958, Saudi Arabia and Kuwait granted separate concessions to a Japanese company for exploration in the Arabian Gulf offshore from their jointly-controlled Neutral Zone. These concessions provided for payments of royalties, rents and taxes representing 56 per cent of the profits from oil to Saudi Arabia and 57 per cent to Kuwait; they promised the construction of local refineries once a certain level of throughput was reached; and the governments were given options to purchase 10 per cent of the stock of the company once production began (which the governments exercised during 1961). Moreover, the Japanese Arabian Oil Company was to exercise its concession rights through an operating company which would engage in refining, transport and marketing; and the government's tax share of profits could extend to all these integrated activities.

How far these new and different types of concession would offer the host countries better terms remained to be seen: it was not until 1960–61, as this book was being written, that any of them were beginning to deliver crude from the Middle East to market. It was not absolutely certain, considering the state of the market into which they were beginning to put this crude, and the limited marketing facilities of at least some of them, that the revenue per barrel that the governments would get would necessarily be larger than the share some were getting under 50–50 agreements. This at any rate, was the confident argument of some existing companies; and certain governments in the Middle East were commercially-minded enough to know the value of world-wide marketing facilities in a soft market for oil. The Shell concession offshore from Kuwait, signed in January, 1961, is the latest development of the concession pattern of any major company in the Middle East—a major company, incidentally, that had until this been relatively weakly represented in the Middle East so far as 'cost oil' was concerned. Its provisions were outlined at the beginning of this book. Among other provisions, it allows the state to buy its way into the operating company—at cost—though its offer of extremely favourable terms for any Kuwait share of oil may well seem a better bargain to the government than trying to sell the oil independently. It provided for relinquishment of unexplored territories, and for the possible establishment of a refinery in Kuwait. It was, moreover, a concession of somewhat shorter term than any in which any other major company was engaged in the Middle East—forty-five years. And Shell, unlike any other major company in the area, would be operating on its own, without corporate partners who would have to be persuaded to agree with anything that it chose to do.

At the end of 1943, a mission headed by Everette Lee DeGolyer, a well-known oil geologist, reported to the Petroleum Reserves Corporation that had been set up by the Roosevelt Administration, that the centre of gravity of world oil production was shifting from the Gulf-Caribbean to the Middle East-Persian Gulf area and was likely to continue to shift. It reckoned, at that time, that in Kuwait there might be reserves of 9 billion barrels, in Iran 6–7 billion barrels, in Saudi Arabia 5 billion barrels, and in Qatar a billion barrels.

Nearly twenty years ago, that was prescience. Today, the shift it envisaged is very nearly taken for granted, and the reserves it guessed at have been proved many times over. In the whole Middle East, at the end of 1961, proven reserves totalled 188,000 million barrels, 60 per cent of the world's total; and though the Middle East in that year produced only a quarter of the world's oil, it was overwhelmingly the largest source of the crude oil moving in international trade, supplying 5 million barrels a day out of the total of 10 million barrels traded. It is generally held to contain the areas of lowest-cost petroleum output in the world. Though net profits after tax on oil may have rivalled it at times in other areas such as Venezuela, in none does the high reserve-production ratio impose so little obligation upon the oil developer to invest in further exploration. Production from most areas in the region, moreover, could rapidly be stepped up if the need arose, without significant danger of depletion of any major reservoir.

If the development of Middle East oil since the war has been virtually explosive, its impact upon the traditional societies within whose lands it was found has not been much less so. It has, first, arbitrarily divided the region into three groups of countries, the great producers, the oil transit countries, and the other have-nots. These divisions cut across the political and tribal linkage within Arab nationalism—and to some extent across the traditional spheres of interest of the former tutelary powers, though these between the wars had substantially adjusted their pattern of interests in the Middle East to take account of where the oil happened to lie. The access of riches to some parts, but not others in the region—and often within countries to some groups but not most people—has begun to influence the political structure and connexions of the Middle East countries. Oil happened to be produced in countries ruled by different absolutisms, benevolent or not. The republics of the region, with their differing brands of democracy, are for the most part countries without oil exports to make their fortunes, though General Qasim in 1958 moved Iraq from one of these rather uncertain categories to another. Political turbulence, since the war, has affected the big exporters as well as countries without much foreign income from oil: Iran and Iraq as well as Egypt and Syria.

The great producers of oil—three of them Arab countries, and one not—vary both in political stability and in their attitudes towards the industry that has unlocked their wealth. Kuwait, which to the visitor seems the most stable and contented, is a tiny country of immense wealth. It covers only square miles and the vast majority of these are empty. Its 300,000 inhabitants, of whom only about 100,000 are Kuwaiti nationals, live in the seaport that is its capital city, or in the 'company town' and oil terminal of Ahmadi twenty miles along the coast. In 1960 its national income, of which more than 90 per cent derives from oil directly or indirectly, must have been of the order of £500 million, about £500 a year for each Kuwaiti national. Its other inhabitants, largely expatriates or transients from elsewhere in the Middle East or from Europe, are well paid for their specialist services, but can hardly be said to partake of the national wealth in quite the same way.

PRODUCERS FOR EXPORT

Kuwait is the largest producer of oil in the Middle East, not simply because its oil is the cheapest. Its most rapid growth of output occurred during the years when Iranian oil could not be traded to the world, which the Iranians do not forget. Neither Iran, Saudi Arabia, nor Iraq has ever yet recognized the full sovereignty of Kuwait.

In the twenties the shaikhdom of Kuwait had to establish itself against the house of Saud. From 1899 to 1961, Kuwait was under some degree of British protection; in 1922, its boundaries, including the neutral zone with Saudi Arabia, were delineated by treaty. In 1961 the British government formally withdrew all its reserved powers and recognized the absolute sovereignty of Kuwait: this was immediately followed by claims from Iraq's General Qasim that the state was an Iraqi province. First British troops, and later a force from other Arab countries, had to be sent to Kuwait to support its independent status.

Under the Gulf-Anglo-Iranian concession granted in 1934, drilling began in 1936; but the wells were plugged in 1942, and it was not until June, 1946, that commercial shipments of crude oil began from the first terminal installation at Mina al Ahmadi. During the whole of 1946, the country produced just under 800,000 barrels of crude oil. In 1950, it had risen to 7 million barrels a day. During the three years of the dispute over the Iranian nationalization it rose to 47 million tons a year; and by 1961, it amounted to 82 million tons a year or 1,644,000 barrels a day, the daily rate being twice as much as the year's output in 1946. Two other producers have producing concessions from the state. The American Independent group, Aminoil (owned by a group of sizeable American companies) produces oil from the Neutral Zone between Kuwait and Saudi Arabia under a concession from the Shaikh: the Getty group operates in the same area under a concession from the King of Saudi Arabia. And in the area of the Gulf offshore from this neutral zone, a Japanese company is now producing under concessions from each ruler: these were among the first to breach, openly, the generally ruling 50:50 principle.

A very large amount of this small state's revenue has been invested in education and in medical services; there are seventy superbly-equipped schools, a secondary school and technical and commercial colleges. The state finances higher education at overseas universities for all young Kuwaiti nationals who it believes can benefit from it; in the last few years the first sprinkling of these graduates has been returning— to a rather bewildering profusion of important jobs in the civil service, local commerce, or the oil industry. Large amounts of Kuwaiti capital have flowed overseas to finance, in particular, construction in Beirut and Cairo, and it is now offering low-interest loans to less fortunately placed Arab countries.

Saudi Arabia, in 1960, was the second largest producer in the Middle East; in area, though not in population, the largest country, with probably about a million square miles within its partly undefined frontiers. The ruling Saud family provides religious as well as temporal leaders. The nation is an absolutist monarchy with a considerable tinge of xenophobia; local Aramco employees, for example, live under fairly strictly isolated conditions. From an oil production of 1,395,000 barrels a day in 1960, the state receives revenues amounting to about £250 million a year; its wells have been producing for more than twenty years. The Dhahran structure was the first developed, followed by the Qatif and Abqaiq fields; since the war a huge structure known as Ghawa, some 150 miles long, has gradually been mapped out with the drill. Aramco has also offshore fields, Safaniya and Manifa, in production; these were among the first in the Middle East. According to the statistics, Kuwait has the largest reserves in the Middle East, with the Arabian figure not far below it; many oilmen believe that Saudi Arabia's may eventually turn out to be even larger. About a third of Aramco crude leaves the country via TAPline to Sidon in Lebanon; the remainder goes out from ocean terminals, or via a submarine pipeline to Bahrain Island, a refining centre with some limited production of its own.

The Saudi kingdom has invested somewhat less of its oil revenues in social development than for example Kuwait, though Aramco has developed social services to a considerable extent for its own fairly large local labour force. Education and technical training, however, tend to separate these Arabian workers to some extent from the rest of the population, which is a good deal less prosperous. Much of the country's budget goes on internal security and on subsidies to the many nomadic tribes under Saudi tutelage; large sums, also, on maintaining the numerous royal family in what Arabs may think of as Occidental luxury. Relations between Aramco and the royal house have not always been happy: its department of oil affairs, in particular, has been perhaps more active than those of other countries in searching out what it complains to be inequitable treatment under the concession agreement.

Iran, the oldest-established and until nationalization in 1951, the leading producer in the Middle East, was, in 1961, only the third with an output of 58 million tons a year or 1,186,000 barrels a day. This nation has a population of 16 million, by far the largest in the area; though Muslims, the majority are not Arabs. Iran is a monarchy, today somewhat more stably established than ten years ago; its government has still to deal with undercurrents of political unrest. Formally, Iran owns its own oil, and its National Oil Company takes part in the exploitation even of the area controlled by the international consortium; at the beginning of the sixties, NIOC was inclined to complain that in practice its responsibilities were still not taken sufficiently seriously by the managers of the consortium, whom the Persians were apt to think of as 'still BP'. The national company has done a certain amount of exploration in the remainder of Iran; in 1956, it brought in a spectacular discovery at Kum in central Iran, but has not established any significant field worth developing. In the consortium territory, the longest established field is Masjid-i-Sulaiman, still producing some 50,000 barrels a day; but by far the largest of the area's nine producing fields is Agha Jari (some 600,000 barrels a day), while output from the relatively new Gach Saran field is due for a rapid increase. Abadan, with a capacity of about 400,000 barrels a day, is still the largest refinery in the world, though a somewhat inefficient plant by modern standards. With the switch to refining in market areas since the war, its products now go mainly to Far Eastern markets, and it operates below capacity.

Iran still openly expresses dissatisfaction with the limited growth of its output in comparison with such states as Kuwait, which has 40 per cent more output and no more than an eightieth of its population. It has been extremely cautious in its attitude towards the interest taken in oil by, for example, the Arab league; it has defined its role in OPEC as that of a 'catalyst', though it has been under Iranian leadership that the organization has developed its secretariat and services. Its relations with Arab neighbours are not always particularly easy.

In July, 1958, when the former royal régime was overthrown in Iraq by a military revolution, the new government, under General Qasim, inherited some outstanding negotiations with the Iraq Petroleum Company. The new government's claims, somewhat elaborated from those of the old, were for a very substantial change in a concession covering an oil industry that was producing, in 1960, at the rate of about a million barrels a day—practically as high a rate as Iran's, with the capacity to increase output a good deal more rapidly. Iraq is only about half as large as Iran, with a third of the population; the country has good land, a fair rainfall in the north, and in general rather more economic resources apart from oil than any of the other major oil-producing countries.

The famous Kirkuk structure of IPC, which was first discovered in 1927, has been one of the most prolific fields in the history of the oil industry; its cumulative output is now approaching two billion barrels. Its disadvantage is in location; it is 500 miles from tidewater, along the pipelines to Tripoli and Banias. The Mosul field in northern Iraq is on its way towards exhaustion, and must be the only field in the Middle East where oil is produced (to meet the minimum required under its concession) at a loss. In the south, the Basrah Petroleum Company, also owned by IPC, has comparatively rich fields at Zubair and Rumaila, these fields having the advantage of proximity to the Persian Gulf. Between 1958 and 1961 the government and IPC were deadlocked in negotiation over a series of outstanding issues: the amortization of 'dead rents', relinquishment of a very large proportion of the company's concession area, the utilization of gas now being flared in some of the country's oilfields, and the implementation of a half-forgotten clause in the original IPC concession which provided for a preferential issue of shares to Iraqi nationals should IPC ever go to the market. The operating companies concerned did agree to relinquish 75 per cent of their total concession areas straight away and another 15 per cent over a period; and offered the alternative of taking the Iraq government in as a 20 per cent partner in developing the final 15 per cent that they would otherwise have handed over. The government did not regard this as sufficient. Negotiations broke down again; and in December 1961 the government published a law restricting the companies to their operations in well under 1 per cent of the original concession area. This was the first unilateral action on such a scale since the nationalization of oil in Iran in 1951.

By the end of 1961, therefore, the international oil companies that own IPC were deadlocked in dispute with the Iraq government, as Anglo-Iranian had been with the Iranian government ten years before. The deadlock, however, was more peaceable. The government had cut off, in outlining IPC's 'unexplored areas', some 40 per cent of the group's proved oil reserves, mainly in the northern Rumaila field of the Basrah concession. This did not, however, leave IPC remotely short of oil. Nor, except in Mosul, was the ban on further exploration immediately inconvenient (and even there it saved money on what had in recent years been an expensive, contractually necessary, but fruitless form of investment). The shareholders of IPC did not cease their 'offtake' of oil; this indeed, in early 1962, was rising slightly, though not as much as it would otherwise have done. General Qasim threatened more measures to put pressure on the operating companies, and began to draft a general petroleum law to govern new concessions that Iraq might grant other developers (in the seized areas, which included very large reserves of proved oil). But up to the time this book was completed he was showing no firm disposition to interfere with IPC's oil production—alias his own oil revenues. Neither side, in short, seemed inclined to turn the deadlock into open conflict—though there were pressures upon the Iraq government that might render continued quiescence politically impossible, and on the other hand signs that the corporate partners in IPC did not see wholly eye to eye in dealing with the government.

These along with the Persian Gulf peninsula of Qatar, which produces about 174,000 barrels of crude a day for export, are the main producers among the Middle East countries: the oil industry is concerned with other nations in the area mainly as transit countries. Vast amounts of oil move through the United Arab Republic, via the Suez Canal and the pipelines from Iraq and Saudi Arabia. Nationalization of the Canal in 1956 did not arise specifically from a desire to get a bigger revenue from this oil movement, but as a result of the refusal of Western finance for the High Dam at Aswan. Egypt could be classed in various of the categories of government exerting influence on oil that have been used in this book, from that of the nations seeking self-sufficiency to that of the consumer country putting pressure on its refining and marketing companies. It has a number of minor deposits, producing about half of its oil requirements, and has of late been offering new concessions, generally for rather small areas by Middle East standards. But its main influence in the region has recently been as a present leader of Arab nationalism.

The influence of the state that has been built up by President Nasser's authoritarian military government is very considerable throughout the Middle East. Egyptian teachers, from the largest reservoir of educated Arabs in the whole area, have influence in other Arab countries: both Saudi Arabia and Kuwait, in periods of political emergency in the area, have shown themselves reluctant openly to dissociate themselves from UAR policies. Moreover, the whole Suez affair and its aftermath was not, on the whole, calculated to weaken Egyptian influence in the region. It emphasized the bargaining strength

—up to a point—of a transit country athwart the main oil trade route: but also the logistic ability of the Western oil companies to make good supplies in the West and to move a large proportion of exports from the Persian Gulf by other routes. This odd trial of strength devalued Egyptian military pretensions, yet showed that President Nasser, over a few years, could get most of his way politically and economically despite defeat. It demonstrated the influence of these underdeveloped and uncommitted nations in the United Nations. It showed the Arabs, once again, the alarming strength of Israel. And the sorry affair of the Suez Canal pilots demonstrated that some of the claims of the West to a monopoly of technical competence were arrant nonsense. That point, politically unimportant in itself, might in the medium run be as important as any other implication of Suez for the oil industry in the Middle East.

Syria and Lebanon, the other two important transit countries, have in recent years been anxious to get full value for their geographical position. Effectively, the maximum price of such a transit position is the difference in cost to the operator of making use of the short cut or doing without it. This is very considerable for Iraq oil from the key Kirkuk field: the ban on access to the sea via Israel robs the oil producer of much of his bargaining power here. But of late, as was seen in Chapter IV, the value of the short cut to Saudi Arabian oil has become much more doubtful: at present levels of tanker freights, TAPline cannot compete with big tankers sailing from the Gulf.

These Muslim countries of the Middle East form the greatest centre of oil exports in the world, with the largest reserves and—in spite of high government revenues—the lowest costs on crude production anywhere. But they are not the only significant oil exporters in the Eastern hemisphere. There is one other, older exporting area and one new one (both as it happens, also, largely Muslim by religion) the East Indies and North Africa.

Oil production in the East Indies, from Borneo, Sumatra, and Brunei was one of the foundations of both the Royal Dutch and the Shell companies that later came together; Caltex and Stanvac, now split into its component parts of the Jersey and Mobil groups, also have production there. In the postwar years, rehabilitation of the fields after destruction during the war against Japan was slow; political strife between the newly independent government of Indonesia and the Dutch, former rulers of most of its territories, did not help matters. In 1959, the Indonesian government proclaimed 'nationalization' of oil operations there. But nobody seemed clear what this meant. It appeared probable that the individual companies operating there would have to work out new contracts or concessions with the Indonesian government—though there were signs that these deals might turn out to be no more onerous than some 50:50 arrangements elsewhere. But production in Indonesia, as in Borneo, had ceased to rise (though the Caltex group has located large new reserves there recently). In 1961, production from the East Indies was about 25 million tons a year, or 500,000 barrels of crude a day; from the whole Far East area, 550,000 barrels a day. This is still one of the world's main export refining areas, and about a third of the oil trade of South-East Asia is still done in petroleum products.

During the next few years, a number of substantial new oil-exporting areas will be growing in importance as suppliers to Western Europe—at the same time, incidentally, as the newer Japanese, Italian and American ventures in the Persian Gulf area are beginning to offer their production at full rate on to the international market. The French effort in the Sahara has been discussed already: its oil will soon be followed to Europe by growing quantities of Libyan production. These new exporting areas—which were the only two of major significance to be opened up for oil in the late fifties—are very often discussed as 'alternative sources' to the Middle East, and it is obvious that to expand production they must compete in the main markets of oil from the region. But it should also be recognized that Libya, at any rate, is an Arab country that welcomes private enterprise in oil, but is no longer inclined to accept less favourable terms for the development of it than other host governments receive. And the Sahara, developed largely by French efforts with French capital, is now being transformed overnight from a largely nationalized enterprise ready to accept low prices from Algeria in order to pump this oil into new markets in France and the European Economic Community to a foreign enterprise operating in the territory of another Arab government, not so far away from the Middle East.

Both these areas are still only at the beginning of their development. Libyan output, in commercial terms, only began in September 1961. Saharan output, in 1961, had increased rapidly to 320,000 barrels a day. But the most optimistic hopes for 1965, do not put its output above 800,000 barrels a day, or something approaching four-fifths of present production in Iraq. As supplementary sources of oil, taking much of the expansion in southern European demand, these countries will hold the growth of output in the Middle East below what it might have been; but on present estimates, they could hardly halt this growth in any Middle East country.

Much has been said about the probable extent of the oil riches of the Sahara: surprisingly little, by comparison, about the oil resources and possibilities of Libya, which leads some oilmen to feel that these are greater than anyone is anxious to admit. Drilling began there in 1956; shows of oil were recorded in 1957, and in June, 1959, Jersey Standard brought in its 'Zelten No. 1' in an area about 200 miles south of Benghazi, reporting an initial flow of 17,500 barrels a day, which is a big find for anywhere. Other companies, particularly Oasis, a joint subsidiary of certain big American newcomers to international oil, had very rich discoveries not long after. Jersey is on its own in Libya (as Shell is off Kuwait). This partly reflects the concessionary circumstances: Libya in 1955 enacted a petroleum law (with the assistance of the oil companies) that cuts up the country into a fairly large number of exploration areas, with limits to the total acreage for which any company can hold permits in each of four major zones of the country. Reconnaissance permits are granted for a year, followed by fifty-year concessions, with compulsory relinquishment of total acreage that will bring any holding down to a third or a quarter of the original area in ten years; there is provision for 50–50 sharing of profits. In the first five years of exploration, 19 companies had taken out exploratory concessions. In 1961, as relinquished acreage from the first of these began to come up for re-letting, the Libyan government in its turn amended its legislation, ending the possibility of a 25 per cent depletion allowance provided in its 1955 law.

This did not necessarily affect the bargains that existing producers had achieved. Guesses in oil journals put the proven reserves of Libya at perhaps 3,000 million barrels at end-1961, considerably less than those of the Sahara; but the oil search had been going on for only about half as long. Some people in the industry believed that Zelten was one of the most important finds that Jersey Standard had made for many years (though the oil lay in conditions where pressure might have dropped away rapidly, and Esso had to embark on a huge water injection project, bringing water to the field from the coast, shortly after it began deliveries in 1961); and that Libya in general might become even more important to the oil industry in the sixties than the Algerian Sahara.

This North African territory, again, is a nation that through its former connexions with Italy had the chance of 'association' with the European common market—and conceivably, if the issue were pressed on behalf of the Sahara, of similar preferential access to the E.C.C. for its oil. It is one of the new producing areas, indeed, upon which in the early sixties some European consumers have been building hopes, probably exaggerated, of sufficient diversity in oil sources to hold down oil prices and curb the ambitions of other producer governments. Libya, however, seemed inclined to align itself with other producing governments, provided these would accept its right to fairly rapid initial growth. Another of these areas on which hopes are being built is Nigeria, where a modest production is now emerging. Yet a reminder of the difficulty, for commercial developers of oil, of putting more emphasis on sources outside the Middle East was given yet again in 1962 when the shaikhdom of Abu Dhaki, down on the Trucial Coast of the Persian Gulf, came into production. This barren little place, tiny in area and population, has oil onshore and offshore, justifying production from two separate concessions; by drilling a handful of wells inland and out in the Gulf, the IPC group and a BP-CFP consortium respectively have located oil structures that together may well have reserves comparable to those discovered by so massive an effort in the Sahara.

During the middle fifties, when the upsurge of world oil demand seemed unlikely to weaken, and countries expected prices to stay firm, the pressure of host governments upon the oil companies operating in the Middle East was mainly for bigger shares than the established 50 per cent of an income they expected to go on growing. As the market slipped into surplus, the emphasis changed. The governments became more cautious in proposing changes in their concessionary relationship with the companies, and their pressure shifted towards the maintenance of posted prices on which profit shares are paid regardless of the actual prices realized, and increases of export offtake. So far, in spite of price cuts in 1959, and again—though the companies have not yet officially recognized them—in 1960, a continued rise in offtake has maintained their income and indeed kept it rising somewhat. The cuts in posted prices were, however, recognized in one way at least. They triggered off what had long been discussed as a possibility on both sides of the Middle East oil business—a compact of the governments of oil-exporting countries.

CHAPTER XXI

Producers: Interests in Common

One of the first public statements from Baghdad, after the Iraq government in December 1961 produced legislation seizing 99 per cent of the concession areas of the Iraq, Basrah and Mosul oil companies, was to ask the co-operation and support of its OPEC partners. In particular, these were asked not to benefit at its expense. This came before any proposal to restrict or to cease the increase in output had been announced by the companies concerned. But it was inevitable that Iraq should remember how effective a boycott of Iranian oil had proved after nationalization in 1951, largely because the oil companies were able to step up output in other Middle East countries and Venezuela. These countries, at the first meeting of OPEC in 1960, had agreed not to benefit in this way at the expense of any fellow-member in dispute with an oil company: Iraq was now seeking implementation of this resolution, which the members had reiterated as recently as November 1961. Whether the issue would in practice openly arise in quite this way was not clear at the time this book was completed. The countries concerned would in any case be expecting a continued increase in production. The appeal to a formal organization for support showed in principle, at least, how the formation of OPEC might eventually affect all disputes between governments and oil companies. But it was also symbolic that Iraq did not attend the next OPEC meeting: it was laying claim to Kuwait, and unwilling by any co-operation to acknowledge its fellow-member's independence.

Concerted action among the people in control of the oil supplies entering into world trade is not a new idea, as we have seen in earlier chapters. Some degree of marketing co-operation between major companies, American and British, existed up to the end of the Second World War, though it was not perhaps entirely effective. That was abandoned at the end of the war, partly in response to public and governmental attitudes towards restrictive agreements of this kind. But sometimes the idea of concerted control had come from governments.

It is worth recalling that during the Second World War the governments of the United States and Britain went so far as to sign an agreement on oil, to which other nations would have been invited to adhere, which some oilmen felt might in effect have perpetuated and brought under the control of governments both the 'Red Line' arrangements about joint concession-seeking in the Middle East and the 'As Is' agreements to moderate commercial competition in the international sphere between the major companies.

In August 1944, the two governments reached agreement to promote an international pact that among other things would have provided that

'supplies should be derived from the various producing areas of the world, with due consideration of such factors as available reserves, sound engineering practices, relevant economic factors and interests of producing and consuming countries and with a view to provide full satisfaction to all. . . .'

and

'that the adoption of these principles can best be promoted by an international agreement among all countries interested in the petroleum trade, either as producers or consumers.'

The two governments agreed to set up an International Petroleum Commission with 'partly fact-finding and partly advisory' functions. Oil producers inside the United States suspected that its vague wording implied some form of government-sponsored international cartel; their suspicions, and some opposition in Washington, were understandably aroused by a proposal that action under it should be exempted from the provisions of the anti-trust laws. The agreement was re-written, and signed once again; but even in this revised form, the American Senate would not have it, and it disappeared into that limbo to which so many other 'plans for the post-war future' also found their way. The signatory governments had emphasized the need to conduct the world petroleum trade 'in an orderly manner'; for the next ten years, the major companies took the responsibility for that.

On many occasions during that next decade, proposals were put forward for the 'international control of oil resources', or for the 'regional development of the Middle East'. They came, in the first place, mainly from the West, which did not improve their reception among the nations actually concerned. Some came from private theorists or semi-political bodies; one or two actually from governments, as in 1957 when the Italian government proposed that a financial pool should be created to back economic development of the whole region, with contributions from the United States and Western Europe. In August 1958, following the American landings in the Lebanon, President Eisenhower actually put forward a proposal for an Arab development institution. This was discussed in the United Nations, which invited the Secretary General to confer with the Arab countries on the point, but nothing came of it either.

Nor were similar ideas lacking in the Middle East itself, among politicians and among Arab personalities concerned with oil. The Arab League first took a direct interest in oil at the time of the Palestine War in 1948: it prevailed upon the government of Iraq to force the suspension of shipments through the pipeline to the Haifa refinery at the time, and later, over a period of years, put pressure on oil companies marketing in Israel to withdraw. Apart from this, it recognized oil as a possibly unifying economic interest among countries to whose unifying political interests it was dedicated. In 1951 it set up an 'Oil Experts' Committee', and in 1954, it decided to establish a permanent Petroleum Department. It was this department, under the directorship of Mr. Mohammed Salman, an Iraqi engineer, who organized the Arab Oil Congresses in 1949 and 1951; after the second, Mr. Salman became the petroleum minister of General Qasim's government in Iraq, and held this position at the time of the 'forced relinquishment' of the undeveloped areas of the concessions there. It was within the Arab League's committees that most of the ideas concerning pan-Arab policies for oil were first formulated. Although its membership includes some states that have little effective say in oil, and it could never hope to wield so direct and concentrated an influence as OPEC aspires to, the league's intellectual influence on 'Arab economic aspirations', which are largely aspirations regarding oil, has been and may remain significant.

Its committee of oil experts includes a number of the 'Arab technocrats', but their influence extends beyond it and is one of the strengths of OPEC. The group is real, recognizable, and among the more dynamic elements in the social and governmental pattern of the Middle East. These youngish men differ rather significantly, to the casual observer at least, from the similarly aspiring intelligentsia of other developing societies. Their education is sometimes technological rather than legal. Their ladder of advancement has not been primarily political, but within the semi-technical administrative departments that each of the host governments has necessarily created to handle its contacts with its tenant oil company. They have benefited, within these departments, from the absolute shortage of Arabs educated to understand this industry. The rise of some of them, within these departments, has been meteoric, so that able young men not long out of their twenties are at the heads of departments that deal with the companies, and in some cases are government-appointed directors to their boards.

In some ways, the careers that have been so open to the talents of these young men have possibly made for political stability in certain of these countries. The surplus of briefless advocates and other unemployed intellectuals which has so often featured in nationalist politics in other developing (and developed) countries, seems less evident in the oil-producing Arab countries; and where violent political change has come, it has come mainly from military circles. The graduate, in the oil states, need not lack advancement. Educated 'technocrats' may or may not be, as one of them once suggested, 'well placed to enforce, in the long run, practically every point they mean.' Their personal isolation, in some cases, from the feudal social structure of the states they serve, may be uncomfortable and is certainly vulnerable. But they are entrenched in, and while they are in such short supply often essential to, the absolutist governments of these states. Some of them are radical in temper, which in countries of such glaring contrasts between riches and poverty is not surprising. But their radicalism does not need to express itself in politics. They already have the positions of influence that in other countries political radicals might dream of attaining.

These positions, however, do not guarantee them political influence inside their countries. Their political influence is likely to depend upon their success in dealing, on behalf of the host government, with the oil companies. This in itself might tend to canalize their radicalism into seeking always to improve the bargain that the government gets. The better that bargain, the better their chance of achieving, say, the economic development that they believe their country needs. But the tenant oil company, as a nexus of economic power controlled from outside, is liable to be an affront to their patriotic ambitions anyway. In a sense, therefore, nationalism, radicalism and the favour of the ruling families may all press the 'technocrat' in the same direction—towards seeing what more can be gained from the companies. Moreover these young men, whose position rests largely upon their talents and their scarce technical competence, are certain to see possibilities in common action by at least the oil-producing states; also, perhaps, personally but not unworthily, the strength that their own positions can gain from participation and recognition on a larger than national stage. Their training will help them to appreciate the possibility of joint economic and technical action among host governments.

Some of the proposals for specific concerted action regarding Middle East oil have come from politicians in countries that do not produce oil. M. Emile Bustani, a Levanese businessman and politician of much wealth, sophistication and political influence, has on more than one occasion suggested that the oil-producing countries should use some of their revenues to back development of the whole Middle East. In 1959, at the first Arab Petroleum Congress, he proposed that these countries should lend 5 per cent of their annual oil revenues, at a nominal rate of interest, to an Arab development bank. At the second congress, in 1960, he advised the host governments to satisfy their aspirations for fuller control of the development of their oil by buying up control of the great oil companies with which they do business. His views are individualist, practical, sometimes almost too wittily phrased to gain their full effect. They come, also, from a country concerned only with the transit of oil, not with its production. Arab solidarity has not yet persuaded those countries that do have oil to sacrifice much of it to benefit those that have not; and the foundation of OPEC, in a sense, re-emphasized that distinction.

Other specific proposals have concerned fuller participation, on a joint scale, in the oil business. Such have been the proposals for an Arab tanker company and an Arab-owned common carrier pipeline. Neither has yet come to pass, though tankers have been ordered for a Kuwaiti company (as well as for the National Iranian Oil Company). The pipeline project, much discussed in 1957, was avowedly to be based upon the profits available then from TAPline; one of the points made, at a time when the pipelines from Iraq to the Mediterranean were in course of repair, was that if it were owned jointly by Arab countries no one of them would ever be prepared to cut the line. The sharing of capital contributions—and of the profits from the operation—is said to have been the subject of some argument between producers and transit countries. Within a year or two, however, there was a world surplus of tankers and even TAPline alone was working well below capacity: Arab investment in pipelines looked less attractive.

The formation of national oil companies in each producing country, again, was one of the recommendations of the first Arab Petroleum Congress, and the Arab League has long advocated fuller participation by the governments in the later stages of oil operations. This has been partly advocated as a way of taking increasing responsibility for the development of the countries' natural resources; but largely, of course, as one of the possibilities of increasing the governments' share in the proceeds of oil. In the late fifties, many critics in the producing countries had argued that large proportions of the profit properly attributable to crude oil production were in fact siphoned off into later stages of the business, so that host countries did not get their fair half-share of them. By the time that this argument became generally discussed, at any rate, it looks to have been unfounded: in some consuming countries, indeed, governments were complaining that refining and marketing affiliates of countries drawing oil from the Middle East and Venezuela were showing fictitious losses because their 'parents' chose to take all their profits at the level of production. But suspicion about the oil companies' apparent ability to take most of their profits where they choose remains. Naturally, Arab critics of this industry are less ready than Western to believe that the companies really choose to take most of their profits within Arab tax jurisdiction; and certainly this has never been proved by the companies with chapter and verse.

Venezuela was represented, by observers, at the first Arab Petroleum Congress; for the first time, all the great oil exporting countries were sitting down together. Eighteen months later, it was one of the founder members of OPEC. In the meantime two leading government personalities concerned with oil in Venezuela and in Saudi Arabia, Dr. Perez Alfonzo and Shaikh Abdullah Tariki (then Arabia's oil minister) —had both committed themselves to proposals for 'international proration' to hold down supplies in accordance with demand and therefore to stabilize the price of oil. The emergence of world oil surplus had logically shifted the emphasis to stabilizing the rates of profit from which one drew one's revenues. Venezuela had been the leader in unilateral action to increase its share of oil profits, by its new income tax in 1958; but the results, as its colleagues noted, were not certain to be what it had hoped. Refusal to recognize price cuts that were made without their prior agreement, which was the formula that OPEC governments adopted in late 1960, was another possible reaction to the consequences of surplus in oil. But what would be more fundamentally attractive to these governments—as it is attractive to independent oilmen in Texas, and has at times in the past been attractive to the international oil companies—would be to arrange things so that the potential surplus simply did not happen.

In the United States, as we have seen in an earlier chapter, proration does effectively control the volume of domestic oil coming on to the market, even if it works untidily and with some awkward side-effects. Since import restrictions were imposed in the United States, total supplies from home and abroad are now regulated; and in effect, whatever its motives, the whole complex of American oil legislation tends to operate as a price support programme. It operates inside one nation; and though state governments are responsible for the output controls, the law that prevents widespread evasion of these controls is federal, as are the import restrictions that have had to be invoked to aid proration. Among the states, proration has succeeded mainly through this federal backing and because one dominant producer, Texas, has been prepared to act as the balance-wheel, taking the biggest cuts in its own output to stabilize total supplies, even though some states do not control production at all. These circumstances may be essential to any successful proration of oil supplies. If so, they raise questions about the practicability of international proration even if it were agreed to be desirable.

Shaikh Abdullah Tariki, who put forward proposals on the subject first in Texas in May 1960, did not specify the formula that he would propose to regulate the output of the oil-exporting countries that might join in such a scheme; but at the second Arab Petroleum Congress in November that year the kind of formula that one might use was discussed by one of his advisers. Mr. M. J. Sladic, an American consultant, suggested that the factors to be taken into consideration might be

(1) the average annual net export achieved during any three-year period preceding proration. Nations would be entitled to declare an average rate at less than the maximum achieved in the past if they wished, in order to conserve their resources;
(2) the proportion of each nation's reserves to the total reserves of all net exporting nations; and
(3) estimates of net world demand.

The formula he proposed would be 'the maximum declaration plus the product of the ratio of the exporting nation's reserves to the total reserves of all nations ready to export above their maximum declaration, and the difference between net world demand and the total of all nation's declarations'. Mr. Sladic made allowance for the introduction into such a scheme of new exporting nations; and also, notionally at least, for problems that might arise for companies whose production in any given area was held down through proration to a level that would sharply reduce their return on investment. He recognized the difficulties that would be encountered in carrying through any such scheme—such as the need to standardize estimates of reserves, conservation practice, the forecasting of market demand, and any necessary estimates of return on investment. He noted that in countries where producing leases are fragmented, proration inside each member's territory would probably be necessary; but added that in the Middle East, where most production is already 'unitized' through the large concessions, this would hardly be necessary.

That formulae could be worked out to govern an international proration scheme is not in doubt; and the international 'infra-structure' necessary to administer it might be formed and might just possibly be able to work. But two main obstacles to such a scheme seemed very hard to overcome: namely, that consumer countries would regard it as an oil producers' cartel run by governments, and that it would effectively remove a large part of the managerial control that oil companies possess over their own businesses. These two objections are linked. For the international oil companies' right to supply any given market from whatever source they choose means flexibility in maintaining supplies; and this is the main guarantee that consumer countries rely on when increasing their dependence on petroleum imports.

For the host governments themselves, the intrinsic difficulties of proration would mainly arise from reconciling the different interests of the different member countries. First, the major exporters would have to allow a disproportionate share of the growth of demand, however small this might be to start with, for newcomers and potential entrants to the world oil market. Secondly, the interests of the Middle East would have to be reconciled with those of Venezuela, at a time when that exporting country's 'natural markets' in North America are being protected against its supplies. Third, even within the Middle East there are some jealousies. Iran, for example, feels that it is entitled to the leadership in volume that it lost with nationalization and has never regained. Although Iran is a member of OPEC, spokesmen from the Shah downwards have expressed great scepticism towards ideas of proration or international market-sharing—which if based on any recent period for production or exports would give Kuwait and Saudi Arabia substantially higher shares at its expense. And even if some working arrangement could be arrived at, one concomitant of the world surplus that was indirectly responsible for bringing OPEC into being remains the existence of very large amounts of 'shut-in' capacity in North America and elsewhere. Any collision of interests with the international companies—which might well come under pressure themselves from consumer countries' governments if these feared coercion by a producers' cartel—might force some of that shut-in capacity back into production. The biggest exporters operating any proration scheme might have to take substantial reductions in output themselves if they hoped to hold up the price to consumer countries. In any proration scheme, as indeed in any co-operative arrangement to restrict production, somebody, and usually the largest producer or group of producers, has to 'act like Texas'.

This proposal was not one that appealed to all the founder members of OPEC: and proration would no doubt have appealed even less to any of the newer oil-exporting countries whom these founders might hope to recruit. In its first year of existence, the organization, under the coolly sensible directorship of Mr. Fuad Rouhani of Iran, set up a head-quarters in Geneva, and began the organization of a variety of studies on points where the governments felt they lacked information to back their views. Attitudes to OPEC among the Western companies differed: some were apprehensive about its ambitions, while others hoped that the fuller understanding of their own commercial behaviour that it was certainly out to gain might make its members better disposed towards them. OPEC's resolution at meetings during 1961 were firm but temperate in wording: their main emphasis was upon securing detailed and accurate information about various aspects of the international oil industry that are not often discussed very openly. Membership of OPEC was open to all exporting countries, though with rather restricted voting powers. Qatar joined the organization in 1961, and in spring 1962 Indonesia and Libya were also accepted as members. The Sahara remained outside, while it remained French; but it seemed possible that the new nationalist government might well join. If it did, OPEC would have all the world's significant crude petroleum exporters within its ranks, except Russia. And several of its members were sure that if it came to putting the screws on the Western oil companies, Russia would at least co-operate with OPEC.

Location of its headquarters in Geneva was a sensible move: it offered the possibility of more direct contact with governments at the other end of the oil business. Those governments had already in their own different ways also been intervening—none of these governments' concern with oil can reasonably be called 'interfering'—in the oil business. In both kinds of government there were politicians inclined to argue that more direct contact between producers and consumers at this level need not in any way mean a collision of interests: and that it might serve both of their interests better than they are served now. During the sixties, these more direct contacts will almost certainly increase in scope. Does that imply the likelihood of some shrinkage in the role of the international oil business itself?

Part Three

CHAPTER XXII

Pressure from Producers

One of the first acts of the Organization of Petroleum Exporting Countries after it set up headquarters in Geneva in 1961 was to commission three Western economic intelligence agencies to look into the economic behaviour of the Western oil companies. These agencies reported, in the first place, in time for the OPEC meeting of spring 1962: their remits included studies of the rate of return on oil investment in production and other operations, of the pricing of crude oil and products, and of the financial arrangements between companies and host governments. These subjects, as patient readers of this book may appreciate, offer plenty of meat for study—and argument. The arguments, from interested personalities in the host countries, had never been lacking: what was new in OPEC's better organized approach was the determination that from now on such arguments need never again lack any documentation and briefing that the best impartial consultancy available anywhere can make available.

The subjects of these first commissioned studies were wide enough to comprise very large areas of delicacy and probable controversy between the companies operating internationally and the OPEC governments. It is no secret that they were contemplated within the major companies, which were most directly concerned, with somewhat mixed feelings. But the precedent set by these studies may turn out to have been more important than their immediate content. It served notice on the international oil industry that within a very short time they would have to expect countries negotiating with them that have access to OPEC to be as well briefed as they are themselves.

These companies needed no notice that the petroleum exporting countries were dissatisfied with their existing financial arrangements with the industry, and bent on changing them. Since the late fifties, many ideas had been in the air about the revision of the basic financial

311

relationships between these governments and the oil companies. And though the initiative came largely from the governments, oilmen were not lacking, even within the most conservative of companies, to feel that the existing formulae promised, for the future, little but trouble. It was easier, admittedly, to find people who felt the international companies had 'painted ourselves into a corner', or who would agree that the time had come for 'a breakthrough', than people who had a solution that they were confident about themselves, or that they could persuade many of their colleagues was worth taking seriously. But much more widely than was perhaps evident from their public pronouncements, there existed an acceptance within the companies—resigned or even bitter rather than hopeful—of the likelihood of considerable change soon.

From the side of the governments, the elements coming into prominence in new concession agreements and in demands for revision of existing ones, as this decade began, were 'participation' for host governments in the production (and, they would hope, in later stages of operations) of oil from beneath their land; the demand, whether as formal partners or not, for consultation with host governments over prices; the returning element of 'relinquishment'; and continuing desire, under one formula or another, for 'more than 50:50'.

Several newcomers to the Middle East, during the middle and later fifties, had made deals offering participation to host governments, and at the end of 1960 Royal Dutch Shell, in Kuwait, made a deal that appeared to break ranks and follows suit. Its initiative then, it asseverated, could still be reconciled with the formula 50:50. These assurances were less than convincing to other major companies: but that the terms were what Shell had to pay to get the chance of 'cost oil' that it needed in the Middle East, nobody doubted (moreover, several of them had also gone well beyond 50:50 in their own, unsuccessful bids for this concession). Shell, again, is reported to have been the first of these established companies owning shares in IPC, to inquire with any hopefulness into the chances of some agreement on Iraqi participation in the equity of this operating company. What the companies later offered, and Iraq turned down, was not participation in IPC: but it was participation in production—if only in areas that the companies had agreed to relinquish later anyway.

From 1961 onwards, the Middle East governments began to achieve the practice of participation in, for example, the operations of the Japanese and Italian companies that had first made agreements providing for this five or six years before. Moreover, the few new deals made in the Middle East during 1961 mostly incorporated some possibility of optional 'participation' for the government concerned. And while the major international companies were still unwilling to concede as a right in the revision of past agreements what they might have to offer in new ones, they or their associates were at the same time accepting quite high percentages of government partnership in exploring new territories in, for example, South America and India, or in producing gas in Holland.

The demand for participation, in Iraq, had come along with what has, of late, become another highly fashionable claim—for the 'relinquishment' of unexplored territories from the original concession areas. There had been no provision for this in the original Iraq agreements, or indeed in most of the original agreements that parcelled out oil concessions in the Middle East. Surrender of land that one has not chosen to explore, after a certain period had elapsed, has, however, long been a feature of concessions in many countries where these are granted in mining laws. It came into the Middle East with the original agreement in Saudi Arabia, and was also put into a clause in the Iran Consortium agreements of 1953 (though there the option to relinquish is left with the oil companies); it was later accepted, though no provision for it existed in the concession, in Kuwait. The principle seems equitable; and in line with the 'most-favoured-nation' principle that generally holds good in the Middle East and is fairly explicit in the Iraq agreements, the partners in IPC did not attempt to hold out against relinquishment there, though what they offered was not finally accepted by the Iraq government. There is no automatic connexion between relinquishment and participation. But it may on occasion occur, as it did in Iraq, that the one, in an established oil-producing country, might provide the opportunity for the other, whether the government chose to share ownership of the land given back with producing companies already there or with newcomers.

Access to the rest of these countries for new developers, possibly on new terms, might be more serious for the established companies. It could threaten a potential surge of extra oil on to the world market, from areas that have so far been sterilized for 'orderly development'. It might mean new twists in the concession formulae to which, over the years, they might have to consider accommodating their own concessions. Yet opening new taps to increase the world's surplus of oil would surely tend to shift the initiative further towards marketing even than it is shifting already; and to that degree, it might reduce the ultimate pressures that producers can apply to the whole integrated operations of the international industry.

Certainly relinquishment, forced or voluntary, would bring in fresh capital to the Middle East; this is still an intensely attractive area, in physical prospects, for any oil company, new or established, that is still prepared to spend large amounts of money on exploration, and most companies, including the established majors, still are. The host governments, like many producing companies, would probably be prepared to take a chance on the possibility that by the time their oil was in production it would be marketable at some remunerative price. Some suppliers of fresh capital—from America, Europe, or even the Soviet bloc—would no doubt be prepared to accept a low integrated return, or its equivalent, in order to gain a growing share of the world oil business at the expense of the major companies; or might argue that yet cheaper oil, against the preconceptions of this industry, might unlock completely new layers of demand in various parts of the world.

The chances of finding oil in unexplored or untested areas in such countries must be taken as far better than in some of the countries where it has never yet been found. To the extent that host governments have capital to invest, oil in such areas should rank fairly high among potential activities in which to invest it—even if the apparent return on production is an exaggerated one, the return really available might compare well with, say, secondary manufacturing industries. But even off the shores of Kuwait, say, you cannot be certain of finding oil. And in a period when it is difficult to find markets for all the oil being developed already, the advantages of participation by the governments of producing countries in the joint development of relinquished areas are, objectively, debatable. Better to get some bonuses and drive a hard bargain with some private bidder? Or devote as much capital as the government can spare or assemble itself and venture alone in a national producing company?

Government participation in oil operations, with capital that the nation genuinely subscribes, has many obvious attractions in principle and in national sentiment. As one British civil servant commented in 1961, 'How should we like to have Arabs running our steel industry?' And the sooner the national companies begin operating on their own responsibility in this business, the better. It is simply bad luck that these companies should have commenced business in a period when the market for oil is so soft; but possible, at least, that they ought to be able to make better than knockdown bargains with the private companies operating in their countries.

Participation by the governments as minority partners in the existing operating companies owned by private foreign business, on the face of it, looks attractive. But the more one considers the possibility, the more potential difficulties appear in a relationship between a government partner, wanting responsibility and initiative, and a local operating company that possesses very little of either. Any self-respecting government entering such a partnership would expect some say in the key decisions of the business: yet these key decisions are in fact taken elsewhere, by the international companies of which the local operating joint companies or consortia are generally mere technical instruments. The setting of prices is one of those key decisions, in which governments are claiming a share already. Deciding the volume of offtake from one operating country as against another is the next; it is a function of the international integrated supplier, but governments as partners in local operating companies would be vitally affected by the decisions. With the best will in the world, a government participating in the operations—and the profits—of an operating company in its own country would in its own national interest be at pains to secure the largest possible production from that one country. At present the offtake from each country is governed partly by agreements between the major shareholders in each jointly-owned company, but basically by the incentive of each such integrated major to maximize its own net integrated return across a wide network of business around the globe. How would these governmentally-urged but at present powerless operating companies 'compete' for greater custom from these international oil buyers—and others? And would any resultant changes in the balance of oil logistics make for more economical oil supply in the world, or less? ('Economical' here perhaps begs a question: but it is not used simply from the standpoint of a consumer interested in cheap oil. It is used to mean the supply of requirements around the world at the lowest practicable real cost, regardless of the prices paid and of how any profits made are shared).

Responsible government participation in local producing companies that are mainly owned by private integrated companies elsewhere, if and when it comes, may put considerable strain on the links of integration inside companies producing oil in a large number of different places. It might, in theory at least, put less strain or simpler strains upon any integrated companies that produced mainly in one area and shipped the oil to one market or group of markets. Such a company might not at least be faced within the group with choices between two or more producing companies in which it had local governments as partners. Its refining and marketing organizations, even then, would have to consider the costs of operation with alternative crude oils, unless their 'own' had some special advantage. That is one reason why the 'national preference company', even or perhaps particularly if the consumer government on which it depended for the preference were involved too, might fit conveniently into some 'participation' formula.

But it can hardly be argued that a flow of trade depending upon special government dispensations at one end (or both) is likely to minimize real cost. And outside such special cases, it could be argued that responsible government participation in producing companies could only become effective if the internationally integrated companies were to 'divorce', in effect if not in form, their logistic function of matching demand from their central choice of supply, and in effect to put their requirements out to tender from their own (and other?) producing companies.

The governmental-cum-private producing companies would then, in principle, be free to offer their oil on the most advantageous terms to these major middlemen, with their considerable integrated command of markets, and to other independent buyers, to whom these countries indeed sell oil today. Some might find, if they made the terms right, that their offtake of oil rose. If so, that of others would be likely to fall (unless, indeed, all these government-influenced companies were ready to push prices down to a level that might stimulate an even greater increase in consumption, which somehow one imagines would not be their first intention). The integrated middlemen (ignoring for a moment all the problems of disentanglement) would retain the countervailing power of going elsewhere for their oil. The cost advantage of cheap oil from elsewhere against more expensive oil from which one stood to draw part of the profits would set a series of interesting problems for these integrated buyers, and the further ramifications of tax credits and final net integrated return on investment would add a further set of twists. But it would be too much to argue that these complications, presuming it were possible to get from the present situation to the one we have postulated, would make logical commercial behaviour impossible for the integrated marketers. Is their commercial logic so much simpler nowadays?

In circumstances of surplus, indeed, such a shift of responsibility for

producing—and selling—crude more completely within national jurisdiction would seem most likely to have one rapid result, whatever its
later repercussions. It would break the artificially posted prices for
Middle East crude. That might be a good thing for the world oil
market—though there ought to be simpler ways to get there than
divorcement. But would it be a good thing for the participating governments? More important, would they think it so? (It might be unwise to
hazard any hasty answer to the first of those questions. But, at present,
it would surely not be difficult to guess the answer to the second.)

That is obviously not the only conclusion to which government
participation in operating companies might lead. It postulates an
extreme solution, which could be reached only through a considerable
upheaval of established property relationships; and one imagines that
the integrated companies concerned would contemplate the process
with as much distaste as the governments of host countries might find
cause, in hindsight, to contemplate its eventual consequences. But it
may illustrate that the current situation may be more advantageous for
host revenues tied to the posted price of crude oil than a greater
accession of commercial responsibility might be. And it perhaps suggests also that the exaggerated apparent return on assets invested in oil
production in the Middle East might be slashed automatically by a
structural change towards anything rather more closely resembling an
independently competitive free market.

Participation that amounted in fact only to getting an eventually
larger percentage of the profit shown at posted prices, without any real
share in the control of the business, would be another thing, which some
companies at least are already more disposed to offer. But could this
be expected to satisfy the reasonable ambitions of the able and aspiring
nationalists even as long as the 50:50 formula has satisfied them? It may
seem on the one hand reactionary to doubt whether most of these host
governments are yet quite aware of the rigours of commercial partnership in a soft world market for oil; and on the other hand perversely
radical to doubt whether further halfway houses between here and full
'partnership' could long satisfy the nationalist aspirations that they
whet. Yet one must bear in mind the limited experience of many of
these countries in meeting the problems of industry, let alone an internationally integrated one. Some of their nationals are most skilled
traders in merchandise or even in international currency; but few of
them have any industry other than this one within their borders.
Ignorance of anything but oil, and disregard of the oil industry beyond

one's borders, is in no way a reproach; it can be encountered, for example, in Texas. But it may make anything approaching genuine government partnership in sections of this complex private business unwise to assume or to promise, in the short run. It is hard to escape the feeling that when the exporting countries venture into full participation in the oil business—as logically in time they must—they would be best placed as participants in their own national companies.

The present is a time when no honest businessman would be inviting innocent newcomers into his risks in the oil market as partners. There are too many newcomers, some far from innocent ones, in it already. If host governments were any more directly involved in this business than they are today, they might simply hamper the ability and resolution of their commercial partners in reacting logically to competition. Their stake in the industry's present arrangements, indeed, already does so.

For even now, logical commercial behaviour for the integrated companies could be politically explosive. As one person prominent in a major international company put it to me at the end of 1960, 'On paper at least, returns on investment in oil operations in the Eastern hemisphere appear to be exceptionally high. That appearance is deceptive; but the apparent returns on production, in particular, keep on attracting more new capital in. One solution that might eventually discourage new capital from entering this business, and perhaps eventually clear some of the recent entrants out, would be to make posted prices more realistic—demonstrating that investment in integrated oil operations in this hemisphere yields no more nowadays than a normal manufacturing return'. There is hard economic logic there—though sceptics would probably argue that there might be almost no bottom to the depths to which you would have to drive down the apparent return on production before you drove out of it newcomers who have invested their money already.

But any move towards realism in posted prices would mean pushing the postings for crude oil produced in the Middle East down at any rate to the levels at which large-scale discounted deals have been made and continue to be made (for example, the prices that Japanese oil buyers consistently get and regularly publish). And any such course, as things stand, would be politically impossible.

For, as things stand today, any posted prices cuts that brought these more into line with the actual prices paid in independent deals would correspondingly reduce the governments' revenue per barrel, and cut down the increase in total revenue upon which they will probably have been counting. The Middle East governments have understandable reasons to object to another drastic slash in their revenue per barrel, decided upon from outside without reference to them. While postings remain stable, their revenues are protected from the discounts granted to individual buyers: in the Middle East, taxes are levied to bring revenues up to 50 per cent of the posted prices less allowable costs, regardless of the actual price charged in particular deals. So if in their own interests the oil companies felt it might be necessary and salutary to make postings realistic, this could only be made acceptable, if at all, by revisions of the formulae under which governments draw income from oil production.

Revisions have been made before in the history of the oil concession of the Middle East; and though the companies involved find it essential to insist always upon the principle of sanctity of contract, it could be said that some of the agreements are almost in a state of continuous redefinition of detail. The occasional basic revisions have come about partly under pressure from governments; but in the form of change chosen the companies concerned have often taken most of the initiative. When one looks at these 'breakthroughs', one could almost say that they occurred at times when circumstances beyond the control of the contracting parties had begun to make it difficult to go on fulfilling the intent or the equity of the original agreement, rather than the letter of it. Some people in the industry feel that such a change in circumstances has come about with the onset of a world surplus of oil that seems likely to last for some time.

The 'breakthrough' that most people on both sides of Middle East oil remember best (perhaps unfortunately) is the last one: the shift to 50:50 that was initiated at the end of 1950 and carried through to its full present form by the mid-fifties. This was basically a shift from a fixed royalty of four shillings gold per ton of oil to an income tax charged as 50 per cent of profits shown at posted prices. That royalty had originally been tied to gold as a hedge against exchange instability, inflation or deflation, which during the thirties it provided. But when crude oil prices veered sharply upwards during the war years, the price of gold remained frozen; the original gold hedge in the royalty was nullified, and in effect the intent of the earlier agreements, to give the governments a revenue that was likely to rise in value at least as much as the price of oil, was no longer being carried out.

When the new 'profit-sharing' tax formula was introduced, it offered the governments considerable benefits. By the time that it was modified

319

to exclude discounts to shareholder companies, in the middle fifties, it offered the governments such impressive increases over their revenues before that ever since most discussions of further improvements in revenue from oil have tended to be discussed simply in terms of the percentages in this 'profit-sharing' both by governments that would like to push their percentage up and by companies maintaining that 50:50 ought to be inviolable. But it might still be worth remembering that the earlier 'gold' royalty itself derived from a revision of the Anglo-Iranian concession in the early thirties, and was made to give the government concerned a higher and more stable revenue. That was a shift from basing government revenues partly on a percentage of profits, which at the time were so low as to give it virtually no revenue at all, to the fixed royalty based on volume. It is by no means automatically true that what is nowadays called 'profit-sharing'—i.e. an income tax basis against which certain royalties can be set off—will always be the most advantageous financial arrangement for a host country, particularly in dealings with an industry where over the years prices are fairly often under downward competitive pressure.

When the companies and the governments moved to 50:50, the possibility of a fall in prices seems hardly to have been given much practical consideration by either group of bargainers. The subsequent move into surplus, indeed into rather similar circumstances to those reigning in the thirties, was a change neither could have prevented, though it might have been foreseen. If this change were to be taken as the justification for another basic revision of the formula, in which direction ought it to be revised?

Many Arabs would argue that the simplest way to deal with falling prices is to revise upward the percentage of profits to which the government is entitled. But this still begs the question, 'More than 50 per cent of what?' If the companies were to agree to concede 60 per cent of profits on the prices actually realized, there might not be too much difference from what they pay in taxes to the host countries now. The 50:50 formula applied on posted prices appears nowadays to represent at least 57:43 in favour of the governments on the prices actually paid; by the time this book appears the effective shares may have moved further. But whatever percentage became general, if the prices concerned continued to sag, the government's revenues per barrel would sag too. So, unless their volume of exports rose more than in proportion, their total revenues from oil would start declining.

If governments became concerned with 'realizations'—prices arising from the real state of the market—that, again, could become a source of friction. Would the governments be satisfied that the prices realized—particularly on sales to affiliates of integrated companies—were made at the most advantageous figures possible? Arabs might answer that a higher percentage should still be based on posted prices; that the governments' consent should be necessary before these should be changed; and that the governments should then refuse to let posted prices go down. The integrated companies, however, cannot avoid realism in meeting competition across large sectors of their market for products, and some of their sales of crude. Such a course would simply push down their integrated return on operations even further, and reduce their willingness to go on developing this business. Over any long period of surplus, profit-sharing formulae, whatever the percentage ruling, seem liable to lead inexorably to the governments' seeking first to control prices, and second to their trying to organize some producer-controlled cartel to try to make those prices stick.

The only circumstances in which the companies might find it practicable to cut posted prices for crude as the prices actually paid are being forced to slip, would be by revising their formulae in the direction of insulating the governments' revenues from the effect of cuts in postings. This might mean, in some way or another, moving back towards a larger element of flat-rate revenue per barrel for the governments; and a smaller element varying with the swings of the market; either a return towards the royalty pattern, or supplementary payments for the governments at any time that it became commercially expedient to cut postings, to make up what would otherwise be their loss in revenue per barrel. This would mean accepting a principle that has not been accepted in the Middle East since the change from royalty to 50:50—that the governments' level of revenue per barrel should be taken as virtually irreducible. Of late, in practice, their annual revenues from oil have been taken as irreducible, though even that has never been spelt out as a formal principle in any agreement. The steady and fairly high rate of growth in offtake of oil from these countries, at the time that cuts were made in posted prices in 1959 and 1960, made it possible to demonstrate that the host governments' total oil revenues for the next year, in spite of a somewhat lower revenue per barrel, would still come out higher. The chance that this could be true again in any further cut in posted prices, from now on, has been becoming smaller. Offtake from the Middle East, no doubt, will go on growing. But its years of phenomenally rapid increase in volume have perhaps already passed.

Any revision of formulae to leave the companies free to move prices as they thought fit for the market, but to protect government revenue per barrel, would be criticized as 'giving more than 50:50'; and it would do so, of course, as soon as posted prices were cut. But in practice this is happening anyway—by the payment of a 50 per cent tax according to posted prices that on some sales cannot be realized, and also by invoicing crude to affiliates at prices that involve losses at later stages of the integrated operation.

Arrangements that made it possible to cut the posted price but keep the government revenue per barrel stable might even be criticized from the government side as wasting oil at unduly low prices. And certainly the time has passed when any shift right back to a fixed revenue per barrel would be accepted by any government in a producing country: the most that the governments would be likely to accept as desirable for the long term, as well as the short, would be a larger element fixed and a smaller variable element in their revenues, or some supplementary special payments in 'once for all' adjustments of postings towards what the market will currently bear. Certain of the governments might not want to abandon what they have on occasion been encouraged to think of as a modicum of 'partnership', simply in order to let crude oil postings move according to the state of the market. But others have occasionally indicated that they would not be sorry to see some of the newcomers who they feel have 'spoiled the market' forced out or bought up after a period of really sharp competition. And in general, even though stable and growing revenue from oil may not be all that host governments want from this industry, it is certainly one of the prerequisites.

To the outsider who has been told how these formulae have been revised before, it would seem that revision on such lines might be quite feasible if both parties agreed to it—and just possible, indeed, that it might be achieved at not much net cost to the companies concerned. One stumbling block, certainly, may exist in the companies' double tax arrangements. At present there remain vestigial royalty elements in the governments' revenue; these are chargeable against local income tax in bringing this up to 50 per cent of the profits on posted prices. In settling the shareholder oil companies' tax liabilities in their home countries, this royalty is ordinarily excluded as a cost of operation, charged before arriving at taxable income; only the foreign income tax paid can actually be credited against the home tax payable.

If, for example, the host government were to go on charging a 50 per cent income tax on profits, but ceased to offset the royalty paid against this, it would get more revenue per barrel, and more of it fixed; or might retain the same revenue if the posted price and hence the profit were cut. The larger foreign tax payment (because royalty was not offset) would create a larger tax credit for use wherever the internationally-integrated company was able to use its home tax liability on other foreign income. But whether this would be of any use to the international company would depend very much on the extent to which the tax credits to which it was already entitled happen to be utilized already. If the tax credit available already exceeded its home tax liability on total foreign income (as, after depletion allowances are set off against total income, those of American integrated companies often do), then an increase in foreign tax credit would be of no help in offsetting the cost of the higher tax in the producing country to an integrated company. Circumstances might however arise that could increase companies' American tax liability on foreign income—such as the Kennedy Administration's advertised desire to reduce foreign depletion allowances. If that happened—the companies hope it will not—then additional tax credit overseas might become extremely useful, and the net cost of allowing foreign governments a higher tax share, or a stable revenue per barrel when posted prices went down, might be considerably reduced.

More than one tax system's treatment of corporations trading abroad are involved here, and only the professional can assess the implications of any given proposal within them. But without being cynical, the outsider may be inclined to feel that if companies and host governments were able to agree that a new formula to put a floor under government revenues but allow freedom to move these posted prices would be advantageous to both, a formula for doing this with the least possible extra net cost in tax to the companies concerned might possibly be worked out. The income tax authorities in Britain have never proved themselves unco-operative for long with the oil companies over questions that so significantly affect Britain's position in the Middle East and its balance of payments. The internal revenue authorities in the United States have perhaps an inherently stiffer attitude towards oil companies as such. But when it has come to major revisions in agreements, co-operation from the Treasury Department has sometimes been forthcoming.

There might well be some logic in some such revision of the formulae setting government revenues from oil—and not simply because of a particular situation in the world oil market when prices happen to be dropping. In public relations terminology, the whole concept of 'profit-sharing' in tax arrangements has too often been clothed in phrases that suggest Arab governments are 'partners' in this business. This was always disingenuous; nowadays such terminology seems to be of little use to either side of the oil bargain. In the United States and Britain income taxes take some 53–54 per cent of the profits of business firms. But one does not often have companies in either country describing their governments as 'profit-sharing partners' in their enterprise.

This is not to question the fairness of the actual amounts of revenue that host governments draw from the oil produced by companies operating in their areas. It certainly does not seem demonstrable that the actual revenues of say 70–80 cents a barrel that host governments in the Middle East enjoy under the 50:50 principle are in any obvious way 'unfair'. From the consumer's point of view, particularly since the market moved into surplus, their take may seem a pretty substantial one. Equally, there may be considerable merit in the 50:50 formula as a simply understandable formula of apparent fairness for oil ventures in new territories, where the eventual commercial advantages of producing any oil that is found can vary immensely. Newcomers to oil exploration, before oil is found, ought to be prepared to accept whatever arrangements are ruling in the business they hope to enter.

The attractiveness of 50:50, from the beginning, was that it sounded like a principle of fairness. But in fact does it embody any principle at all? Why should the share of profits in any given oil deal be 50:50, rather than 40:60, or 60:40? (and in passing it may be noted that examples of both these divisions, in recent years, have been labelled as 'according to the 50:50 principle'). One advantage of enlarging the flat 'per barrel' element in government revenues from oil might be that this at least could be seen to be clearly what in essence it is—the result of a commercial bargain, not some exercise in dubious principle about some 'right' or 'fair' percentage. In ordinary economic terms, the proceeds that these governments draw from the exploitation of oil or other mineral resources would mainly be classed as a rent or a mining royalty —an element in the operator's costs, rather than a share of his profits. One may note that the Hon. Maurice Bridgeman, chairman of British Petroleum, discussing government revenues from oil in his annual report to shareholders for 1961—stoutly defending the fairness of the existing 50:50 deal—spoke of 'the rent we pay our landlords'. It would be unreasonable to attribute any motive to Mr. Bridgeman but the preference for clear English; but this certainly seems the better description. And a rent, like any other price set in a commercial bargain, will tend to be set within a range limited by each bargainer's idea of the cost of doing without the other.

The oil rent in Venezuela, for example, has obviously in recent years been set rather too high—so long as the oil companies were in a position to shift the emphasis of their operations towards better bargains elsewhere. Doing without Middle East oil, on the other hand, has been attempted only once by the West and the oil companies, with relative success but in an expensive emergency operation. Doing without Middle East and Venezuelan oil at once never has. Doing without the oil companies, on the other hand, was attempted once, by Iran; it was a failure. Abadan and Suez are ugly object lessons that neither the petroleum exporting countries, the Western consuming nations, nor the oil companies might care to contemplate as benchmarks setting the limits of successful bargaining; they are on record, rather, as the danger signs showing where good sense foundered in the past. All parties to this bargaining, understandably, have since increased their insurance provisions. The petroleum-exporting countries did so by creating OPEC and agreeing not to benefit at the expense of other member countries involved in disputes with oil companies (a resolution regarded cynically in the West, but liable to become more durable as time passes). The oil companies did so by some diversification of oil development into new productive areas. But neither of these two parties, as yet, seems to have achieved really 'comprehensive cover' through these measures of insurance.

It would be a rash man who would guess what the eventual bargaining pattern between the oil companies and their growing throng of host governments around the world will look like by the middle sixties. It may not remain uniform; at least, it may display diversity with less pretence of uniformity than the many kinds of deal nowadays labelled as 50:50. It may well, wisely or unwisely, come to include significant elements of government minority shareholding in parts of the international companies' operations: the governments' own national oil companies may be playing a larger part, and the 'national preference' companies almost certainly will. Whatever form has then been reached is unlikely to be permanent: at best, the bargaining will still be going on. It has to be recorded, however, that neither party to this bargain between producing interests, industry or host government, is now as firmly placed as in the first postwar decade. A period of inflation is the time to become a partner in a business you do not know much about and which will remain largely outside your control. A period of deflation is not. The consumer is liable to have more power than either partner.

CHAPTER XXIII

Pressure from Consumers

F ew people in the oil business, when this book was written, were
prepared to take the pressures upon them from consumer governments as seriously as those from producer governments; and in the
short run they were obviously right. The dramatic demands, the
explicit or implicit threats to cut off their supplying operations, come
from the host governments in producing countries. Moreover, their
relations with those hosts are ultimately crystallized into contractual
arrangements: improvement or deterioration in such relations either
fortifies an agreement or brings arguments for its modifications. In consuming countries where the oil industry operates simply as a processor
and marketer, its contractual arrangements until recently were only with
private individuals. Its relations with governments, and the favour or
disfavour it receives in their policies, are generally more detached. Some
of these consuming countries, again, are the homes of the great international companies: these companies make a significant contribution
to national wealth and may expect, though they do not invariably
receive it, some special consideration. And yet the world oil market is in
surplus; consumers throughout the importing countries are seeking to
take as much advantage of this as they can; and energy is so vital to
every consuming country nowadays that no government can ignore its
strategic, commercial and fiscal significance. Moreover, there is one
point of uncertainty regarding oil that consumer governments share
with producers. Petroleum is brought to their shores from various
sources, just as it is taken away from the producing countries towards
various destinations, chosen according to the convenience of international companies operating largely beyond their jurisdiction. They
cannot always assume that the companies' commercial convenience will
be more than incidentally identical with their own national interests.

The present circumstances in which this growing concern of consumer governments with oil may grow in importance are those of

327

surplus, which strengthens their leverage. To any other business it would seem a rather odd kind of surplus, since world demand for oil is continuing to grow at about 5 per cent per year. But it is a real surplus of capacity, at most points in the business, over demand: the one has been growing faster than the other. It is no part of this book's purpose, fortunately, to provide specific guesswork about the continuation of rates of growth in the world economy. But most informed forecasts for the sixties—for example, that made in 1961 by the Stamford Research Institute on behalf of the Iranian government as well as of oil companies—imply that demand for oil will continue to grow fairly steadily without the pace accelerating much, though within the total the importance of newly-developing countries, already rising much faster than those already industrialized, will gradually increase.

Can we assume that from now on capacity will grow less fast, so that the slack is gradually taken up? In certain parts of the industry, perhaps. For some years tankers have not been ordered at the rate they were in the late fifties (though it remains surprising how many new orders even a very short-lived kink upwards in freight rates will still bring for the shipyards); and presumably by the mid-sixties a large amount of the oldest existing tonnage will have been scrapped. Refining capacity in Europe, again, has of late been growing a little more slowly than it was, and perhaps more slowly than demand for petroleum products in certain areas. In other parts of the world, however, where this is associated with the defence or penetration of particular markets, investment in refineries is still going on somewhat in advance of what the market potential might really require. Investment in marketing is certainly still growing in most areas of the world. These are responses to a surplus; what about investment in exploration and production, which might be considered as what brings surpluses about? Right across the industry, investment in exploration has certainly fallen a little in recent years; but no major company can cease to explore, and those that find oil in commercial quantities are often under legal obligations to develop it rapidly into production. Some of the newcomers, the possibility of whose oil has been overhanging the market in recent years, are only now actually bringing it on to the market from productive finds in the Middle East and elsewhere.

Some experts feel that the prices of certain refined products, in parts of the world at least, are passing bottom. It may well be that this will show in an alteration of the pattern of product prices, with prices for certain of the middle distillates tending to harden, while those of lighter products such as low-grade gasoline remain soft. Commercial logic might imply some rise in fuel oil prices, too: but here the Russian exports, partly outside ordinary commerce, remain a depressant. But at the time of writing this book it seemed less easy to argue, for any economic reason, that the price of crude oil was reaching bottom—or that it had been forced down far enough to eliminate or frighten off new competition in the oil business.

From the United States outwards, developed countries with established domestic fuel industries are likely to go on valuing their investment in these industries fairly high in the balance against the cheapness of imported energy. Moreover, nothing that has recently developed in the politics of Latin America, the Arab countries or Africa—which comprise virtually all the significant present and imminent exporters of petroleum—could reasonably have reduced these importers' concern with the strategic security of supply. Western Europe will no doubt remain more shamefaced than the United States about maintaining relatively high-cost indigenous fuel industries; but it may not be very much more prepared to run those industries right down to the levels to which unrestricted imports of cheap oil might drive them.

Consumer governments, organizations of governments, and study groups appointed by governments will remain prepared to expatiate upon the benefits that taking full advantage of cheap energy would confer on the West—though their enthusiasm will no doubt continue to vary inversely with their degree of actual responsibility for acting upon such liberal views. Few responsible governments in such countries, however, are prepared wholly or even largely to supplant old or new indigenous fuel industries by imports of cheap energy—which they would probably accept as a factor, but by no means a determining one, in economic growth. To cite Professor E. S. Mason:

'If low-cost energy was essential to economic development, we would expect to find some association between the price of energy and the state of economic development. Plotting national income per capita against energy prices in fact indicates no significant correlation. . . . There are some underdeveloped countries with low and some with high fuel costs. There are also some highly industrialized countries with low and some with high fuel costs. We also sometimes find within a country differences in fuel costs and energy prices almost as wide as average energy cost differences from country to country. Within the United States we have areas where fuel prices are ten times as high as those of the areas of lowest fuel prices.'

There is always a mixture of considerations: the short-run cost of energy, at home or on the external trade balance, possibly invisible income from ownership of international oil companies, the security of supply in the long run, and continuing uncertainty about the terms on which one may be able to continue to import one's fuel. If one were pushing the short-term logic of seeking cheap energy regardless, it could be argued that we might close down, or put on a 'care and maintenance basis', almost all the other fuel production in the world and rely on getting it all, over the next generation, as oil out of Kuwait or Russia. Nobody is prepared to suggest that, at least outside those two countries. Consciously or not, even the most liberal advocates of cheap energy imports put some bounds upon their enthusiasm.

Mixed motives remain evident also in the supra-national economic groupings that have appeared in Western Europe, the world's main importing region for energy. There is a desire to gain the benefits of cheap imports—up to a point; and a readiness to rationalize one's domestic fuel industries—down to a point. But these groups of governments, perhaps more than the single consumer governments, are moreover disturbed at the possibility of being held up by any cartel of producers. They are probably not entirely convinced that the existing commercial controllers of the oil industry are always as competitive in pricing as they might be. But they are certainly even more apprehensive of any incipient cartel of oil-producing governments.

While the surplus lasts, one can certainly expect pressure from many consuming governments to get improved bargains for their countries: and since this will sometimes run across the interests of international companies whose margins are under pressure at the other end too, it is liable to manifest itself at the point of import or processing by affiliates of the international groups. Some of the developing countries, for example, are anxious to take a financial interest in the import or refining of oil products in their countries; and though this was often derided by economists in the first postwar decade as a matter simply of fashion, it has begun to acquire considerably more logic as the world market moved into surplus. It is no longer simply a matter of laying out one's scarce capital, or attracting foreign capital from outside, to tie up in a prestigious but not over-remunerative item of industrial plant. It offers an opportunity of exacting a price on behalf of the country's consumers and their governmental assets, for access to one's probably developing market. This is capital a nation might not otherwise come by, which its owners are ready and anxious to put in to help them maintain or achieve their integrated return on a network of assets reaching back across the world. The newly independent African nations, in particular, are exacting this price of access to their markets, not only by seeking bids for government participation in refineries but by driving quite hard bargains about the pricing of the crude oil put into these refineries. This is a kind of demand for government participation that major and minor oil companies in the world market have perforce become increasingly ready to accept.

Partnerships with consuming governments in refineries or marketing networks, during a period of world oil surplus, may be a fairly logical move for both participants in such joint enterprises. Over the history of the oil industry, the periods of incipient surplus have probably been longer than those of apparent or real shortage; and the toughest buyers of refined products or nowadays of crude oil, who have included governmental import monopolies, may well on the average have had the best bargain prices for their oil and not lost much during the periods of shortage. Government participation in a refinery or an importing concern can generally, liberal principles notwithstanding, guarantee the refinery's products preferential treatment in the internal market. 'Processing rights' may be guaranteed to existing marketers (but seldom to any new ones): but the partner in refining can generally hope for the lion's share of any expansion (until the time comes for an extension or another refinery). In such deals, the commercial partner must be assumed to know his own mind; so must the government. One may have ideological objections to state trading of any kind, or objections in simple fairness to governments which give their own trading bodies, or partnerships with commercial associates, privileged treatment in competition with purely private competitors. But that does not make their behaviour less likely or in their own interests less logical.

Privileged access to markets can be offered to producing countries, not merely to oil companies seeking outlets. What one of the major groups has christened 'the national preference companies' could grow in importance and increasingly affect the operations of private oil companies in the world market. Two of the examples in the limelight at the time this book was written, the Italian ENI and the French Saharan companies, were in a sense special cases: ENI because of its ambivalence between acting as a mass importer of Russian oil and developing its own crude sources, and the French through their changing relationship with Algeria and the Sahara.

But the main significance of both was their privileged access to their country's markets, an advantage shared also by the Japanese company in the Middle East. During the sixties, one would not be surprised to see more such privileged enterprises develop. Preferential access to a sizeable market, even when the business that can offer this has a large share of consumer government participation, may well be a tempting incentive to the governments of producing countries in a surplus—and might, as is noted in the last chapter, have certain advantages in an era where producer governments too are seeking 'participation'.

The preference that such markets may offer oil from sources of which they particularly approve can come in various forms. Agreements recommending ideal rules of international trade, over the long run, ought in theory at least to whittle down the opportunity for governments to discriminate between imports by special tariffs or quotas. It may be that in the sixties exceptions to these rules will tend to thin out. It seems at present however rather more likely that developing regional trading areas such as the European Economic Community will reduce trade barriers and trade discrimination within their borders but retain some protection against the outside world. Certainly while France retains any hold on Saharan oil and gas it seems likely to seek preferential treatment for these fuels within its EEC partners' markets—and if necessary specific restrictions on crude as well as products from other sources. Apart from tariff preference, consumer governments are likely while their bargaining advantage lasts to enter into commercial competition in marketing: one has already seen recent examples of somewhat varying types in France, India and Ceylon, while the governmental importing agencies already established elsewhere have been driving hard bargains with oil suppliers short of outlets.

The continuance of surplus might logically be expected, perhaps, to reduce consumer governments' interest in another form of intervention into oil in which some have engaged in recent years—exploration for oil within their own borders. But one rather doubts whether it will wholly deter any government. Has surplus, after all, deterred many international oil companies from going on exploring? A government, certainly, is not moved by one incentive that on occasion may encourage companies to keep up their exploration budgets, the possibility of tax advantage here or there. But the rewards of successful exploration can be so dramatic even for highly developed economies—as for example the gas finds in Southern France and more recently in Holland seem likely to show once more—that some national gamble for such prizes may seem sensible regardless of a surplus that might indeed be gone by the time that any petroleum found comes into production. (The gas at Lacq, it may be noted, was located by French government explorers; that at Slochteren by Shell and Esso working together. But in the development of the Dutch gas too government participation has entered.) Moreover, any petroleum found at home becomes indigenous fuel: a benefit to local economic resources and to the balance of payments, and sometimes another domestic industry queueing up for protection. Many of the private exploration ventures begun since the mid-fifties, moreover, have recognized the logic of this; there has been quite a shift in drilling activity to countries where, if the oil is found, it will command a ready market.

For many developing countries in the sixties, oil now weighs as heavy on the balance of payments as it did in Western Europe in the forties and early fifties. Investment in exploration in these countries, too, is likely to continue, by private companies, joint ventures, or state-hired contractors. But a period during which the actual landed prices of oil slip downward, even if postings should be held immovable for fear of reactions from exporting governments, ought to moderate that import cost. And if the private Western companies are not prepared to moderate the net foreign exchange cost of oil imported by such developing countries—either by spending more in these countries, or investing it there, or in helping them secure other foreign aid from Western countries to offset the cost—there is unfortunately little doubt that the Russians will get much of the business, by quoting low prices and accepting non-convertible currencies. Countries such as India, that is to say, are well placed to put the screws on the Western oil marketer; and they are likely to find this for a time a more profitable course than trying to find their own oil.

Pressure for government participation in importing oil, therefore, seems likely to continue, and companies that complain of it in one country may find it convenient for themselves in another. Ambitions to engage in or share in exploration, however, might moderate somewhat in countries lacking oil, if the surplus lasts. And where such countries find it, they will ensure it preference for internal consumption. This, indeed, may not be quite the violation of received economic doctrine that it might appear at first sight to free traders—and importers. Local petroleum may not be the cheapest oil that a country could lay hands on. But can any country be sure that the operations of its present international suppliers at present ensure that it gets the cheapest? Can it be demonstrated that what gives the best net integrated return to an international supply complex is necessarily the best bargain that each particular country could get?

Most consumer governments, moreover, are not unmixedly anxious to have black oil prices pressed further down, though they might like gasoline prices down further. Indeed, the competition of low-cost fuel oil is one of the reasons why some of the consumer nations have been considering combined energy policies. Does this open any possibility of accommodation between the standpoints of consumer nationalism and producer nationalism?

In mid-1961, discussing hemispheric problems, the Organization of American States did consider petroleum as one of the commodities for which some kind of undefined 'scheme' might be devised; there appears to have been some general sympathy for the idea in parts at least of the American State Department. The idea has obvious parallels with OPEC's ideas about international proration, though the two concepts are not identical. Such a scheme, if it could ever be achieved, might offer exporting countries a very real participation in the international logistics of petroleum; but they would be face to face with the equally direct concern of consumer governments. Is there any real chance that the two groups could overcome mutual distrusts in a world commodity scheme, with both groups of governments in the game?

Such a scheme—with its echoes of the ill-fated Anglo-American Oil Agreement—would mean accepting the control of price fluctuations in the market as a shared common interest of consumers and producers, rather than as imposing such control as a lever against the customer (and to some extent against the oil companies). Certain world commodity schemes have had a limited degree of success before and since the war—mainly covering various pastoral commodities and metals. Moreover, the European Economic Community is in principle committed to encourage such schemes for pastoral commodities; and the idea may gain more general acceptance if the primary producing nations' income continues to fall. But few have concerned commodities for which the increase in demand has been anything like as steady as it is for petroleum; and most of them have dealt with materials in the supply of which internationally integrated companies play only a limited part. Certain metals that have on occasion come under cartels or commodity schemes, such as aluminium, are produced by international, integrated companies; but few of them carry operations as far through from the mineral resource to the final consumer, as many oil companies do. Some form of world commodity agreement for petroleum, in principle, might not be inherently impossible. But it would require the reconciliation of many differing, and some violently opposed interests.

Some penetrating analysts of this industry, such as Dr. Paul Frankel, would argue that such external control, of one kind or another, is a natural response to the peculiar economic behaviour to which this industry tends uncontrolled. He has suggested that when one such form of control, such as was exercised in the international oil market by the major companies after the war, breaks down, some other will have to be instituted to replace it. It is for this reason that he has suggested that the 'informal prorationing' that was once possible among the major companies may have to be replaced by something that brings in other interests as well. Even the casual observer may feel convinced that the pressure by the governments at both ends of this business for greater influence over the oil market—control necessitated partly by what Dr. Frankel calls 'lack of self-balancing factors in the market'—will recur and strengthen if no more conventional stabilization comes about. But there are more forms than one in which control might be re-established in this international market, at least temporarily. And it is perhaps likely that for some years we shall see continued evolution of the existing patterns of the industry rather than any quite radical shift in its organization.

For no such scheme could ever come into existence, in a free world, without the co-operation of the oil companies, whose financial stake in this is the largest of all. And whether any scheme controlled largely by governments with different interests could ever fit in with the major companies' widely and differently dispersed patterns of commercial interest is very doubtful. (Where governments and companies have co-operated in emergency schemes, as for example during the Suez crisis, these have been essentially governments of one kind, representing consumers.) This industry has, admittedly, adapted itself to many distortions and emergencies imposed from outside upon its pattern of commercial operations. But no emergency that it has met successfully ever postulated any continuing supervision over its main job of management, in a business that it is conducting successfully on the basis of unquestionable legal rights of ownership.

Politically, too, the parent countries of the existing international oil companies are among the most powerful of the Western world; these would tend to line up against any control that abrogated the property rights of the oil industry. Indeed, the whole current of thinking in the industrialized countries of the West, while not averse to some extension of national or even supra-national control, does for the present seem more favourable towards private enterprise than it may have done, say, at the end of the last war. Planning is coming back into vogue; but planning without socialism and certainly without expropriation.

The most important consuming countries, so far, are all based mainly upon private enterprise. Property is guaranteed rights within a stable and comprehensive legal system; when companies come to argue with such governments, they are arguing about the same things within the same frame of reference. This makes their relationships with such governments easier than with the governments of most producing nations, though no less complicated in detail (as the companies perforce concerned with European energy policies have certainly found out). It does not guarantee the continuance of the present structure of the industry, within and between nations. The influence of the American and British governments, moreover, may not always be exerted towards the precise *status quo* in the international oil industry: at the time that this book was being written, one was peering towards new frontiers in trade as well as security, and the other was bowing to the wind of change in its relations with formerly dependent countries. Neither attitude was irrelevant to the circumstances and conduct of the oil industry in its relations with governments everywhere.

CHAPTER XXIV

The Business in Between

None of the interests concerned with the international oil trade—consuming nations, exporting nations, or the companies in between—wants the oil to stop flowing; but all would like to see it flowing on slightly different terms. There are, however, inherent limitations to the extent to which most consumer governments, at any rate, would push what might seem to be their short-run self interest; and whether or not this is true of the exporting nations, there are some obvious commercial limitations upon the extent to which any of these could push up their rewards from oil. Each group of governments may think of the companies, from time to time, as ganging up with the other against it; the oil business may sometimes consider the possibility of these two ultimate bargainers combining to squeeze the middleman, but has never yet had to face such a reality. Ideologically, not many governments outside the Communist sphere appear to cherish much desire to take oil operations inside their borders entirely under government ownership; this industry is beset primarily by pragmatic nationalism, rather than theoretical socialism. Equally, few substantial companies in the oil business generally behave as if they believe in *laisser faire*, though some on occasion feel constrained to talk as if they did. They may be driven into extremes of short-run competitive behaviour from time to time; but most prefer a steadier form of competition looking towards their interests in at any rate the medium run. And whatever their philosophical attitudes towards government intervention in business, oilmen in practice have had years of experience in living with it.

Nowadays, bargaining between governments and companies about many aspects of the oil business goes on virtually without pause; and that it should not stop is perhaps more important to the world than the precise nature of the formulae discussed. But the central subject of the bargaining is being looked at a little differently. It is no longer simply a

337   W

question of what a government, say, should get out of oil as a reward for geographical ownership: it is shifting round to what the company should get out of it as a reward for business enterprise. This question of the proper rate of return for the risk-taking international entrepreneur in this business is what, in essence, the bargaining always has been about; but today it is being openly discussed as such. And indeed, if producing and consuming governments were ever to get together over the industry's head, they would be faced with the same questions. What are the essential—and irreducible—functions of this prodigious middleman, the international oil industry? And how much return does one need to offer capital to enter or stay in it?

One easy and partly adequate answer to the second question may seem to excuse governments from considering the first. The going price that capital needs in each part of the business, the governments may answer, is simply the lowest rate of return that any fresh entrepreneurs coming into the business are prepared to accept. Let each producing government get the best terms it can on any fresh concessions that it grants; and then squeeze the holders of its existing concessions to come into line. On this reasoning relinquishment deals would have an additional attraction for the governments; they might enable a continuing series of fresh bargains to be struck, with the extra benefits of each being translated back, in due course, to all existing deals. The Libyan government, so recent an entrant into the business, has clearly learned this game: it had begun revising its oil law even before a barrel of commercial oil had been shipped. And at the other end of the oil business, consumer governments have learned this game too. Using their bargaining power in a buyer's market for products, they are exacting special arrangements from some of the major companies that are less advantageously placed in marketing, or from newcomers seeking to enter their markets; then making similar demands on those already established.

Such pressures, tactical considerations in bargaining at both ends of this business, do not remove the question of the essential functions of risk capital in this business and of the return that needs to be paid on integrated operations to make them worth while. Specialized deals of one kind and another, particularly those linking production in given countries to consumption in given countries, will probably multiply. But is or is not the role of the internationally integrated company, operating across the world market, essential to this industry? And if so, what is it worth?

Fractions of the answer to these questions are given daily by the major oil companies themselves. In deciding what they need not do themselves and can hire other people to do, they at once demonstrate what can be decentralized and put a price on the physical performance of it. A host government can hire an exploration contractor: the quotation it gets, set largely by what company customers will pay, should enable it to decide whether it would rather invest in the equipment— and the men—itself, and will also give it an idea of the rate of return that capital invested in the physical operations concerned, without the element of risk, can competitively command. (If it wants to know what the risk, it might ask Petrobras). It can finance its own tankers—or bargain with Messrs. Onassis and Niarchos. It can perhaps conclude refining contracts for its own production or 'royalty crude' with independent refiners. Consuming governments can fairly easily ascertain the amount of capital required and the minimum return that some marketers find acceptable for entry into a market: the capital cost of entry, today, will usually be fairly high, but the rate of return acceptable will depend entirely on whether the marketer is integrated, and how much oil he can get rid of elsewhere. These are all functions of which the internationally integrated company, on occasion, is ready to divest itself, paying the going rate on other people's capital to do the job, though generally retaining most of the choices, and hence the risks itself. It may, similarly, have some of its technical research done outside, though it cannot delegate the technical management function of identifying, at any time, what its key technical problems really are.

What then, are the central functions that it cannot leave to anyone outside? And what rate of return is necessary to get these functions, apart from the many physical operations that it can hire, performed efficiently in the short, the medium and possibly the long run? Asked these questions, various oilmen offer a variety of overlapping answers. But to an outsider the essential operational function of an internationally integrated oil company may seem to be logistic—the disposition of supplies from many sources to meet many different demands, and the setting of relative prices. Its main technical and social function may be one of selecting and training good managers of all nationalities and imbuing them with wider than national experience in management. Its main financial function is perhaps that of acting as a specialized investment bank with exceptional experience in a particularly risky and complex technology, with a long enough view to ensure the steady development of an internationally essential resource. And all these functions, as exercised today, need an international viewpoint detached from the special interest of any one nation—which makes such a company, perforce, a political as well as an economic middleman between nations.

The logistic function of each internationally integrated oil company is carried out, within its limits, as a kind of 'invisible hand'. It produces, moves, and markets oil around the world not quite simply according to the 'principle of comparative costs' of free trade economics, but in accordance with the maximizing of net return after tax across its whole integrated chain of oil operations in many countries. Physically, as we have seen, the resulting movement of oil from source to market may turn out much the same as might be expected to arise from the operation of the law of comparative costs in a freely competitive international market. It is true that neither producing nor consuming governments, considering the structure of this industry and the assorted interests of the many integrated companies involved, are likely to trust that these companies' decisions best serve all interests quite as much as classical economists would have producers and consumers trust the free play of market forces. Tax considerations, moreover, enter into each company's logistic exercise; and other not simply economic incentives that an integrated company may have to consider A as against B also arise largely from the different governmental pressures under which it does business in different places. One may regret these complications of taxation and these political pressures, or accept them as inevitable. What one can hardly do is to argue that any new set of operators, set up by governments likely to follow their own individual economic interests rather than the broader medium-run interest of world oil development in general, would be less susceptible to political pressures—or that they could automatically perform this operation with greater efficiency than that with which oil is nowadays moved from well to market.

It has to be borne in mind that any regulation of permitted exports imposed politically from outside the companies might be likely on balance to cut across their tax advantages here and there, raising the cost of the operation and the tax liability involved, and reducing the net return on the capital employed in it. That reduction, certainly, would no doubt arise largely from the particular dispersion of interests of particular companies. Moreover, taxes are things a government can alter to suit its own convenience, as oil companies have plenty of reason to know. But whether any concert of governments at either end of the oil business or both could 'maximize the return' or reduce the net expenditure of resources on this central exercise of oil management to the degree

that uncommitted third parties—
tegrated companies—can in practi

Developing and properly employ
those managers who have to identify
search—is not less important. Any of
substantial asset to this industry, in w
been invested: developing a succession
tinuous exercise, and cannot be done on
company generates experience embodied
generates capital. Some businessmen wo
calibre that international oil has now in qu
be trained or would not stay in organizatio
governments: I do not find that ideological …g. The
quality of French technicians in the Sahara, ...gnor Mattei's gas
marketing men—or so far as one can judge from outside by results, of
Mr. Gurov's Soviet oilmen—does not seem to me necessarily inferior
to that of their counterparts in the privately-owned groups. Venezuelans
and Arabs, to the extent that they are given the chance, are already
proving their abilities in oil management. On the other hand, there are
dangers that political decisions affecting a government-dominated company might frustrate intelligent action for reasons wholly foreign to its
business interest more often than in the privately-owned group (though
neither frustration nor bureaucracy is absent there either).

Anyone who has seen anything of the fairly ruthless process of
cost-cutting set in train by the biggest international oil groups over
the last few years may retain doubts, too, whether any government-
owned organization could set about slimming itself so drastically. The
strength of political considerations and influence, at any rate, might
slow such a process. Without belittling the efforts in recent years to
recruit and train nationals of the oil-producing states inside the major
companies, it is objectively a pity that the process has not been ever
faster, and that responsible top management in the great international
companies is still almost exclusively confined to white Westerners. But
the internationally integrated oil company can, at its best, offer a
possibility of employment all round the world, in different national
situations but not of them, that may bring a refinement of managerial
judgment for international operations difficult to achieve either if
governments played a more dominant role in the oil trade or if the
demand for employment of 'nationals first' develops much further
everywhere.

function of the integrated oil company, which
upon the question of the return that capital in this
es, seems to me to be its activity as a generator and in-
apital, a specialized investment bank. It happens that this
ry since the war has generated and retained internally most
the capital that it goes on investing in such great amounts: but the
deployment rather than the provenance of these capital resources seems
to me the essential function. The exceptional risks involved in exploration and the huge rewards that accrued for the lucky risk-taker, no
doubt, set the pattern of self-financing. Oilmen who struck it rich
acquired the money as well as the taste for more gambling in oil, while
few capitalists outside felt competent to risk sums of such magnitude
in so chancy a business (until this acquired special tax advantages in
some countries). From time to time, the business began to look less
chancy, and attracted large amounts of outside capital in: much of it has
stayed, but some of the outsiders, again and again in the history of this
industry, have burned their fingers and withdrawn. The latest influx
of new capital occurred when it began to become clear how fabulous a
money-spinner the Middle East, in a favourable market, could be.
We are not over the results of that yet. Moreover, it was the exceptional profits earned there that made possible the virtually complete
self-financing of the major companies in the fifties. This may not
recur.

Decisions about the deployment of further capital investment in this
industry—which venture to back where next, out of the many propositions constantly on offer—is the ultimate job that no internationally-
integrated company would consider delegating to outsiders in its normal
business operations. It might be hard for individual governments, or
some 'democratic' committee of producer and consumer governments
to get these decisions right as often as the industry, on balance, manages
to do. No sensible oilman would suggest that investment policy is
always right now, or always decided now purely in economic terms
without the least attention to political considerations. Like other
heavily-capitalized industries since the war, the world petroleum
industry has been subject to 'fashions' in investment, waves of imita-
tive capital expenditure that predictably and fairly quickly have led to
surpluses in particular stages of the business. Moreover, the tax incentives thrown in by some governments to encourage investment in particular stages of it still seem to be encouraging so much investment as to
prolong situations of surplus.

Ought the industry to be investing as much in looking for oil as it still is? Is heavy investment in refining and marketing justified to hold or extend the share that every company has of every market? Is petrochemicals quite the escape route to higher returns than can be obtained on oil that it seemed to these central oil managers a few years ago? How far should the industry be looking for gas on its own (and whenever it finds gas, how ought it to price the stuff in relation to oil products)? These are not questions about which anyone can be confident of getting the right answer all the time. But long experience in having to consider them is a pretty valuable commodity. So is a degree of insulation from sectional political interest in selecting answers—and the degree that even now these investment managers still enjoy may on balance be of considerable service to the whole international economy.

Each international oil group's spread of interests, true, will be biased or lopsided in one way or another, giving it a different background for decision from other groups in the industry (or from some ideally-weighted cross-section of the 'whole' world oil industry. But who would do the weighting?). Not every decision or initiative from even the most broadly-based groups is popular with other oil companies or always, considered in hindsight, advantageous for the industry as a whole. But it is usually less one-sided than the decision a single national government engaged in oil might take, and less simply null than the lowest common denominator of decision acceptable to several such governments around a table might be; also, nowadays at least, more open to test in the market.

Governments seeking to discover the proper rate of return on capital in the oil business, I have suggested, might find that many of the physical operations, provided they assumed all the risk themselves, could perhaps be financed for the bare cost of borrowing the money. The oil companies are indeed doing this today with fairly low-coupon bonds (though their credit may still be rather better than that of most governments). Moreover, the need to keep producer government revenues stable and hence posted prices of crude up has of late involved the integrated companies in showing only nominal rates of return or even losses on their later stages of operations, even though the total integrated return is actually earned on the whole operation. That exaggerates the return on production to an embarrassingly high level; and with an irony that the companies may consider somewhat cruel, they are now being questioned, by the very governments who benefit

343

from its remaining high, about the justification of such a high return. It is possible to mount some rationalizations to support the belief of many oilmen that the profit not only is, but should be, 'in the crude'. But in the Middle East, the prices that put it there were a result of decision, not of any automatic working of market forces. Many of the governments dealing with them still credit the few large international companies, at any rate, with unaltered powers of decision over the world oil market. But in the meantime, across huge areas of their operations, these companies have become far more susceptible to the competition of other companies and the countervailing power of consumers. It would be hardly too much to say that the rate of return on production, in the Middle East, which arose from deliberate decisions by these companies (and the governments of the United States and Britain), has remained high because they have become almost helpless to change it.

In contrast to this continuing high rate of apparent return on production, at the beginning of the sixties, some of the major companies in the oil industry were showing an integrated return in the Eastern hemisphere (on production and everything else) that was lower than the return capital could get less riskily in normal manufacturing in developed countries. The excess profits taxes that some people in the Middle East are now talking about, like the increase in tax that Venezuela brought in a few years ago, would in effect depress the return even further on this 'downstream' (and in value much larger) investment. This idea illustrates some of the difficulties that would arise in practice from the idea often toyed with in government departments all around the world—of imposing upon the oil industry some kind of 'international public utility' rate of return. Assume that governments could agree on what rate of return they would consider proper for internationally integrated companies in this business (which enjoy neither the guaranteed monopoly nor the relative freedom from risk that are ordinarily associated with public utilities). Can one see different governments agreeing about how much of that controlled rate of return ought to be shown at each stage of the business—in all the different countries concerned?

Part of the seemingly excessive return on Middle East crude, it is clear, arises simply from accounting that was once convenient for the companies and is now the reverse. The Eastern hemisphere comparison is admittedly not the ideal one. Economically, there seems no reason why the profits on Middle East oil—made all the way down the stream, wherever they may be shown—should need automatically to cover investment in less remunerative oil operations elsewhere. This they were able to do to some considerable extent during the earlier postwar years. In circumstances of oligopoly, the companies adjusted the prices down more slowly than they might have come down in an utterly competitive market; kept in being some higher-cost producing areas that utter competition from low-cost Middle East oil might have put out of business; and themselves financed from the profits much of the further investment that utterly competitive entrepreneurs might have had to seek from the world's capital market. The producer governments shared these profits of oligopoly made during that period, and have been protected from the later decline in those profits as the degree of oligopoly crumbled. The consumer governments shared the security of supplies that a large part of the profits left with the companies were invested to bring about. Both, inevitably, feel that the others, along with the companies, did too well out of it.

One key question that producer governments, here, put to the companies goes to the heart of the international situation of these companies, and is one that producers would have to argue out with consumer governments, throughout any joint public utility operation that they might combine to set up. How much investment in exploration does the international oil industry need to go on doing—and where? This is a direct confrontation of producer versus consumer interests, as well as of the short-term interest of any producing area against the long-term interest of international companies, or any conceivable successors to them as continuing suppliers of oil.

It is hardly going to be possible to persuade a Kuwaiti or a Saudi Arabian, sitting on what may be a century's oil at the rate it is now being taken out, that the entrepreneurial net return on developing his oil need be such as to allow exploration elsewhere for the purpose of finding a developing capacity that might eventually replace, but will immediately compete with, production in Arabia. 'Explore, yes,' one can imagine him saying. 'Explore here! Find the next Burgan and the next Abqaiq, or drill up the reserves here—and a sight more easily, in all probability, than by wasting years and millions in Papua or Nigeria.' Any established producing government's enthusiasm about the need for financing exploration is likely to be temperate and somewhat localized. One might indeed suspect the same of certain major companies that are particularly well-placed in single regions, if it were not for the growing interest, always potentially unwelcome, of host governments

345

there. This governmental interest has limited the extent to which any oil company dare 'accentuate the positive' of one rich region. So its business incentive to keep up with the rest, maintaining or improving its share of proved oil reserves, is supplemented by a concern with the security of maintainable supplies that makes diversification of investment in the search for oil an end in itself.

This is one of the kinds of questions of management, quite apart from direct bargaining over price and offtake, that would come up again and again for answer in any world commodity scheme for oil, any proration scheme, or any other machinery by which diverse governments may seek to take over or regulate this business that works in between them. It is possible from the outside to have some doubts about the total rate of exploration of the international oil industry in given periods, and to feel that the tax incentives which help to engender it, representing the frozen decision of certain governments long ago to encourage local oil development, now encourage it everywhere to a degree that exacerbates and prolongs surplus. But that makes it no easier to see how other governments would answer the same set of questions—particularly governments with opposite kinds of interests in oil.

For this diversification, this high rate of exploration in unlikely places as well as likely, is something in which the consumer government's interest is strong and almost unmixed. Such a government may not be anxious to have oil prices forced down to levels that would put its own domestic fuel industries out of business. But it certainly prefers, at any time, to have just a little more oil on tap than it really requires, and from as many different sources as possible. (It is indeed likely, nowadays, to promote exploration for oil within its own borders; and if it finds any, to protect this even more zealously than it does coal.) Equally, the governments of prospective areas for exploration, which have as yet found no oil but not much of anything else either, have certainly an interest in attracting the oil entrepreneur to take his gamble in their land, where he may win so much for them along with himself.

One cogent if partial answer from the middlemen to this question of how much further exploration, and where, the profits made on oil from established producing areas should be partly utilized to finance would no doubt be that if you want consumers to switch to oil they will have to feel safe in doing so. The great consuming countries, in spite of some protection of their home fuel industries, have in fact been switching to oil as a general fuel at a pretty rapid pace. It is doubtful whether the additional productive capacity that has been brought into being since the Suez incident has actually made much difference to the West's ability, after an interruption of supplies, to get all the oil it needs at low cost. But the implicit assurance that diverse sources of oil are constantly being explored, as part of the normal behaviour of the international oil industry, does play a part in the policies of consumer governments.

The companies operating internationally, of course, have other motives for going on exploring as well as keeping consumers confident. They want to find it, if they can, really near to developing markets. They want to balance their supplies and marketing capacity in the short run and maintain their competitive position in the long run and to pre-empt possible discoveries in new areas. They are quite often concerned, in bidding for new concessions, less with finding new oil quickly than in making sure it is 'in strong hands'—which can mean that it may not soon become so bitterly competitive with established producing areas as established host governments fear. The established groups are no more anxious for 'competition amongst the many' than any established producing government. But there is no reason why the corporate and national rivals of both should accept this joint 'oil establishment' as uniquely entitled to conduct this business.

In this many-sided bargaining, indeed, some of the key issues lie really between governments—the landlord from whose territory the oil comes, his neighbours who would like a bonanza too, and the ultimate consumer who finally pays the price and confers a value on it. The entrepreneurs who put their capital into developing the resource and finding it a market for the producing nation, or into securing a cheap and convenient fuel for the consumer, are already being squeezed at both ends of the business they have built up. In theory, they might become quite resigned to sit back and let landlords and customers wrangle over some of the refinements of this ultimate bargain. Some people in the companies, at times, are prepared to debate upon the possibilities of 'retreating to the marketing function' and using their buying power fully against the producing companies that they presently own; or even of shifting large parts of their aggregated capital out of the oil business. So far, however, the industry as a whole has certainly not resigned itself to letting producer and consumer governments argue over its head. The entrepreneurs distrust further government encroachment on their business. They fear that even if confrontation were to demonstrate to governments of both kinds that the shared problems of oil are less simple than they look from one side alone, whatever was finally worked out would still tend to be at the companies' expense. These fears are naturally self-interested. Can one argue that they are not realistic?

One quite useful service of this industry to the world economy, to the outsider, may seem to be simply that it does not leave consuming countries to argue direct with producers, and that in this trade the governments whose interests are opposed remain relatively insulated from one another. Like other international institutions in a world where nationalism is not visibly declining, it cannot expect to be popular. It is certainly not an ideal international economic phenomenon. Its control is heavily biased towards the Western industrialized countries, though most of its production comes from underdeveloped countries. In economic performance, it is at best workably rather than fully competitive; and its frequent attempts to reduce instability do not guarantee any rapid re-adjustment back into equilibrium. The very large companies that play so large a part within it display some considerable built-in resistances to change, in spite of operational flexibility; they are also quite dominating aggregations of economic power in some of the countries where they operate, and indeed large and rather remote, suspect ones to most of the countries where they do business. Their formal duty is to shareholders, not to the national aspirations of the countries where they work. This may sometimes hamper their ability to adjust their dealings with governments—particularly when they fear that the end of successive adjustments must eventually be at their shareholders' expense, which is certainly a considerable possibility. The big company's interest in survival is always likely to counsel moderation in short-term gains. But if its managers have a feeling of '*après moi la deluge*'—and clearheaded men at the top of the integrated companies might have some excuse for such a feeling—are they justified in foregoing short-term gains for the sake of amicable future relations with governments that they do not honestly believe can stay amicable?

From some but not all the governments they have to deal with, private enterprise can probably claim some theoretical approval. But in theory this approval attaches to atomistically competitive private enterprise: in practice, also, to private enterprise operating wholly within a government's own economic sphere. The oil business is not quite either of these. There is no general and automatic acceptance of its private, international 'legitimacy'. It can act as a cushion, if not an arbiter, between the claims of different countries, without the political friction that continuous confrontation of national interests would cause. Yet at both ends of its business, the governments may doubt whether in the last resort it is responsible to anyone. They may feel confronted with some kind of 'Shell Company of Atlantis'. Every international oil company, in a sense, must seem to those who deal with it to live on an imaginary island.

What may seem to constitute the companies' virtues, on a world view, are not much more likely to be popular with governments than their defects. Whatever bounds different governments put upon their legitimate interest in this business, the international oil industry from now on seems fairly certain to have to get accustomed to operating with governments breathing down its neck. That may be uncomfortable, but not impossible.

The internally integrated companies are still, even now, glad enough to go on ploughing capital into this business: it would be stupid to suggest that they have been driven to a point where it is really losing its fascination or its rewards for them. But there could obviously come a limit to the readiness of international capital to invest in this international business, if these growing encroachments should begin even more seriously to whittle down the independent efficiency of international operations, the security of tenure, and in a market like the present the total integrated return. There are other forms of investment into which capital and management of the quantity and quality that the international oil industry deploys could go—and which could, at some point, become equally attractive. And there is at present no prospect of any alternative structure formed out of overlapping nationalism that offers a hope of handling this international job of logistics and of deploying investment with anything like the same, reasonably impartial efficiency.

There is still plenty of room for legitimate bargaining about sharing the wealth that the international development of oil is bringing into being. But the bargaining needs to be conducted in the recognition that the capitalist is worthy of his hire; and that his labour—which is ultimately one of reaching a fair balance between different commercial and national interests at many points, as a continuing operation—cannot be avoided. The international oil industry, and within it the major oil companies, have not yet fully fitted themselves for and into their role as an international economic institution; there remain, oddly enough, considerable vestiges of nationalist arrogance in their own makeup and behaviour. But if this international institution did not exist it would be necessary to invent one.

This book arose from an attempt to understand an industry from outside, and is necessarily incomplete. It began as a challenge, and became a pleasure. The attempt continues. But a book has to end somewhere.

J.E.H.

Hampstead, 1962.

Table I

WORLD ENERGY CONSUMPTION, COMMERCIAL FUELS:
Orders of Magnitude

	1929	1937	1950	1960	1970 (forecast)
Million metric tons Coal Equivalent					
Solid Fuels	1,367	1,361	1,569	2,263	3,060
Hydro-Electricity	14	22	41	82	150
Natural Gas	76	115	273	596	1,340
Oil	255	328	636	1,492	2,680
Total	1,712	1,826	2,519	4,433	7,230*
Percentages					
Solid Fuels	80	75	62		
Hydro-Electricity	1	1	2		
Natural Gas	4	6	11		
Oil	15	18	25		
	100	100	100	100	100*

* Includes est. 20 million tons CE of nuclear electricity

Source: Figures to 1950, 'World Energy Supplies' United Nations. 1961 and forecast 1971, oil company estimates.

Table IV

CRUDE OIL RESERVE AND PRODUCTION POSITION OF MAJOR INTERNATIONAL COMPANIES

	GROSS CRUDE OIL RESERVES, END 1958 Million tons					CRUDE OIL PRODUCTION, 1959 Million tons					PRODUCTION: RESERVE RATIO Years				
	U.S.A.	Other Western Hemisphere	Eastern Hemisphere	TOTAL Excl. U.S.A.	TOTAL Incl. U.S.A.	U.S.A.	Other Western Hemisphere	Eastern Hemisphere	TOTAL Excl. U.S.A.	TOTAL Incl. U.S.A.	U.S.A.	Other Western Hemisphere	Eastern Hemisphere	TOTAL Excl. U.S.A.	TOTAL Incl. U.S.A.
Gulf Oil[1]	225	125	4,350	4,475	4,700	19	9	41	50	69	11.8	13.9	106.1	89.5	68.1
Standard Oil (New Jersey)	515	1,480	2,685	4,165	4,680	25	71	30	101	126	20.6	20.8	89.5	41.2	37.1
Texaco	305	185	2,350	2,535	2,840	25	12	24	36	61	12.2	15.4	97.9	70.4	46.6
Standard Oil (California)	250	70	2,350	2,420	2,670	16	4	24	28	44	15.6	17.5	97.9	86.4	60.7
Socony Mobil	175	70	1,410	1,480	1,655	12	8	18	26	38	14.6	8.8	78.3	56.9	43.6
British Petroleum[2]	—	—	6,670	6,670	6,670	—	—	63	63	63	—	—	105.9	105.9	105.9
Royal Dutch/Shell[1]	145	620	1,635	2,255	2,400	19	53	31	84	103	7.6	11.7	52.7	26.8	23.3
Cie. Francaise des Pétroles[2]	—	—	1,275	1,275	1,275	—	—	14	14	14	—	—	91.1	91.1	91.1

[1] All the reserves attributable to Gulf's 50% share in Kuwait are included under Gulf Oil. Royal Dutch/Shell, however, has long-term supply contracts for a substantial part of Gulf's Kuwait production and so has a special relationship to these reserves.
[2] Excluding B.P.'s interests in Canada and Trinidad and C.F.P.'s in Canada.

Source: Petroleum Economics Ltd.

Table V

SHAREHOLDINGS OF MAIN MIDDLE EAST OIL CONCESSIONS

Countries and Concessions	British Petroleum	Compagnie Française des Pétroles	Gulf Oil	Standard Oil of New Jersey	Socony Mobil	Royal Dutch/ Shell	Standard Oil of California	Texas Company
ABU DHABI								
Onshore concession[1]	(23.75%)	(23.75%)	—	(11.875%)[2]	(11.875%)[2]	(23.75%)	—	—
Offshore concession	50%	50%						
BAHREIN							50%	50%
IRAN								
Consortium	40%	6%	7%	7%	7%	14%	7%	7%
IRAQ								
IPC, BPC, MPC concessions[1]	23.75%	23.75%	—	11.875%[2]	11.875%[2]	23.75%	—	—
KUWAIT								
Onshore concession	50%		50%					
Offshore concession						100%[3]		
QATAR[1]	(23.75%)	(23.75%)	—	(11.875%)[2]	(11.875%)[2]	(23.75%)	—	—
SAUDI ARABIA	—	—	—	30%	10%	—	30%	30%

[1] IPC owns Qatar and Abu Dhabi (onshore) operating companies. [2] Exercised through half ownership of Near East Development Corporation, which owns 23.75 per cent of I.P.C. stock. [3] Kuwait Government has right to buy 20 per cent at cost when oil is developed commercially.

Short Bibliography

Ayres, Eugene, and Scarlott, Charles. *Energy Sources: the Wealth of the World.* McGraw Hill. New York, 1952.

Cassady, Ralph jr. *Price Making and Price Behaviour in the Petroleum Industry.* Yale University Press. New Haven, 1954.

Chase Manhattan Bank. Monographs:
Future Growth and Financial Requirements of the World Petroleum Industry. New York, 1956.
Investment Patterns in the World Petroleum Industry. New York, 1956.
Future Growth of the World Petroleum Industry. New York, 1961.
Capital Investments by the World Petroleum Industry. New York, 1961.

de Chazeau, Melvin E., and Kahn, Alfred E. *Integration and Competition in the Petroleum Industry.* Yale University Press. New Haven, 1959.

Economic Commission for Europe. *The Price of Oil in Western Europe.* Geneva. United Nations, 1955. *Relationship Between Coal and Black Oils in Western Europe.* Geneva. United Nations, 1954.

First National City Bank. Monographs:
Petroleum in the Eastern Hemisphere. New York, 1959.
Oil Prospects and Profits in the Eastern Hemisphere. New York, 1961.
Future Price and Availability Trends for Hydrocarbon Raw Materials outside the United States. New York, 1961.

Frankel, Paul H. *Essentials of Petroleum: A Key to Oil Economics.* Chapman & Hall. London, 1946. 'Integration in the Oil Industry'. *Journal of Industrial Economics*, Oxford, July 1953. 'The Significance of Marginal Capacity in the Oil Industry'. *Journal of Industrial Economics.* March 1962.

Leeman, Wayne A. *The Price of Middle East Oil.* Cornell University Press. Ithaca, 1962.

Lenczowski, George. *Oil and State in the Middle East.* Cornell University Press. Ithaca, New York, 1960.

Levy, Walter J. 'World Oil in Transition'. *The Economist*, 1961.

357

SHORT BIBLIOGRAPHY

Longrigg, Stephen H. *Oil in the Middle East: Its Discovery and Development*. Oxford University Press. Revised edition, 1961.

Maclean, John H., and Haigh, Robert W. *The Growth of Integrated Oil Companies*. Graduate School of Business Administration, Harvard University, Boston, 1954.

Organization of European Economic Co-operation. Two independent reports:
Europe's Growing Needs of Energy. How Can They Be Met? (by a commission headed by Sir Harold Hartley) Paris, 1956.
Towards a New Energy Pattern in Europe (by a commission headed by Professor E. A. G. Robinson) Paris, 1960.

Ovens, David. *Crude Oil Prices: The Next Five Years in Competitive Aspects of Oil Operations*. Institute of Petroleum, London, 1958.

Penrose, E. T. 'Profit Sharing Between Producing Countries and Oil Companies in the Middle East'. *The Economic Journal*. London, June 1959. 'Middle East Oil; The International Distribution of Profits and Income Taxes'. *Economica*. London, August 1960.

Schurr, Sam H. and Netschert, Bruce C. *Energy in the American Economy, 1850–1975. Its History and Prospects*. Resources for the Future Inc. The Johns Hopkins Press, Baltimore, 1960.

Shwadran, Benjamin. *The Middle East, Oil, and Great Powers*. Council for Middle Eastern Affairs Press. New York, 1959.

Tugendhat, Georg. 'A World Market in Upheaval'. *Fortune*. October 1960. *The Political Economy of Energy*. Three lectures to The London School of Economics, 1959.

United States Federal Trade Commission. *The International Petroleum Cartel*. Washington, 1952.

Zimmermann, Erich W. *Conservation in the Production of Petroleum*. Yale University Press. New Haven, 1957.

Index

INDEX

INDEX